NATURAL PHILOSOPHY
OF
CAUSE AND CHANCE

NATURAL PHILOSOPHY
OF
CAUSE AND CHANCE

BY

MAX BORN

BEING
THE WAYNFLETE LECTURES
DELIVERED IN THE COLLEGE OF ST. MARY MAGDALEN,
OXFORD, IN HILARY TERM, 1948
TOGETHER WITH A NEW ESSAY,
"SYMBOL AND REALITY"

DOVER PUBLICATIONS, INC., NEW YORK

Published simultaneously in Canada by General Publishing Co., Ltd., 222 Adelaide St. W., Toronto, Canada.

Published in the United Kingdom by Constable and Company Limited, 10 Orange Street, London W. C. 2.

This Dover edition, first published in 1964, is an unabridged and unaltered republication of the work first published by the Oxford University Press in 1949, to which has been added two new appendices: Addendum (1964) and "Symbol and Reality," a new English translation of a lecture given at the June, 1964 meeting of Nobel Laureates at Lindau, Germany.

This Dover edition is published by special arrangement with Oxford University Press.

Library of Congress Catalog Card Number: 64-18840

Manufactured in the United States of America

Dover Publications, Inc.
180 Varick Street
New York 14, N.Y.

PREFACE TO THE DOVER EDITION

SINCE these lectures were delivered and printed sixteen years ago physics has vastly expanded, and I have become too old to follow it up. When I was approached with the plan of a new edition I felt unable to bring the text up to date, for it would have meant writing a new book. However, this is not a textbook, but a survey of the scientific scene from my own philosophical standpoint. Since this has not changed with the years, I proposed an unchanged reprint. I have, however, added two new appendices: in one I list a few outdated passages and indicate the results of new research; the other is a lecture recently delivered at the Lindau Conference of Nobel Laureates, on the central philosophical problem of scientific objectivity.

M. B.

1964

PREFACE

A DRAFT of these lectures, written before they were delivered, contained considerably more technicalities and mathematics than the present text. Facing a large audience in which physicists and mathematicians were presumably a minority, I had to change my plans and to improvise a simplified presentation. Though this did not seem difficult on the platform of the Hall of Magdalen College, Oxford, the final formulation for publication was not an easy task. I did not like replacing rigorous mathematical reasoning by that mixture of literary style, authority, and mystery which is often used by popularizing and philosophizing scientists. Thus, the idea occurred to me to preserve the mathematics by removing it to a detailed appendix which could also contain references to the literature. The vast extension of the latter, however, compelled me to restrict quotations to recent publications which are not in the text-books. Some of these supplements contain unpublished investigations of my school, mainly by my collaborator Dr. H. S. Green. In the text itself I have given up the original division into seven lectures and replaced it by a more natural arrangement into ten chapters.

I have to thank Dr. Green for his untiring help in reading, criticizing, and correcting my script, working out drafts of the appendix, and reading proofs. I am also indebted to Mr. Lewis Elton not only for proof-reading but for carefully preparing the index. I have further to thank Albert Einstein for permission to publish sections of two of his letters.

My most sincere gratitude is due to the President and the Fellows of Magdalen College who gave me the opportunity to plan these lectures, and the leisure to write them down for publication.

I wish to thank the Oxford University Press for the excellent printing and their willingness to follow all my wishes.

M. B.

CONTENTS

NOTATION

THE practice of representing vector quantities by means of **clarendon type** in print is now well established, and used throughout these lectures. For dealing with cartesian tensors, the notation of Chapman and Milne, explained in the first chapter of Chapman and Cowling's book *The Mathematical Theory of Non-Uniform Gases* (C.U.P., 1939) is used; this consists in printing tensors in sans serif type.

The following examples will suffice to show how vector and tensor equations are translated into coordinate notation.

$$\mathbf{a} = \mathbf{b} \rightarrow a_k = b_k \quad (k = 1, 2, 3)$$

$$\mathbf{a}.\mathbf{b} = \sum_{k=1}^{3} a_k b_k$$

$$\mathsf{a} = \mathsf{b} \rightarrow a_{kl} = b_{kl} \quad (k, l = 1, 2, 3)$$

$$\mathsf{a}.\mathbf{b} = \mathbf{c} \rightarrow \sum_{l=1}^{3} a_{kl} b_l = c_k \quad (k = 1, 2, 3)$$

$$\mathbf{a}.\mathsf{b}.\mathbf{c} = \sum_{k,l=1}^{3} a_k b_{kl} c_l$$

$$\mathbf{a} \wedge \mathbf{b} = \mathbf{c} \rightarrow a_2 b_3 - a_3 b_2 = c_1, \quad \text{etc.}$$

$$\frac{\partial a}{\partial \mathbf{x}} = \operatorname{grad} a = \mathbf{b} \rightarrow \frac{\partial a}{\partial x_k} = (\operatorname{grad} a)_k = b_k \quad (k = 1, 2, 3)$$

$$\frac{\partial}{\partial \mathbf{x}}.\mathbf{a} = \operatorname{div} \mathbf{a} = \sum_{k=1}^{3} \frac{\partial a_k}{\partial x_k}$$

$$\frac{\partial}{\partial \mathbf{x}}.\mathsf{a} = \operatorname{div} \mathsf{a} = \mathbf{b} \rightarrow \sum_{l=1}^{3} \frac{\partial a_{lk}}{\partial x_l} = (\operatorname{div} \mathsf{a})_k = b_k \quad (k = 1, 2, 3)$$

$$\frac{\partial}{\partial \mathbf{x}} \wedge \mathbf{a} = \operatorname{curl} \mathbf{a} = \mathbf{b} \rightarrow \frac{\partial a_3}{\partial x_2} - \frac{\partial a_2}{\partial x_3} = (\operatorname{curl} \mathbf{a})_1 = b_1, \quad \text{etc.}$$

NATURAL PHILOSOPHY
OF
CAUSE AND CHANCE

I
INTRODUCTION

THE notions of cause and chance which I propose to deal with in these lectures are not specifically physical concepts but have a much wider meaning and application. They are used, more or less vaguely, in everyday life. They appear, not only in all branches of science, but also in history, psychology, philosophy, and theology; everywhere with a different shade of meaning. It would be far beyond my abilities to give an account of all these usages, or to attempt an analysis of the exact significance of the words 'cause' and 'chance' in each of them. However, it is obvious that there must be a common feature in the use of these notions, like the theme in a set of variations. Indeed, cause expresses the idea of necessity in the relation of events, while chance means just the opposite, complete randomness. Nature, as well as human affairs, seems to be subject to both necessity and accident. Yet even accident is not completely arbitrary, for there are laws of chance, formulated in the mathematical theory of probability, nor can the cause–effect relation be used for predicting the future with certainty, as this would require a complete knowledge of the relevant circumstances, present, past, or both together, which is not available. There seems to be a hopeless tangle of ideas. In fact, if you look through the literature on this problem you will find no satisfactory solution, no general agreement. Only in physics has a systematic attempt been made to use the notions of cause and chance in a way free from contradictions. Physicists form their notions through the interpretation of experiments. This method may rightly be called Natural Philosophy, a word still used for physics at the Scottish universities. In this sense I shall attempt to investigate the concepts of cause and chance in these lectures. My material will be taken mainly from physics, but I shall try to regard it with the attitude of the philosopher, and I hope that the results obtained will be of use wherever the concepts of cause and chance are applied. I know that such an attempt will not find favour with some philosophers, who maintain that science teaches only a narrow aspect of the world, and one which is of no great importance to man's mind. It is true that many scientists are not philosophically minded and have hitherto shown much skill and ingenuity but little wisdom. I need hardly to enlarge on this subject. The practical applications of science have given us the means of a fuller and richer life, but also the means of destruction and devastation on a vast scale. Wise men would have considered the consequences of their activities before starting on them; scientists have failed to do so, and only recently have they become conscious of their responsibilities to society. They have gained prestige as men of action, but they have lost credit as philosophers. Yet history shows that science has played a leading part in the development of human thought. It has not only supplied raw material to philosophy by gathering facts, but also evolved the fundamental concepts on how to deal with them. It suffices to mention the Copernican system of the universe, and the Newtonian dynamics which sprang from it. These originated the conceptions of space, time, matter, force, and motion for a long time to come, and had a mighty influence on many philosophical systems. It has been said that the metaphysics of any period is the offspring of the physics of the preceding period. If this is true, it puts us physicists under the obligation to explain our ideas in a not-too-technical language. This is the purpose of the following lectures on a restricted though important field. I have made an attempt to avoid mathematics entirely, but failed. It would have meant an unbearable clumsiness of expression and loss of clarity. A way out would have been the reduction of all higher mathematics to elementary methods in Euclidean style—following the celebrated example of Newton's *Principia*. But this would even have increased the clumsiness and destroyed what there is of aesthetic appeal. I personally think that more than 200 years after Newton there should be some progress in the assimilation of mathematics by those who are interested in natural philosophy. So I shall use ordinary language and formulae in a suitable mixture; but I shall not give proofs of theorems (they are collected in the Appendix).

In this way I hope to explain how physics may throw some light on a problem which is not only important for abstract knowledge but also for the behaviour of man. An unrestricted belief in causality leads necessarily to the idea that the world is an automaton of which we ourselves are only little cog-wheels. This means materialistic determinism. It resembles very much that religious determinism accepted by different creeds, where the actions of men are believed to be determined from the beginning by a ruling of God. I cannot enlarge on the difficulties to which this idea leads if considered from the standpoint of ethical responsibility. The notion of divine predestination clashes with the notion of free will, in the same way as the assumption of an endless chain of natural causes. On the other hand, an unrestricted belief in chance is impossible, as it cannot be denied that there are a great many regularities in the world; hence there can be, at most, 'regulated accident'. One has to postulate laws of chance which assume the appearance of laws of nature or laws for human behaviour. Such a philosophy would give ample space for free will, or even for the willed actions of gods and demons. In fact, all primitive polytheistic religions seem to be based on such a conception of nature: things happening in a haphazard way, except where some spirit interferes with a purpose. We reject to-day this demonological philosophy, but admit chance into the realm of exact science. Our philosophy is dualistic in this respect; nature is ruled by laws of cause and laws of chance in a certain mixture. How is this possible? Are there no logical contradictions? Can this mixture of ideas be cast into a consistent system in which all phenomena can be adequately described or explained? What do we mean by such an explanation if the feature of chance is involved? What are the irreducible or metaphysical principles involved? Is there any room in this system for free will or for the interference of deity? These and many other questions can be asked. I shall try to answer some of them from the standpoint of the physicist, others from my philosophical convictions which are not much more than common sense improved by sporadic reading. The statement, frequently made, that modern physics has given up causality is entirely unfounded. Modern physics, it is true, has given up or modified many traditional ideas; but it would cease to be a science if it had given up the search for the causes of phenomena. I found it necessary, therefore, to formulate the different aspects of the fundamental notions by giving definitions of terms which seem to me in agreement with ordinary language. With the help of these concepts, I shall survey the development of physical thought, dwelling here and there on special points of interest, and I shall try to apply the results to philosophy in general.

II

CAUSALITY AND DETERMINISM

THE concept of causality is closely linked with that of determinism, yet they seem to me not identical. Moreover, causality is used with several different shades of meaning. I shall try to disentangle these notions and eventually sum them up in definitions.

The cause-effect relation is used mainly in two ways; I shall illustrate this by giving examples, partly from ordinary life, partly from science. Take these statements:

'Overpopulation is the cause of India's poverty.'

'The stability of British politics is caused by the institution of monarchy.'

'Wars are caused by the economic conditions.'

'There is no life on the moon because of the lack of an atmosphere containing oxygen.'

'Chemical reactions are caused by the affinity of molecules.'

The common feature to which I wish to draw your attention is the fact that these sentences state timeless relations. They say that one thing or one situation A causes another B, meaning apparently that the existence of B depends on A, or that if A were changed or absent, B would also be changed or absent. Compare these statements with the following:

'The Indian famine of 1946 was caused by a bad harvest.'

'The fall of Hitler was caused by the defeat of his armies.'

'The American war of secession was caused by the economic situation of the slave states.'

'Life could develop on earth because of the formation of an atmosphere containing oxygen.'

'The destruction of Hiroshima was caused by the explosion of an atomic bomb.'

In these sentences one definite event A is regarded as the cause of another B; both events are more or less fixed in space and time. I think that these two different shades of the cause–effect relation are both perfectly legitimate. The common factor is the idea of dependence, which needs some comment. This concept of dependence is clear enough if the two things connected are concepts themselves, things of the mind, like two numbers or two sets of numbers; then dependence means what the mathematician expresses by the word 'function'. This logical dependence needs no further analysis (I even think it cannot be further analysed). But causality does not refer to logical dependence; it means dependence of real things of nature on one another. The problem of what this means is not simple at all. Astrologers claim the dependence of the fate of human beings on the constellations of stars. Scientists reject such statements—but why? Because science accepts only relations of dependence if they can be verified by observation and experiment, and we are convinced that astrology has not stood this test. Science insists on a criterion for dependence, namely repetitive observation or experiment: either the things A and B refer to phenomena, occurring repeatedly in Nature and being sufficiently similar for the aspect in question to be considered as identical; or repetition can be artificially produced by experiment.

Observation and experiment are crafts which are systematically taught. Sometimes, by a genius, they are raised to the level of an art. There are rules to be observed: isolation of the system considered, restriction of the variable factors, varying of the conditions until the dependence of the effect on a single factor becomes evident; in many cases exact measurements and comparison of figures are essential. The technique of handling these figures is a craft in itself, in which the notions of chance and probability play a decisive part—we shall return to this question at a later stage. So it looks as if science has a methodical way of finding causal relations without referring to any metaphysical principle. But this is a deception. For no observation or experiment, however extended, can give more than a finite number of repetitions, and the statement of a law—B depends on A—always transcends experience. Yet this kind of statement is made everywhere and all the time, and sometimes from scanty material. Philosophers call it Inference by Induction, and have developed many a profound theory of it. I shall not enter into a discussion of these speculations. But I have to make it clear why I distinguish this principle of induction from causality. Induction allows one to generalize a number of observations into a general rule: that night follows day and day follows night, or that in spring the trees grow green leaves, are inductions, but they contain no causal relation, no statement of dependence. The method of inductive thinking is more general than causal thinking; it is used in everyday life as a matter of course, and it applies in science to the descriptive and experimental branches as well. But while everyday life has no definite criterion for the validity of an induction and relies more or less on intuition, science has worked out a code, or rule of craft, for its application. This code has been entirely successful, and I think that is the only justification for it—just as the rules of the craft of classical music are only justified by full audiences and applause. Science and art are not so different as they appear. The laws in the realms of truth and beauty are laid down by the masters, who create eternal works.

Absolute values are ideals never reached. Yet I think that the common effort of mankind has approached some ideals in quite a respectable way. I do not hesitate to call a man foolish if he rejects the teaching of experience because no logical proof is forthcoming, or because he does not know or does not accept the rules of the scientific craft. You find such super-logical people sporadically among pure mathematicians, theologians, and philosophers, while there are besides vast communities of people ignorant of or rejecting the rules of science, among them the members of anti-vaccination societies and believers in astrology. It is useless to argue with them; I cannot compel them to accept the same criteria of valid induction in which I believe: the code of scientific rules. For there is no logical argument for doing so; it is a question of faith. In this sense I am willing to call induction a metaphysical principle, namely something beyond physics.

After this excursion, let us return to causality and its two ways of application, one as a timeless relation of dependence, the other as a dependence of one event fixed in time and space on another (see Appendix, **1**). I think that the abstract, timeless meaning of causality is the fundamental one. This becomes quite evident if one tries to use the term in connexion with a specific case without implicit reference to the abstraction. For example: The statement that a bad harvest was the cause of the Indian famine makes sense only if one has in mind the timeless statement that bad harvests are causes of famines in general. I leave it to you to confirm this with the other examples I have given or with any more you may invent. If you drop this reference to a general rule, the connexion between two consecutive events loses its character of causality, though it may still retain the feature of perfect regularity, as in the sequence of day and night. Another example is the time-table of a railway line. You can predict with its help the arrival at King's Cross of the 10 o'clock from Waverley; but you can hardly say that the time-table reveals a cause for this event. In other words, the law of the time-table is deterministic: You can predict future events from it, but the question 'why?' makes no sense.

Therefore, I think one should not identify causality and determinism. The latter refers to rules which allow one to predict from the knowledge of an event A the occurrence of an event B (and vice versa), but without the idea that there is a physical timeless (and spaceless) link between all things of the kind A and all things of the kind B. I prefer to use the expression 'causality' mainly for this timeless dependence. It is exactly what experimentalists and observers mean when they trace a certain phenomenon to a certain cause by systematic variation of conditions. The other application of the word to two events following one another is, however, in so common use that it cannot be excluded. Therefore I suggest that it should be used also, but supplemented by some 'attributes' concerning time and space. It is always assumed that the cause precedes the effect; I propose to call this the principle of antecedence. Further, it is generally regarded as repugnant to assume a thing to cause an effect at a place where it is not present, or to which it cannot be linked by other things; I shall call this the principle of contiguity.

I shall now try to condense these considerations in a few definitions.

Determinism postulates that events at different times are connected by laws in such a way that predictions of unknown situations (past or future) can be made.

By this formulation religious predestination is excluded, since it assumes that the book of destiny is only open to God.

Causality postulates that there are laws by which the occurrence of an entity B of a certain class depends on the occurrence of an entity A of another class, where the word 'entity' means any physical object, phenomenon, situation, or event. A is called the cause, B the effect.

If causality refers to single events, the following attributes of causality must be considered:

Antecedence postulates that the cause must be prior to, or at least simultaneous with, the effect.

Contiguity postulates that cause and effect must be in spatial contact or connected by a chain of intermediate things in contact.

III

ILLUSTRATION: ASTRONOMY AND PARTICLE MECHANICS

I SHALL now illustrate these definitions by surveying the development of physical science. But do not expect an ordinary historical treatment. I shall not describe how a great man actually made his discoveries, nor do I much care what he himself said about it. I shall try to analyse the scientific situation at the time of the discovery, judged by a modern mind, and describe them in terms of the definitions given.

Let us begin with the oldest science, astronomy. Pre-Newtonian theory of celestial motions is an excellent example of a mathematical and deterministic, yet not causal, description. This holds for the Ptolemaic system as well as for the Copernican, including Kepler's refinements. Ptolemy represented the motion of the planets by kinematic models, cycles, and epicycles rolling on one another and on the fixed heavenly sphere. Copernicus changed the standpoint and made the sun the centre of cyclic planetary motion, while Kepler replaced the cycles by ellipses. I do not wish to minimize the greatness of Copernicus' step in regard to the conception of the Universe. I just consider it from the standpoint of the question which we are discussing. Neither Ptolemy nor Copernicus nor Kepler states a cause for the behaviour of the planets, except the ultimate cause, the will of the Creator. What they do is, in modern mathematical language, the establishment of functions,

$$x_1 = f_1(t), \qquad x_2 = f_2(t), \qquad \ldots,$$

for the coordinates of all particles, depending on time. Copernicus himself claimed rightly that his functions, or more accurately the corresponding geometrical structures, are very much simpler than those of Ptolemy, but he refrained from advocating the cosmological consequences of his system. This question came to the foreground long after his death mainly by Galileo's telescopic observations, which revealed in Jupiter and his satellites a repetition of the Copernican system on a smaller scale.

Descartes's cosmology can be regarded as an early attempt to establish causal laws for the planetary orbits by assuming a complicated vortex motion of some kind of ether, and it is remarkable that this construction satisfies contiguity. But it failed because it lacked the main feature of scientific progress; it was not based on a reasonable induction from facts. Of course, no code of rules existed, nor did Descartes's writings provide it at that time. The principles of the code accepted to-day are implicitly contained in the works of Galileo and Newton, who demonstrated them with their actual discoveries in physics and astronomy—in the same way as Haydn established the rules of the sonata by writing lovely music in this form.

Galileo's work precedes Newton's not only in time but also in logical order; for Galileo was experimenting with terrestrial objects according to the rules of repetition and variation of conditions, while Newton's astronomical material was purely observational and restricted.* Galileo observed how a falling body moves, and studied the conditions on which the motion depends. His results can be condensed into the well-known formula for the vertical coordinate of a small body or 'particle' as a function of time,

$$z = -\tfrac{1}{2}gt^2, \tag{3.1}$$

where g is a constant, i.e. independent not only of time but also of the falling body. The only thing this quantity g can depend upon is the body towards which the motion is taking place, the earth—a conclusion which is almost too obvious to be formulated; for if the motion is checked by my hand, I feel the weight as a pressure directed downwards towards the earth. Hence the constant g must be interpreted as a property of the earth, not of the falling body.

Using Newton's calculus (denoting the time derivative by a dot) and generalizing for all three coordinates, one obtains the equations

$$\ddot{x} = 0, \qquad \ddot{y} = 0, \qquad \ddot{z} = -g, \tag{3.2}$$

which describe the trajectories of particles upon the earth with arbitrary initial positions and velocities.

These formulae condense the description of an infinite number of orbits and motions in one single simple statement: that some

* See Note 1 of Appendix Two, p. 213.

property of the motion is the same for the whole class, independent of the individual case, therefore depending only on the one other thing involved, namely the earth. Hence this property, namely the vertical acceleration, must be 'due to the earth', or 'caused by the earth', or 'a force exerted by the earth'.

This word 'force' indicates a specification of the general notion of cause, namely a measurable cause, expressible in figures. Apart from this refinement, Galileo's work is just a case of ordinary causality in the sense of my definition.

Yet the law (3.2) involves time, since the 'effect' of the force is an acceleration, the rate of change of velocity in time. This is the actual result of observation and measurement, and has no metaphysical root whatsoever. A consequence of this fact is the deterministic character of the law (3.2): if the position and the velocity of a particle are given at any time, the equations determine its position and velocity at any other time.

In fact, any other time in the past or future. This shows that Galileo's law does not conform to the postulate of antecedence: a given initial situation cannot be regarded as the cause of a later situation, because the relation between them is completely symmetrical; each determines the other. This is closely connected with the notion of time which Galileo used, and which Newton took care to define explicitly.

The postulate of contiguity is also violated by Galileo's law since the action of the earth on the moving particle needs apparently no contact. But this question is better discussed in connexion with Newton's generalization.

Newton applied Galileo's method to the explanation of celestial motions. The material on which he based his deductions was scanty indeed; for at that time only six planets (including the earth) and a few satellites of these were known. I say 'deductions', for the essential induction had already been made by Kepler when he announced his three laws of planetary motion as valid for planets in general. The first two laws, concerning the elliptic shape of the orbit and the increase of the area swept by the radius vector, were based mainly on Tycho Brahe's observations of Mars, i.e. of one single planet. Generalized by a sweeping induction to *any* planet they are, according to Newton, equivalent to the statement that the acceleration is always directed towards the sun and varies inversely as the square of the distance r from the sun, μr^{-2}, where μ is a constant which may differ from planet to planet. But it is the third law which reveals the causal relation to the sun. It says that the ratio of the square of the period and the cube of the principal axis is the same for all planets—induced from data about the six known planets. This implies, as Newton showed (see Appendix, **2**), that the constant μ is the same for all planets. Hence as in Galileo's case, it can depend only on the single other body involved, the sun. In this way the interpretation is obtained that the centripetal acceleration μr^{-2} is 'due to the sun', or 'caused by the sun', or 'a force exerted by the sun'.

The moon and the other planetary satellites were then the material for the induction which led to the generalization of a mutual attraction of all bodies towards one another. The most amazing step, rightly admired by Newton's contemporaries and later generations, was the inclusion of terrestrial bodies in the law derived from the heavens. This is in fact the idea symbolized by the apocryphal story of the falling apple: terrestrial gravity was regarded by Newton as identical with celestial attraction. By applying his laws of motion to the system earth–moon, he could calculate Galileo's constant of gravity g from geodetical and astronomical data: namely,

$$g = \frac{4\pi^2 R^3}{r^2 T^2}, \tag{3.3}$$

where r is the radius of the earth, R the distance between the centres of earth and moon, and T the time of revolution of the moon (sidereal month).

The general equations for the motion of n particles under mutual gravitation read in modern vector notation

$$\ddot{\mathbf{r}}_\alpha = -\mathrm{grad}_\alpha V, \tag{3.4}$$

$$V = \frac{1}{2}\sum_{\alpha,\beta=1}^{n} \frac{\mu_\beta}{r_{\alpha\beta}}, \tag{3.5}$$

where $\mathbf{r}_\alpha$ is the position vector of the particle α ($\alpha = 1, 2, \ldots, n$), $r_{\alpha\beta} = |\mathbf{r}_\alpha - \mathbf{r}_\beta|$ the distance of two particles α and β, V the potential of the gravitational forces.

Newton also succeeded in generalizing the laws of motion for other non-gravitational forces by introducing the notion of mass, or more precisely of inertial mass. Newton's method of representing his results in an axiomatic form does not reveal the way he obtained them. It is, however, possible to regard this step as a case of ordinary causality derived by induction. One has to observe the acceleration of different particles produced by the same non-gravitational (say elastic) forces at the same point of space; they are found to differ, but not in direction, only in magnitude. Therefore, one can infer by induction the existence of a scalar factor characteristic for the resistance of a particle against acceleration or its inertia. This factor is called 'mass'. It may still depend on velocity as is assumed in modern theory of relativity. This can be checked by experiment, and as in Newton's time no such effect could be observed, the mass was regarded as a constant.

Then the generalized equations of motions read

$$m_\alpha \ddot{\mathbf{r}}_\alpha = \mathbf{F}_\alpha, \tag{3.6}$$

where m_α ($\alpha = 1, 2, \ldots, n$) are the masses and $\mathbf{F}_\alpha$ the force vectors which depend on the mutual distances $r_{\alpha\beta}$ of all the particles. As in the case of gravitation, they may be derivable from a potential V by the operation

$$\mathbf{F}_\alpha = -\operatorname{grad}_\alpha V, \tag{3.7}$$

where V is a function of the $r_{\alpha\beta}$. The most general form of V for forces inverse to the square of the distance would be ($\sum'_{\alpha,\beta}$ means summing over all α, β except $\alpha = \beta$)

$$V = \sum_{\alpha,\beta}' \frac{\mu_{\alpha\beta}}{r_{\alpha\beta}}, \tag{3.8}$$

where $\mu_{\alpha\beta}$ are constants; comparison with (3.4) and (3.5) shows, however, that these must have the form

$$\mu_{\alpha\beta} = m_\alpha \mu_\beta. \tag{3.9}$$

Newton applies further a law of symmetry, stated axiomatically, namely that action equals reaction, or $\mu_{\alpha\beta} = \mu_{\beta\alpha}$, from which follows

$$\mu_\beta = K m_\beta, \tag{3.10}$$

where K is a universal constant, the constant of gravitation. Hence the constants of attraction or gravitational masses μ_α are proportional to the inertial masses m_α.

Neither Newton himself, nor many generations of physicists and astronomers after him have paid much attention to the law expressed by (3.10). Astronomical observations left little doubt that it was correct, and it was proved by terrestrial observations (with suitable pendulums) to hold with extreme accuracy (Eötvos and others).* Two centuries went by before Einstein saw the fundamental problem contained in the simple equation (3.10), and built on it the colossal structure of his theory of general relativity, to which we have to return later.

But this is not our concern here. We have to examine Newton's equations from the standpoint of the principle of causality. I hope I have made it clear that they imply the notion of cause exactly in the same sense as it is always used by the experimentalist, namely signifying a verifiable dependence of one thing or another. Yet this one thing is, in Galileo's and Newton's theory alike, a peculiar quantity, namely an acceleration. The peculiarity is not only that it cannot be seen or read from a measuring tape, but that it contains the time implicitly. In fact, Newton's equations determine the motion of a system in time completely for any given initial state (position and velocity of all particles involved). In this way, 'causation' leads to 'determination', not as a new metaphysical principle, but as a physical fact, like any other. However, just as in Galileo's simpler case, so here the relation between two consecutive configurations of the system is mutual and symmetrical. This has a bearing on the question whether the principle of antecedence holds. As this applies, according to our definition, only to the cause–effect relation between single events, one has to change the standpoint. Instead of considering the acceleration of one body to be caused by the other bodies, one considers two

* See Note 2 of Appendix Two, p. 213.

consecutive configurations of the whole system and asks whether it makes sense to call the earlier one the cause of the later one. But it makes no sense, for the relation between the two states is symmetrical. One could, with the same right, call the later configuration the cause of the earlier one.

The root of this symmetry is Newton's definition of time. Whatever he says about the notion of time (in *Principia*, Scholium I) as a uniform flow, the use he makes of it contains nothing of a flow in one direction. Newton's time is just an independent variable t appearing in the equations of motion, in such a way that if t is changed into $-t$, the equations remain the same. It follows that, if all velocities are reversed, the system just goes back the same way; it is completely reversible.

Newton's time variable t is obviously an idealization abstracted from simple mechanical models and astronomical observations, fitting well into celestial motion, but not into ordinary experience. To us it appears that life on earth is going definitely in one direction, from past to future, from birth to death, and the perception of time in our mind is that of an irresistible and irreversible current.

Another feature of Newton's dynamics was repugnant to many of his contemporaries, in particular the followers of Descartes, whose cosmology, whatever else its shortcomings, satisfied the principle of contiguity, as I have called the condition that cause and effect should be in spatial contact. Newton's forces, the quantitative expressions for causes of motion, are supposed to act through empty space, so that cause and effect are simultaneous whatever the distance. Newton himself refrained from entering into a metaphysical controversy and insisted that the facts led unambiguously to his results. Indeed, the language of facts was so strong that they silenced the philosophical objections, and only when new facts revealed to a later generation the propagation of forces with finite velocity, was the problem of contiguity in gravitation taken up. In spite of these difficulties, Newton's dynamics has served many generations of physicists and is useful, even indispensable, to-day.

IV

CONTIGUITY

MECHANICS OF CONTINUOUS MEDIA

ALTHOUGH I maintain that neither causality itself nor its attributes, which I called the principles of antecedence and contiguity, are metaphysical, and that only the inference by induction transcends experience, there is no doubt that these ideas have a strong power over the human mind, and we have evidence enough that they have influenced the development of classical physics. Much effort has been made to reconcile Newton's laws with these postulates. Contiguity is closely bound up with the introduction of contact forces, pressures, tensions, first in ordinary material bodies, then in the electromagnetic ether, and thus to the idea of fields of forces; but the systematic application of contiguity to gravitation exploded Newton's theory, which was superseded by Einstein's relativity. Similar was the fate of the postulate of antecedence; it is closely bound up with irreversibility in time, and found its first quantitative formulation in thermodynamics. The reconciliation of it with Newton's laws was attempted by atomistics and physical statistics; the idea being that accumulations of immense numbers of invisible Newtonian particles, atoms, or molecules appear to the observer to have the feature of irreversibility for statistical reasons. The atoms were first hypothetical, but soon they were taken seriously, and one began to search for them, with increasing success. They became more and more real, and finally even visible. And then it turned out that they were no Newtonian particles at all. Whereupon the whole classical physics exploded, to be replaced by quantum theory. Looked at from the point of view of our principles, the situation in quantum theory is reversed. Determinism (which is so prominent a characteristic of Newton's theory) is abandoned, but contiguity and antecedence (violated by Newton's laws) are preserved to a considerable degree. Causality, which in my formulation is independent of antecedence and contiguity, is not affected by these changes:

scientific work will always be the search for causal interdependence of phenomena.

After this summary of the following discussion, let us return to the question why violation of the principles of contiguity and antecedence in Newton's theory was first accepted—though not without protest—but later amended and finally rejected. This change was due to the transition from celestial to terrestrial mechanics.

The success of Newton's theory was mainly in the field of planetary motion, and there it was overwhelming indeed. It is not my purpose to expand on the history of astronomy after Newton; it suffices to remember that the power of analytical mechanics to describe and predict accurately the observations led many to the conviction that it was the final formulation of the ultimate laws of nature.

The main attention was paid to the mathematical investigation of the equations of motion, and the works of Lagrange, Laplace, Gauss, Hamilton, and many others are a lasting memorial of this epoch. Of all these writings, I shall dwell only for a moment on that of Hamilton, because his formulation of Newton's laws is the most general and elegant one, and because they will be used over and over again in the following lectures. So permit me a short mathematical interlude which has nothing directly to do with cause and chance.

Hamilton considers a system of particles described by any (in general non-Cartesian) coordinates $q_1, q_2, \ldots$; then the potential energy is a function of these, $V(q_1, q_2, \ldots)$ or shortly $V(q)$, and the kinetic energy T a function of both the coordinates and the generalized velocities $\dot{q}_1, \dot{q}_2, \ldots$, $T(q, \dot{q})$. He then defines generalized momenta

$$p_\alpha = \frac{\partial T}{\partial \dot{q}_\alpha}, \tag{4.1}$$

and regards the total energy $T+V$ as a function of the q_α and p_α. This function

$$T+V = H(q, p) \tag{4.2}$$

is to-day called the Hamiltonian.

The equations of motion assume the simple 'canonical' form

$$\dot{q}_\alpha = \frac{\partial H}{\partial p_\alpha}, \qquad \dot{p}_\alpha = -\frac{\partial H}{\partial q_\alpha}, \tag{4.3}$$

from which one reads at once the conservation law of energy,

$$\frac{dH}{dt} = 0, \qquad H = \text{const.} \tag{4.4}$$

It is this set of formulae which has survived the most violent revolution of physical ideas which has ever taken place, the transition to quantum mechanics.

Returning now to the post-Newtonian period there was, simultaneous with the astronomical applications and confirmations of the theory, a lively interest in applying it to ordinary terrestrial physics. Even here Newton had shown the way and had calculated, for instance, the velocity of sound in a fluid. Eventually the mechanics of elastic solids brought about a modification of Newton's definition of force which satisfies contiguity. Much of this work is due to the great mathematician Cauchy. He started, as many before him, by treating a solid as an aggregate of tiny particles, acting on one another with Newtonian non-contiguous forces of short range—anticipating to some degree the modern atomistic standpoint. But there was of course, at that time, no evidence of the physical reality of these particles. In the physical applications all traces of them were obliterated by averaging. The form of these results suggested to Cauchy another method of approach where particle mechanics is completely discarded. Matter is considered to be a real continuum in the mathematical sense, so that it has a meaning to speak of a force between two pieces of matter separated by a surface. This seems to be, from our modern standpoint, a step in the wrong direction, as we know matter to be discontinuous. But Cauchy's work showed how contiguity could be introduced into mechanics; the importance of this point became evident when the new method was applied to the ether, the carrier of light and of electric and magnetic forces, which even to-day is still regarded as continuous—though it has lost most of the characteristic properties of a substance and can hardly be called a continuous *medium*.

In this theory all laws appear in the form of partial differential equations, in which the three space-coordinates appear together with the time as independent coordinates.

I shall give a short sketch of the mechanics of continuous media.

Mass, velocity, and all other properties of matter are considered continuously distributed in space. The mass per unit volume or density ρ is then a function of the space coordinates, and the same holds for the current of mass $\mathbf{u} = \rho\mathbf{v}$ (namely the quantity of mass passing through a surface per unit area and unit time). The conservation (indestructibility) of mass then leads to the so-called continuity equation (see Appendix, **3**)

$$\dot{\rho}+\operatorname{div}\mathbf{u} = 0. \tag{4.5}$$

Concerning the forces, one has to assume that, if the substance is regarded as separated into two parts by a surface, each part exerts a push or pull through this surface on the other which, measured per unit area, is called tension or stress. A simple mathematical consideration, based on the equilibrium conditions for the resultant forces acting on the surfaces of a volume element, shows that it suffices to define these tension forces for three non-coplanar surface elements, say those parallel to the three coordinate planes; the force on the element normal to x being $\mathbf{T}_x$ with components T_{xx}, T_{xy}, T_{xz}, the other two forces correspondingly $\mathbf{T}_y$ (T_{yx}, T_{yy}, T_{yz}) and $\mathbf{T}_z$ (T_{zx}, T_{zy}, T_{zz}). Then the force on a surface element with the normal unit vector

$$\mathbf{n}\ (n_x, n_y, n_z)$$

is given by

$$\mathbf{T}_n = \mathbf{T}_x n_x+\mathbf{T}_y n_y+\mathbf{T}_z n_z. \tag{4.6}$$

Application of the law of moments to a small volume element shows (see Appendix, **3**) that

$$T_{yz} = T_{zy}, \quad T_{zx} = T_{xz}, \quad T_{xy} = T_{yx}. \tag{4.7}$$

Hence the quantities T form a symmetrical matrix, the *stress tensor*

$$\mathsf{T} = \begin{pmatrix} T_{xx} & T_{xy} & T_{xz} \\ T_{yx} & T_{yy} & T_{yz} \\ T_{zx} & T_{zy} & T_{zz} \end{pmatrix}. \tag{4.8}$$

Newton's law applied to a volume element then leads to the equations

$$\rho\frac{d\mathbf{v}}{dt} = \operatorname{div}\mathsf{T}, \tag{4.9}$$

where div T is a vector with the components

$$(\text{div }\mathsf{T})_x = \frac{\partial T_{xx}}{\partial x}+\frac{\partial T_{xy}}{\partial x}+\frac{\partial T_{xz}}{\partial x}, \quad ..., \tag{4.10}$$

and d/dt the operator

$$\frac{d}{dt} = \frac{\partial}{\partial t}+v_x\frac{\partial}{\partial x}+v_y\frac{\partial}{\partial y}+v_z\frac{\partial}{\partial z}, \tag{4.11}$$

which is called the 'convective derivative'.

(4.9) together with (4.5) are the new equations of motion which satisfy the postulate of contiguity. They are the prototype for all subsequent field theories. In the present form they are still incomplete and rather void of meaning, as the stress tensor is not specified in its dependence on the physical conditions of the system—just in the same way as Newton's equations are void of meaning if the forces are not specified with their dependence on the configuration of the particles. The configuration of a continuous system cannot be described by the values of a finite number of variables, but by certain space functions, called 'strain-components'. They are defined in this way: A small (infinitesimal) volume of initially spherical shape will be transformed by the deformation into an ellipsoid; the equation of this has the form

$$e_{11}x^2+e_{22}y^2+e_{33}z^2+2e_{23}yz+2e_{31}zx+2e_{12}xy = \epsilon, \tag{4.12}$$

where ϵ is an (infinitesimal) constant, measuring the absolute dimensions, and $e_{11}, e_{22},..., e_{12}$ are six quantities depending on the position x, y, z of the centre of the sphere. These e_{ij} are the components of the *strain tensor* e.

In the theory of elasticity it is assumed that the stress components T_{ij} are linear functions of the strain components e_{ij} (Hooke's law).

In hydrodynamics the relation between T and e involves space- and time-derivatives of e_{ij}. In plastic solids the situation is still more complicated.

We need not enter into these different branches of the mechanics in continuous media. The only important point for us is this: Contact forces spread not instantaneously but with finite velocity. This is the main feature distinguishing Cauchy's contiguous mechanics from Newton's non-contiguous. The simplest example is an elastic fluid (liquid or gas). Here the stress tensor T has only diagonal elements which are equal and represent the pressure p. The configuration can also be described by one variable, the density ρ or, for a given mass, the volume V. The relation between p and V may be any function $p = f(V)$—we shall have to remember this later when we have to deal with thermodynamics. For small disturbances of equilibrium the general equations reduce to linear ones; any quantity ϕ in an isotropic fluid (change of volume or pressure) satisfies the linear wave equation

$$\frac{1}{c^2}\frac{\partial^2\phi}{\partial t^2} = \Delta\phi, \tag{4.13}$$

where Δ is Laplace's differential operator

$$\Delta = \text{divgrad} = \frac{\partial^2}{\partial x^2}+\frac{\partial^2}{\partial y^2}+\frac{\partial^2}{\partial z^2}, \tag{4.14}$$

and c a constant which is easily found to mean the phase velocity of a plane harmonic wave

$$\phi = A\sin\frac{2\pi}{\lambda}(x-ct).$$

The equation (4.13) links up mechanics with other branches of physics which have independently developed, optics and electromagnetism.

ELECTROMAGNETIC FIELDS

The history of optics, in particular Newton's contributions and his dispute with Huygens about the corpuscular or wave nature of light, is so well known that I need not speak about it. A hundred years after Newton, the wave nature of light was established by Young and Fresnel with the help of experiments on diffraction and interference. Wave equations of the type (4.13) were used as a matter of course to describe the observations, where now ϕ means the amplitude of the vibration.

But what is it that vibrates? A name, 'ether,' was ready to hand, and its ability to propagate transverse waves suggested that it was comparable to an elastic solid. In this way it came to pass that the ether-filled vacuum was the carrier of contact forces, spreading with finite velocity. They existed for a long period peacefully beside Newton's instantaneous forces of gravitation, and other similar forces introduced to describe elementary experiences in electricity and magnetism. These forces are usually connected with Coulomb's name, who verified them by direct measurements of the intensity of attraction and repulsion between small charged bodies, and between the poles of needle-shaped magnets. He found a law of the same type as that of Newton, of the form μr^{-2}, where the constant μ depends on the state of electrification or magnetization respectively of the interacting particles; by applying the law of action and reaction μ can be split into factors, $\mu = e_1 e_2$ in the electric case, where e_1, e_2 are called the charges. It must, however, have been remarked that this law was already established earlier and with a higher degree of accuracy by Cavendish and Priestley by an indirect reasoning, with the help of the fact that a closed conductor screens a charged particle from the influence of outside charges; this argument, though still dressed up in the language of Newtonian forces, is already quite close to notions of field theory.

It was the attempt to formulate the mechanical interactions between linear currents (in thin wires) in terms of Newtonian forces which entangled physics in the first part of the nineteenth century in serious difficulties. Meanwhile Faraday had begun his investigations unbiased by any mathematical theory, and accumulated direct evidence for understanding electric and magnetic phenomena with the help of contact forces. He spoke about pressures and tensions in the media surrounding charged bodies, using the expressions introduced in the theory of elasticity, yet with considerable and somewhat strange modifications. Indeed, the strangeness of these assumptions made it difficult for his learned contemporaries to accept his ideas and to discard the well-established Newtonian fashion of description. Yet seen from our modern standpoint, there is no intrinsic difference between the two methods, as long as only static and stationary phenomena are considered. Mathematical analysis shows that the resultant forces on observable bodies can be expressed either as integrals over elementary contributions of the Newtonian—or better Coulombian—type acting over the distance, or by surface integrals of tensions derived from field equations. This holds not only for conductors *in vacuo*, but also for dielectric and magnetizable substances; it is true that in the latter case the Coulombian forces lead to integral equations which are somewhat involved, but the differential equations of the field are, in spite of their simpler aspect, not intrinsically simpler. This is often overlooked in modern text-books. However, in Faraday's time this equivalence of differential and integral equations for the forces was not known, and if it had been, Faraday would not have cared. His conviction of the superiority of contact forces over Coulombian forces rested on his physical intuition. It needed another, more mathematically-minded genius, Clerk Maxwell, to find the clue which made it impossible to accept forces acting instantaneously over finite distances: the finite velocity of propagation. It is not easy to analyse exactly the epistemological and experimental foundations of Maxwell's prediction, as his first papers make use of rather weird models and the purity of his thought appears only in his later publications. I think the process which led to Maxwell's equations, stripped of all unnecessary verbiage and roundabout ways, was this: By combining all the known experimental facts about charges, magnetic poles, currents, and the forces between them, he could establish a set of field equations connecting the spatial and temporal changes of the electric and magnetic field strength (force per unit charge) with the electric charge density and current. But if these were combined with the condition that any change of charge could occur only by means of a current (expressed by a continuity equation analogous to (4.5); see Appendix, **4**), an inadequacy became obvious. In the language of that time, the result was formulated by saying that no open currents (like discharge of condensers) could be described by this theory. Therefore something was wrong in the equations, and an inspection showed a suspicious feature, a lack of symmetry. The terms expressing Faraday's induction law (production of electric force by the time variation of the magnetic field) had no counterpart obtained by exchanging the symbols for electric and magnetic quantities (production of magnetic force by the time variation of the electric field). Without any direct experimental evidence Maxwell postulated this inverse effect and added to his equations the corresponding term, which expresses that a change of the electric field (displacement current) is, in its magnetic action, equivalent to an ordinary current. It was a guess based on a belief in harmony. Yet by some mathematical reasoning it can be connected with one single but highly significant fact which sufficed to convince Maxwell of the correctness of his conjecture—just as Newton was convinced of the correctness of his law of gravitation by one single numerical coincidence, the calculation of terrestrial gravity from the moon's orbit. Maxwell showed that his modified equations had solutions representing waves, the velocity, c, of which could be expressed in terms of purely electric and magnetic constants; for the vacuum c turned out to be equal to the ratio of a unit of charge measured electrostatically (by Coulomb's law) and electromagnetically (by Oersted's law). This ratio, a quantity of the dimensions of a velocity, was known from measurements by Kohlrausch and Weber, and its numerical value coincided with the velocity of light. That could hardly be accidental, indeed, and Maxwell could pronounce the electromagnetic theory of light.

The final confirmation of Maxwell's theory was, after his death, obtained by Hertz's discovery of electromagnetic waves.

I cannot follow the further course of events in the establishment of electromagnetic theory. I only wish to stress the point that the use of contact forces and field equations, i.e. the establishment of contiguity, in electromagnetism was the result of a long struggle against preconceptions of Newtonian origin. This confirms my view that the question of contiguity is not a metaphysical one, but an empirical one.

We have now to see whether the laws of electromagnetism satisfy the principle of antecedence. An inspection of Maxwell's equations (see Appendix, **4**) shows that a reversal of time, $t \rightarrow -t$, leaves everything, including the continuity equation, unchanged, if the electric density and field are kept unchanged while the electric current and magnetic field are reversed. This is a kind of reversibility very similar to that of mechanics, where a change of the sign of all velocities makes the system return to its initial state. The difference is only a practical one: a change of sign of all current densities and the whole magnetic field is not as simple to perform as that of a finite set of velocities. The situation is best seen by considering an electromagnetic wave spreading from a point source; the corresponding solution of Maxwell's equation is given by so-called retarded potentials which express the electromagnetic state at a point P for the time t in terms of the motion of the source at the time $t-r/c$, where r is the distance of P from the source. But there also exist other solutions, advanced potentials, which refer to the later time $t+r/c$ and represent a wave contracting towards the source.

Such contracting waves are of course necessary for solving certain problems. Imagine, for instance, a spherical wave reflected by a concentric spherical mirror. However, such a mirror must be absolutely perfect to do its duty, and there appears to be something improbable about the occurrence of advanced potentials in nature. For the description of elementary processes of emission of atoms or electrons one has supplemented Maxwell's equations by the rule that only retarded solutions are allowed. In this way a kind of irreversibility can be introduced and the principle of antecedence satisfied. But this is altogether artificial and unsatisfactory. The irreversibility of actual electromagnetic processes has its roots in other facts which we shall later have to describe in detail. Maxwell's equations themselves do not satisfy the postulate of antecedence.

RELATIVITY AND THE FIELD THEORY OF GRAVITATION

The situation which we have now reached is that which I found when I began to study almost half a century ago. There existed, more or less peacefully side by side, Newton's mechanics of instantaneous action over any distance, Cauchy's mechanics of continuous substances, and Maxwell's electrodynamics, the latter two satisfying the postulate of contiguity. Of these theories,

Maxwell's seemed to be the most promising and fertile, and the idea began to spread that possibly all forces of nature might be of electromagnetic origin. The problem had to be envisaged, how to reconcile Newton's gravitational forces with the postulate of contiguity; the solution was Einstein's general theory of relativity.

This is a long and interesting story by itself which involves not only the notion of cause with which we are concerned here, but other philosophical concepts, namely those concerned with space and time. A detailed discussion of these problems would lead us too far away from our subject, and I think it hardly necessary to dwell on them because relativity is to-day widely known and part of the syllabus of the student of mathematics and physics as well. So I shall give a very short outline only.

The physical problems which led to the theory of relativity were those concerned with the optical and electromagnetic phenomena of fast-moving bodies. There are two types of experiments: those using the high velocity of celestial bodies (e.g. Michelson's and Morley's experiment) and those using fast electrons or ions (e.g. Bucherer's measurement of the mass of electrons in cathode rays as a function of the velocity). The work of Lorentz, FitzGerald, Poincaré, and others prepared the ground for Einstein's discovery that the root of all difficulties was the assumption of a universal time valid for all moving systems of reference. He showed that this assumption has no foundation in any possible experience and he replaced it by a simple definition of relative time, valid in a given coordinate system, but different from the time of another system in relative motion. The formal law of transformation from one space-time system to another was already known, owing to an analysis of Lorentz; it is in fact an intrinsic property of Maxwell's equations. The Lorentz transformation is linear; it expresses the physical equivalence of systems in relative motion with constant velocity (see Appendix, **5**).

Einstein's theory of gravitation is formally based on a generalization of these transformations into arbitrary, non-linear ones; with the help of these one can express the transition from one system of reference to another accelerated (and simultaneously deformed) one. The physical idea behind this mathematical formalism has been already mentioned: the exact proportionality of mass, as defined by inertia, and of mass as defined by gravitation, equation (3.10); or, in other words, the fact that in Newton's law of gravitational motion (3.4) the (inertial) mass does not appear.

Einstein succeeded in establishing equations for the gravitational field by identifying the components of this field with the quantities $g_{\mu\nu}$ which define the geometry of space-time, namely the coefficients of the line element

$$ds^2 = \sum_{\mu,\nu} g_{\mu\nu}\, dx^\mu\, dx^\nu, \tag{4.15}$$

where x^1, x^2, x^3 stand for the space coordinates x, y, z, x^4 for the time t.

In ordinary 3-dimensional Euclidean geometry the $g_{\mu\nu}$ are constant and can, by a proper choice of the coordinate system, be normalized in such a way that

$$g_{\mu\mu} = 1, \qquad g_{\mu\nu} = 0 \text{ for } \mu \neq \nu.$$

Minkowski showed that special relativity can be regarded as a 4-dimensional geometry, where time is added as the fourth coordinate, but still with constant $g_{\mu\nu}$, which can be normalized to

$$g_{11} = g_{22} = g_{33} = 1, \quad g_{44} = -1, \quad g_{\mu\nu} = 0 \text{ for } \mu \neq \nu. \tag{4.16}$$

It was further known from the work of Riemann that a very general type of non-Euclidean geometry in 3-dimensional space could be obtained by taking the $g_{\mu\nu}$ as variable functions of x^1, x^2, x^3, and the mathematical properties of this geometry had been thoroughly studied (Levi–Civita, Ricci).

Einstein generalized Riemann's formalism to four dimensions, assuming that the $g_{\mu\nu}$ depend not only on x^1, x^2, x^3, but also on x^4, the time. However, he regarded the $g_{\mu\nu}$ not as given functions of x^1, x^2, x^3, x^4 but as field quantities to be calculated from the distribution of matter. He formed a set of quantities $R_{\mu\nu}$ which can be regarded as a measure of the 'curvature' of space and are functions of the $g_{\mu\nu}$ and their first and second derivatives, and postulated equations of the form

$$R_{\mu\nu} = \kappa T_{\mu\nu}, \tag{4.17}$$

where κ is a constant and the $T_{\mu\nu}$ are generalizations of the tensions in matter, defined in (4.8): one has to supplement the tensor T by a fourth row and column, where T_{14}, T_{24}, T_{34} are the components of the density of momentum, T_{44} the density of energy. These equations (4.17) are invariant in a very general sense, namely for all continuous transformations of space-time, and they are essentially uniquely determined by this property and the postulate that no higher derivatives than the second-order ones should appear.

If the distribution of matter is given, i.e. the $T_{\mu\nu}$ are known, the field equations (4.17) allow one to calculate the $g_{\mu\nu}$, i.e. the geometry of space. Einstein found the solution for a mass point as source of the field, and by assuming that the motion of another particle was determined by a geodesic, or shortest, or straightest line in this geometry, he showed that Newton's laws of planetary motion follow as a first approximation. But higher approximations lead to small deviations, some of which can be observed. I cannot enter into the discussion of all the consequences of the new gravitational theory; Einstein's predictions have been confirmed, although some of them are at the limit of observational technique. But I wish to add a remark about a theoretical point which is not so well known, yet very important. The assumption that the motion of a particle is given by a geodesic is obviously an unsatisfactory feature; one would expect that the field equations alone should determine not only the field produced by particles but also the reaction of the particles to the field, that is their motion. Einstein, with his collaborators Infeld and Hoffmann, has proved that this is in fact the case, and the same result has been obtained independently and, as I think, in a considerably simpler way, by the Russian physicist, Fock.* On the basis of these admirable papers, one can say that the field theory of gravitation is logically perfect—whether it will stand all observational tests remains to be seen.

From the standpoint of the philosophical problem, which is the subject of these lectures, there are several conclusions to be drawn. The first is that now physical geometry, that is, not some abstract mathematical system but the geometrical aspect of the

* See Note 3 of Appendix Two, p. 213.

behaviour of actual bodies, is subject to the cause–effect relation and to all related principles like any other branch of science. The mathematicians often stress the opposite point of view; they speak of the geometrization of physics, but though it cannot be denied that the mathematical beauty of this method has inspired numerous valuable investigations, it seems to me an over-estimation of the formalism. The main point is that Einstein's geometrical mechanics or mechanical geometry satisfies the principle of contiguity. On the other hand, antecedence, applied to two consecutive configurations as cause and effect, is not satisfied, or not more than in electrodynamics; for there is no intrinsic direction in the flow of time contained in the equations. The theory is deterministic, at least in principle: the future or past motion of particles and the distribution of the gravitational field are predictable from the equations, if the situation at a given time is known, together with boundary conditions (vanishing of field at infinity) for all times. But as the gravitational field travels between the particles with finite velocity, this statement is not identical with Newtonian determinism: a knowledge is needed, not only of all particles, but also of all gravitational waves (which do not exist in Newton's theory). Einstein himself values the deterministic feature of his theory very highly. He regards it as a postulate which has to be demanded from any physical theory, and he rejects, therefore, parts of modern physics which do not satisfy it.

Here I only wish to remark that determinism in field theories seems to me of very little significance. To illustrate the power of mechanics, Laplace invented a super-mathematician able to predict the future of the world provided the positions and velocities of all particles at one moment were given to him. I can sympathize with him in his arduous task. But I would really pity him if he had not only to solve the numerous ordinary differential equations of Newtonian type but also the partial differential equations of the field theory with the particles as singularities.

V

ANTECEDENCE: THERMODYNAMICS

WE have now to discuss the experiences which make it possible to distinguish in an objective empirical way between past and future or, in our terminology, to establish the principle of antecedence in the chain of cause and effect. These experiences are connected with the production and transfer of heat. There would be a long story to tell about the preliminary steps necessary to translate the subjective phenomena of hot and cold into the objective language of physics: the distinction between the quality 'temperature' and the quantity 'heat', together with the invention of the corresponding instruments, the thermometer and calorimeter. I take the technical side of this development to be well known and I shall use the thermal concepts in the usual way, although I shall have to analyse them presently from the standpoint of scientific methodology. It was only natural that the measurable quantity heat was first regarded as a kind of invisible substance called caloric. The flow of heat was treated with the methods developed for material liquids, yet with one important difference: the inertia of the caloric fluid seemed to be negligible; its flow was determined by a differential equation which is not of the second but of the first order in time. It is obtained from the continuity equation (see (4.5))

$$\dot{Q} + \operatorname{div} \mathbf{q} = 0 \tag{5.1}$$

by assuming that the change of the density of heat Q is proportional to the change of temperature T, $\delta Q = c\,\delta T$ (where c is the specific heat), while the current of heat $\mathbf{q}$ is proportional to the negative gradient of temperature, $\mathbf{q} = -\kappa \operatorname{grad} T$ (where κ is the coefficient of conductivity). Hence

$$c\frac{\partial T}{\partial t} = \kappa \Delta T, \tag{5.2}$$

a differential equation of the first order in time. This equation was the starting-point of one of the greatest discoveries in mathematics, Fourier's theory of expansion of arbitrary functions in terms of orthogonal sets of simple periodic functions, the prototype of numerous similar expansions and the embryo from which a considerable part of modern analysis and mathematical physics developed.

But that is not the aspect from which we have here to regard the equation (5.2); it is this:

The equation does not allow a change of t into $-t$, the result cannot be compensated by a change of sign of other variables as happens in Maxwell's equations. Hence the solutions exhibit an essential difference of past and future, a definite 'flow of time' as one is used to say—meaning, of course, a flow of events in time. For instance, an elementary solution of (5.2) for the temperature distribution in a thin wire along the x-direction is

$$T-T_0 = \frac{C}{\sqrt{t}}e^{-(cx^2/4\kappa t)}, \qquad (5.3)$$

which describes the spreading and levelling out of an initially high temperature concentrated near the point $x = 0$, an obviously irreversible phenomenon.

I do not know enough of the history of physics to understand how this theory of heat conduction was reconciled with the general conviction that the ultimate laws of physics were of the Newtonian reversible type.

Before a solution of this problem could be attempted another important step was necessary: the discovery of the equivalence of heat and mechanical work, or, as we say to-day, of the first law of thermodynamics. It is important to remember that this discovery was made considerably later than the invention of the steam-engine. Not only the production of heat by mechanical work (e.g. through friction), but also the production of work from heat (steam-engine) was known. The new feature was the statement that a given amount of heat always corresponds to a definite amount of mechanical work, its 'mechanical equivalent'. Robert Mayer pronounced this law on very scanty and indirect evidence, but obtained a fairly good value for the equivalent from known properties of gases, namely from the difference of heat necessary to raise the temperature by one degree if either the volume is kept constant or the gas allowed to do work against a constant pressure. Joule investigated the same problem by systematic experiments which proved the essential point, namely that the work necessary to transfer a system from one equilibrium state to another depends only on these two states, not on the process of application of the work. This is the real content of the first law; the determination of the numerical value of the mechanical equivalent, so much stressed in text-books, is a matter of physical technique. To get our notions clear, we have now to return to the logical and philosophical foundations of the theory of heat.

The problem is to transform the subjective sense impressions of hot and cold into objective measurable statements. The latter are, of course, again somewhere connected with sense impressions. You cannot read an instrument without looking at it. But there is a difference between this looking at, say, a thermometer with which a nurse measures the temperature of a patient and the feeling of being hot under which the patient suffers.

It is a general principle of science to rid itself as much as possible from sense qualities. This is often misunderstood as meaning elimination of sense impressions, which, of course, is absurd. Science is based on observation, hence on the use of the senses. The problem is to eliminate the subjective features and to maintain only statements which can be confirmed by several individuals in an objective way. It is impossible to explain to anybody what I mean by saying 'This thing is red' or 'This thing is hot'. The most I can do is to find out whether other persons call the same things red or hot. Science aims at a closer relation between word and fact. Its method consists in finding correlations of one kind of subjective sense impressions with other kinds, using the one as indicators for the other, and in this way establishes what is called a fact of observation.

Here I have ventured again into metaphysics. At least, a philosopher would claim that a thorough study of these methodological principles is beyond physics. I think it is again a rule of our craft as scientists, like the principle of inductive inference, and I shall not analyse it further at this moment.

In the case of thermal phenomena, the problem is to define the quantities involved—temperature, heat—by means of observable objective changes in material bodies. It turns out that the *concepts of mechanics*, configuration and force, strain and stress, suffice for this purpose, but that the *laws of mechanics* have to be essentially changed.

Let us consider for simplicity only systems of fluids, that is of continuous media, whose state in equilibrium is defined by *one* single strain quantity, the density, instead of which we can also, for a given mass, take the total volume V. There is also only *one* stress quantity, the pressure p. From the standpoint of mechanics the pressure in equilibrium is a given function of the volume, $p = f(V)$.

Now all those experiences which are connected with the subjective impression of making the fluid hotter or colder, show that this law of mechanics is wrong: the pressure can be changed at constant volume—namely 'by heating' or 'by cooling'.

Hence the pressure p can be regarded as an independent variable besides the volume V, and this is exactly what thermodynamics does.

The generalization for more complicated substances (such as those with rigidity or magnetic polarizability) is so obvious that I shall stick to the examples of fluids, characterized by two thermodynamically independent variables V, p. But it is necessary to consider systems consisting of several fluids, and therefore one has to say a word about different kinds of contact between them.

To shorten the expression, one introduces the idea of 'walls' separating different fluids. These walls are supposed to be so thin that they play no other part in the physical behaviour of the system than to define the interaction between two neighbouring fluids. We shall assume every wall to be impenetrable to matter, although in theoretical chemistry semi-permeable partitions are used with great advantage. Two kinds of walls are to be considered.

An *adiabatic wall* is defined by the property that equilibrium of a body enclosed by it is not disturbed by any external process as long as no part of the wall is moved (distance forces being excluded in the whole consideration).

Two comments have to be made. The first is that the adiabatic property is here defined without using the notion of heat; that is essential, for as it is our aim to define the thermal concepts in mechanical terms, we cannot use them in the elementary definitions. The second remark is that adiabatic enclosure of a system can be practically realized, as in the Dewar vessel or thermos flask, with a high degree of approximation. Without this fact, thermodynamics would be utterly impracticable.

The ordinary presentations of this subject, though rather careless in their definitions, cannot avoid the assumption of the possibility of isolating a system thermally; without this no calorimeter would work and heat could not be measured.

The second type of wall is the *diathermanous wall*, defined by the following property: if two bodies are separated by a diathermanous wall, they are not in equilibrium for arbitrary values of their variables p_1, V_1 and p_2, V_2, but only if a definite relation between these four quantities is satisfied

$$F(p_1, V_1, p_2, V_2) = 0. \tag{5.4}$$

This is the expression of thermal contact; the wall is only introduced to symbolize the impossibility of exchange of material.

The concept of temperature is based on the experience that two bodies, being in thermal equilibrium with a third one, are also in thermal equilibrium with another. If we write (5.4) in the short form $F(1, 2) = 0$, this property of equilibrium can be expressed by saying that of the three equations

$$F(2, 3) = 0, \qquad F(3, 1) = 0, \qquad F(1, 2) = 0, \tag{5.5}$$

any two always involve the third. This is only possible if (5.4) can be brought into the form

$$f_1(p_1, V_1) = f_2(p_2, V_2). \tag{5.6}$$

Now one can use one of the two bodies, say 2, as thermometer and introduce the value of the function

$$f_2(p_2, V_2) = \vartheta \tag{5.7}$$

as *empirical temperature.* Then one has for the other body the so-called *equation of state*

$$f_1(p_1, V_1) = \vartheta. \tag{5.8}$$

Any arbitrary function of ϑ can be chosen as empirical temperature with equal right; the choice is restricted only by practical considerations. (It would be impractical to use a thermometric substance for which two distinguishable states are in thermal equilibrium.) The curves $\vartheta = \text{const.}$ in the pV-plane are independent of the temperature scale; they are called *isotherms.*

It is not superfluous to stress the extreme arbitrariness of the temperature scale. Any suitable property of any substance can be chosen as thermometric indicator, and if this is done, still the scale remains at our disposal. If we, for example, choose a gas at low pressures, because of the simplicity of the isothermal compression law $pV = \text{const.}$, there is no reason to take $pV = \vartheta$ as measure of temperature: one could just as well take $(pV)^2$ or $\sqrt{(pV)}$. The definition of an 'absolute' scale of temperature was therefore an urgent problem which was solved by the discovery of the second law of thermodynamics.

The second fundamental concept of thermodynamics, that of heat, can be defined in terms of mechanical quantities by a proper interpretation of Joule's experiments. As I have pointed out already, the gist of these experiments lies in the following fact: If a body in an adiabatic enclosure is brought from one (equilibrium) state to another by applying external work, the amount of this work is always the same in whatever form (mechanical, electrical, etc.) and manner (slow or fast, etc.) it is applied.

Hence for a given initial state (p_0, V_0) the work done adiabatically is a function U of the final state (p, V), and one can write

$$W = U - U_0; \tag{5.9}$$

the function $U(p, V)$ is called the *energy* of the system. It is a quantity directly measurable by mechanical methods.

If we now consider a non-adiabatic process leading from the initial state (p_0, V_0) to the final state (p, V), the difference $U - U_0 - W$ will not be zero, but can be determined if the energy function $U(p, V)$ is known from previous experiment. This difference

$$U-U_0-W = Q \tag{5.10}$$

is called the *heat* supplied to the system during the process. Equation (5.10) is the definition of heat in terms of mechanical quantities.

This procedure presupposes that mechanical work is measurable however it is applied; that means, for example, that the displacements of and the forces on the surface of a stirring-wheel in a fluid, or the current and resistance of a wire heating the fluid, must be registered even for the most violent reactions. Practically this is difficult, and one uses either stationary processes of a comparatively long duration where the irregular initial and final stages can be neglected (this includes heating by a stationary current), or extremely slow, 'quasi-static' processes; these are in general (practically) reversible, since no kinetic energy is produced which could be irreversibly destroyed by friction. In ordinary thermodynamics one regards every curve in the pV-plane as the diagram of a reversible process; that means that one allows infinitely slow heating or cooling by bringing the system into thermal contact with a series of large heat reservoirs which differ by small amounts of temperature. Such an assumption is artificial; it does not even remotely correspond to a real experiment. It is also quite superfluous. We can restrict ourselves to adiabatic quasi-static processes, consisting of slow movements of the (adiabatic) walls. For these the work done on a simple fluid is

$$dW = -p\,dV, \tag{5.11}$$

where p is the equilibrium pressure, and the first theorem of thermodynamics (5.10) assumes the form

$$dQ = dU+p\,dV = 0. \tag{5.12}$$

For systems of fluids separated by adiabatic or diathermanous walls the energy and the work done are additive (according to our definition of the walls); hence, for instance,

$$dQ = dQ_1+dQ_2 = dU+p_1\,dV_1+p_2\,dV_2, \tag{5.13}$$

where

$$U = U_1+U_2.$$

This equation is of course only of interest for the case of thermal contact where the equation (5.6) holds; the system has then only three independent variables, for which one can choose V_1, V_2 and the temperature ϑ, defined by (5.7) and (5.8). Then $U_1 = U_1(V_1, \vartheta)$, $U_2 = U_2(V_2, \vartheta)$, and (5.13) takes the form

$$dQ = \left(\frac{\partial U_1}{\partial V_1}+p_1\right)dV_1+\left(\frac{\partial U_2}{\partial V_2}+p_2\right)dV_2+\left(\frac{\partial U_1}{\partial \vartheta}+\frac{\partial U_2}{\partial \vartheta}\right)d\vartheta = 0. \tag{5.14}$$

Every adiabatic quasi-static process can be represented as a line in the three-dimensional $V_1 V_2 \vartheta$-space which satisfies this equation; let us call these for brevity 'adiabatic lines'.

Equation (5.14) is a differential equation of a type studied by Pfaff. Pfaffian equations are the mathematical expression of elementary thermal experiences, and one would expect that the laws of thermodynamics are connected with their properties. That is indeed the case, as Carathéodory has shown. But classical thermodynamics proceeded in quite a different way, introducing the conception of idealized thermal machines which transform heat into work and vice versa (William Thomson—Lord Kelvin), or which pump heat from one reservoir into another (Clausius). The second law of thermodynamics is then derived from the assumption that not all processes of this kind are possible: you cannot transform heat completely into work, nor bring it from a state of lower temperature to one of higher 'without compensation' (see Appendix, **6**). These are new and strange conceptions, obviously borrowed from engineering. I have mentioned that the steam-engine existed before thermodynamics; it was a matter of course at that time to use the notions and experiences of the engineer to obtain the laws of heat transformation, and the establishment of the abstract concepts of entropy and absolute temperature by this method is a wonderful achievement. It would be ridiculous to feel anything but admiration for the men who invented these methods. But even as a student, I thought that they deviated too much from the ordinary methods of physics; I discussed the problem with my mathematical friend, Carathéodory, with the result that he analysed it and produced a much more satisfactory solution. This was about forty years ago, but still all text-books reproduce the 'classical' method, and I am almost certain that the same holds for the great majority of lectures—I know, however, a few exceptions, namely those of the late R. H. Fowler and his school. This state of affairs seems to me one of unhealthy conservatism. I take in these lectures an opportunity to advocate a change.*

The central point of Carathéodory's method is this. The principles from which Kelvin and Clausius derived the second law are formulated in such a way as to cover the greatest possible range of processes incapable of execution: in no way whatever can heat be completely transformed into work or raised to a higher level of temperature. Carathéodory remarked that it is perfectly sufficient to know the existence of *some* impossible processes to derive the second law. I need hardly say that this is a logical advantage. Moreover, the impossible processes are already obtained by scrutinizing Joule's experiments a little more carefully. They consisted in bringing a system in an adiabatic enclosure from one equilibrium state to another by doing external work: it is an elementary experience, almost obvious, that you cannot get your work back by reversing the process. And that holds however near the two states are. One can therefore say that there exist adiabatically inaccessible states in any vicinity of a given state. That is Carathéodory's principle.

In particular, there are neighbour states of any given one which are inaccessible by quasi-static adiabatic processes. These are represented by adiabatic lines satisfying the Pfaffian equation (5.14). Therefore the question arises: Does Carathéodory's postulate hold for any Pfaffian or does it mean a restriction?

The latter is the case, and it can be seen by very simple mathematics indeed, of which I shall give here a short sketch (see Appendix, **7**).

Let us first consider a Pfaffian equation of two variables, x and y,

$$dQ = X\,dx + Y\,dy, \tag{5.15}$$

* See Note 4 of Appendix Two, p. 213.

where X, Y are functions of x, y. This is equivalent to the ordinary differential equation

$$\frac{dy}{dx} = -\frac{X}{Y}, \tag{5.16}$$

which has an infinite number of solutions $\phi(x,y) = \text{const.}$, representing a one-parameter set of curves in the (x,y)-plane. Along any of these curves one has

$$d\phi = \frac{\partial \phi}{\partial x}dx + \frac{\partial \phi}{\partial y}dy = 0, \tag{5.17}$$

and this must be the same condition as the given Pfaffian; hence one must have

$$dQ = \lambda\, d\phi. \tag{5.18}$$

Each Pfaffian dQ of two variables has therefore an 'integrating denominator' λ, so that dQ/λ is a total differential.

For Pfaffians of three (or more) variables,

$$dQ = X\,dx + Y\,dy + Z\,dz \tag{5.19}$$

this does not hold. It is easy to give analytical examples (see Appendix, **7**); but one can see it geometrically in this way: if in (5.19) dx, dy, dz are regarded as finite differences $\xi - x, \eta - y, \zeta - z$, it is the equation of a plane through the point x, y, z; one has a plane through each point of space, continuously varying in orientation with the position of this point. Now if a function ϕ existed, these planes would have to be tangential to the surfaces $\phi(x,y,z) = \text{const.}$ But one can construct continuously varying sets of planes which are not 'integrable', i.e. tangential to a set of surfaces. For example, take all circular screws with the same axis, but varying radius and pitch, and construct at each point of every screw the normal plane; these obviously form a non-integrable set of planes.

Hence all Pfaffians can be separated into two classes: those of the form $dQ = \lambda\, d\phi$, which have an 'integrating denominator' and represent the tangential planes of a set of surfaces $\phi = \text{const.}$, and those which lack this property.

Now in the first case, $dQ = \lambda\, d\phi$, any line satisfying the Pfaffian equation (5.19) must lie in the surface $\phi = \text{const.}$ Hence an arbitrary pair of points P_0 and P in the xyz-space cannot be connected by such a line. This is quite elementary. Not quite so obvious is the inverse statement which is used in the thermodynamic application: If there are points P in any vicinity of a given point P_0 which cannot be connected with P_0 by a line satisfying the Pfaffian equation (5.19), then there exists an integrating denominator and one has $dQ = \lambda\, d\phi$.

One can intuitively understand this theorem by a continuity consideration: All points P inaccessible from P_0 will fill a certain volume, bound by a surface of accessible points going through P_0. Further, to each inaccessible point there corresponds another one in the opposite direction; hence the boundary surface must contain all accessible points: which proves the existence of the function ϕ, so that $dQ = \lambda\, d\phi$ (see Appendix, **7**).

The application of this theorem to thermodynamics is now simple. Combining it with Carathéodory's principle, one has for any two systems

$$dQ_1 = \lambda_1\, d\phi_1, \qquad dQ_2 = \lambda_2\, d\phi_2, \tag{5.20}$$

and for the combined system

$$dQ = dQ_1 + dQ_2 = \lambda\, d\phi; \tag{5.21}$$

hence

$$\lambda\, d\phi = \lambda_1\, d\phi_1 + \lambda_2\, d\phi_2. \tag{5.22}$$

Consider in particular two simple fluids in thermal contact; then the system has three independent variables V_1, V_2, ϑ, which can be replaced by $\phi_1, \phi_2, \vartheta$. Then (5.22) shows that ϕ depends only on ϕ_1, ϕ_2, and not on ϑ, while

$$\frac{\partial \phi}{\partial \phi_1} = \frac{\lambda_1}{\lambda}, \qquad \frac{\partial \phi}{\partial \phi_2} = \frac{\lambda_2}{\lambda}. \tag{5.23}$$

Hence these quotients are also independent of ϑ,

$$\frac{\partial}{\partial \vartheta}\frac{\lambda_1}{\lambda} = 0, \qquad \frac{\partial}{\partial \vartheta}\frac{\lambda_2}{\lambda} = 0,$$

from which one infers

$$\frac{1}{\lambda_1}\frac{\partial \lambda_1}{\partial \vartheta} = \frac{1}{\lambda_2}\frac{\partial \lambda_2}{\partial \vartheta} = \frac{1}{\lambda}\frac{\partial \lambda}{\partial \vartheta}. \tag{5.24}$$

Now λ_1 is a variable of the first fluid only, therefore only dependent on ϕ_1 and ϑ; in the same way $\lambda_2 = \lambda_2(\phi_2, \vartheta)$. The first equality (5.24) can only hold if both quantities depend only on ϑ. Hence

$$\frac{\partial \log \lambda_1}{\partial \vartheta} = \frac{\partial \log \lambda_2}{\partial \vartheta} = \frac{\partial \log \lambda}{\partial \vartheta} = g(\vartheta), \tag{5.25}$$

where $g(\vartheta)$ is a universal function, namely numerically identical for different fluids and for the combined system.

This simple consideration leads with ordinary mathematics to the existence of a universal function of temperature. The rest is just a matter of normalization. From (5.25) one finds for each system

$$\log \lambda = \int g(\vartheta)\, d\vartheta + \log \Phi, \qquad \lambda = \Phi e^{\int g(\vartheta)\, d\vartheta}, \tag{5.26}$$

where Φ depends on the corresponding ϕ.

If one now defines

$$\left.\begin{aligned} T(\vartheta) &= C e^{\int g(\vartheta)\, d\vartheta}, \\ S(\phi) &= \frac{1}{C} \int \Phi(\phi)\, d\phi, \end{aligned}\right\} \tag{5.27}$$

where the constant C can be fixed by prescribing the value of $T_1 - T_2$ for two reproducible states of some normal substance (e.g. $T_1 - T_2 = 100°$, if T_1 corresponds to the boiling-point, T_2 the freezing-point of water at 1 atmosphere of pressure), then one has

$$dQ = \lambda\, d\phi = T\, dS. \tag{5.28}$$

T is the thermodynamical or absolute temperature and S the entropy.

Equation (5.28) refers only to quasi-static processes, that is, to sequences of equilibrium states. To get a result about real dynamical phenomena one has to apply Carathéodory's principle again, considering a finite transition from an initial state V_1^0, V_2^0, S^0 to a final state V_1, V_2, S. One can reach the latter one in two steps: first changing the volume quasi-statically (and adiabatically) from V_1^0, V_2^0 to V_1, V_2, the entropy remaining constant, equal to S^0, and then changing the state adiabatically, but irreversibly (by stirring, etc.) at constant volume, so that S^0 goes over into S.

Now if any neighbouring value S of S^0 could be reached in this way, one would have a contradiction to Carathéodory's principle, as the volumes are of course arbitrarily changeable. Hence for each such process one must have either $S \geqslant S^0$ or $S \leqslant S^0$. Continuity demands that the same sign holds for all initial states; it holds also for different substances since the entropy is additive (as can be easily seen). The actual sign $\geqslant$ or $\leqslant$ depends on the choice of the constant C in (5.27); if this is chosen so that T is positive, a single experience, say with a gas, shows that entropy never decreases.

It may not be superfluous to add a remark on the behaviour of entropy for the case of conduction of heat. As thermodynamics has to do only with processes where the initial and final states are equilibria, stationary flow cannot be treated: one can only ask, What is the final state of two initially separated bodies brought into thermal contact? The difficulty is that a change of entropy is only defined by quasi-static adiabatic processes; the sudden change of thermal isolation into contact, however, is discontinuous and the processes inside the system not controllable. Yet one can reduce this process to the one considered before. By quasi-static adiabatic changes of volume the temperatures can be made equal without change of entropy; then contact can be made without discontinuity, and the initial volumes quasi-statically restored, again without a change of entropy. The situation is now the same as in the initial state considered before, and it follows that any process leading to the final state must increase the entropy.

The whole chain of considerations can be generalized for more complicated systems without any difficulty. One has only to assume that all independent variables except one are of the type represented by the volume, namely arbitrarily changeable.

If one has to deal, as in chemistry, with substances which are mixtures of different components, one can regard the concentrations of these as arbitrarily variable with the help of semipermeable walls and movable pistons (see Appendix, **8**).

By using thermodynamics a vast amount of knowledge has been accumulated not only in physics but in the borderland sciences of physico-chemistry, metallurgy, mineralogy, etc. Most of it refers to equilibria. In fact, the expression 'thermodynamics' is misleading. The only dynamical statements possible are concerned with the irreversible transitions from one equilibrium state to another, and they are of a very modest character, giving the total increase of entropy or the decrease of free energy $F = U-TS$. The irreversible process itself is outside the scope of thermodynamics.

The principle of antecedence is now satisfied; but this gain is paid for by the loss of all details of description which ordinary dynamics of continuous media supplies.

Can this not be mended? Why not apply the methods of Cauchy to thermal processes, by treating each volume element as a small thermodynamical system, and regarding not only strain, stress, and energy, but also temperature and entropy as continuous functions in space? This has of course been done, but with limited success. The reason is that thermodynamics is definitely connected with walls or enclosures. We have used the adiabatic and diathermanous variety, and mentioned semi-permeable walls necessary for chemical separations; but a volume element is not surrounded by a wall, it is in free contact with its neighbourhood. The thermodynamic change to which it is subject depends therefore on the flux of energy and material constituents through its boundary, which themselves cannot be reduced to mechanics. In some limiting cases, one has found simple solutions. For instance, when calculating the velocity of sound in a gas, one tried first for the relation between pressure p and density ρ the isothermal law $p = c\rho$ where c is a constant, but found no agreement with experiment; then one took the adiabatic law $p = c\rho^\gamma$ where γ is the ratio of the specific heats at constant pressure and constant volume (see Appendix, **9**), which gave a much better result. The reason is that for fast vibrations there is no time for heat to flow through the boundary of a volume element which therefore behaves as if it were adiabatically enclosed. But by making the vibrations slower and slower, one certainly gets into a region where this assumption does not hold any more. Then conduction of heat must be taken into account. The hydrodynamical equations and those of heat conduction have to be regarded as a simultaneous system. In this way a descriptive or phenomenological theory can be developed and has been developed. Yet I am unable to give an account of it, as I have never studied it; nor have the majority of physicists shown much interest in this kind of thing. One knows that any flux of matter and energy can be fitted into Cauchy's general scheme, and there is not much interest in doing it in the most general way. Besides, each effect needs separate constants—e.g. in liquids compressibility, specific heat, conductivity of heat, constants of diffusion; in solids elastic constants and parameters describing plastic flow, etc., and very often these so-called constants turn out to be not constants, but to depend on other quantities (see Appendix, **10**).

Therefore one can rightly say that with ordinary thermodynamics the descriptive method of physics has come to its natural end. Something new had to appear.

VI

CHANCE

KINETIC THEORY OF GASES

THE new turn in physics was the introduction of atomistics and statistics.

To follow up the history of atomistics into the remote past is not in the plan of this lecture. We can take it for granted that since the days of Demokritos the hypothesis of matter being composed of ultimate and indivisible particles was familiar to every educated man. It was revived when the time was ripe. Lord Kelvin quotes frequently a Father Boscovich as one of the first to use atomistic considerations to solve physical problems; he lived in the eighteenth century, and there may have been others, of whom I know nothing, thinking on the same lines. The first systematic use of atomistics was made in chemistry, where it allowed the reduction of innumerable substances to a relatively small stock of elements. Physics followed considerably later because atomistics as such was of no great use without another fundamental idea, namely that the observable properties of matter are not intrinsic qualities of its smallest parts, but averages over distributions governed by the laws of chance.

The theory of probability itself, which expresses these laws, is much older; it sprang not from the needs of natural science but from gambling and other, more or less disreputable, human activities.

The first use of probability considerations in science was made by Gauss in his theory of experimental errors. I can suppose that every scientist knows the outlines of it, yet I have to dwell upon it for a few moments because of its fundamental and somewhat paradoxical aspect. It has a direct bearing on the method of inference by induction which is the backbone of all human experience. I have said that in my opinion the significance of this method in science consists in the establishment of a code of rules which form the constitution of science itself. Now the curious situation arises that this code of rules, which ensures the possibility of scientific laws, in particular of the cause–effect relation, contains besides many other prescriptions those related to observational errors, a branch of the theory of probability. This shows that the conception of chance enters into the very first steps of scientific activity, in virtue of the fact that no observation is absolutely correct. I think chance is a more fundamental conception than causality; for whether in a concrete case a cause–effect relation holds or not can only be judged by applying the laws of chance to the observations.

The history of science reveals a strong tendency to forget this. When a scientific theory is firmly established and confirmed, it changes its character and becomes a part of the metaphysical background of the age: a doctrine is transformed into a dogma. In fact no scientific doctrine has more than a probability value and is open to modification in the light of new experience.

After this general remark, let us return to the question how the notion of chance and probability entered physics itself.

As early as 1738 Daniel Bernoulli suggested the interpretation of gas pressure as the effect of the impact of numerous particles on the wall of the container. The actual development of the kinetic theory of gases was, however, accomplished much later, in the nineteenth century.

The object of the theory was to explain the mechanical and thermodynamical properties of gas from the average behaviour of the molecules. For this purpose a statistical hypothesis was made, often called the 'principle of molecular chaos': for an 'ideal' gas in a closed vessel and in absence of external forces all positions and all directions of velocity of the molecules are equally probable.

Applied to a monatomic gas (the atoms are supposed to be mass points), this leads at once to a relation between volume V, pressure p, and mean energy U (see Appendix, **11**)

$$Vp = \tfrac{2}{3}U, \tag{6.1}$$

if the pressure p is interpreted as the total momentum transferred to the wall by the impact of the molecules. One has now only to assume that the energy U is a measure of temperature to obtain Boyle's law of the isotherms. Then it follows from thermodynamics that U is proportional to the absolute temperature (see Appendix, **9**); one has

$$U = \tfrac{3}{2}RT, \qquad pV = RT, \tag{6.2}$$

where R is the ordinary gas constant. This is the complete equation of state (combined Boyle–Charles law), and one sees that the specific heat of a monatomic gas for constant volume is $\tfrac{3}{2}R$.

I have mentioned these things only to stress the point that the kinetic theory right from the beginning produced verifiable numerical results in abundance. There could be no doubt that it was right, but what did it really mean?

How is it possible that probability considerations can be superimposed upon the deterministic laws of mechanics without a clash?

These laws connect the state at a time t to the initial state, at time t_0, by definite equations. They involve, however, no restriction on the initial state. This has to be determined by observation in every concrete case. But observations are not absolutely accurate; the results of measurements will suffer scattering according to Gauss's rules of experimental errors. In the case of gas molecules, the situation is extreme; for owing to the smallness and excessive number of the molecules, there is almost perfect ignorance of the initial state.

The only facts known are the geometrical restriction of the position of each molecule by the walls of the vessel, and some physical quantities of a crude nature, like the resultant pressure and the total energy: very little indeed in view of the number of molecules (about 10^{19} per c.c.).

Hence it is legitimate to apply probability considerations to the initial state, for instance the hypothesis of molecular chaos. The statistical behaviour of any future state is then completely determined by the laws of mechanics. This is in particular the case for 'statistical equilibrium', when the observable properties are independent of time; in this case any later state must have the same statistical properties as the initial state (e.g. it must also satisfy the condition of molecular chaos). How can this be mathematically formulated? It is convenient to use the equations of motion in Hamilton's canonical form (4.3, p. 18). The distribution is described by a function $f(t, q_1, q_2,..., q_n, p_1, p_2,..., p_n)$ of all coordinates and momenta, and of time, such that $f\,dpdq$ is the probability for finding the system at time t in a given element $dpdq = dp_1...dp_n\,dq_1...dq_n$. One can interpret this function as the density of a fluid in a $2n$-dimensional pq-space, called 'phase space'; and, as no particles are supposed to disappear or to be generated, this fluid must satisfy a continuity equation, of the kind (4.5, p. 20), generalized for $2n$ dimensions, namely (see Appendix, 3)

$$\frac{\partial f}{\partial t} + \sum_k \left(\frac{\partial(f\dot{q}_k)}{\partial q_k} + \frac{\partial(f\dot{p}_k)}{\partial p_k}\right) = 0. \tag{6.3}$$

This reduces in virtue of the canonical equations (4.3), p. 18, to

$$\frac{\partial f}{\partial t} - [H, f] = 0, \tag{6.4}$$

where $[H, f]$ is an abbreviation, the so-called Poisson bracket, namely

$$[H, f] = \sum_k \left(\frac{\partial H}{\partial q_k}\frac{\partial f}{\partial p_k} - \frac{\partial H}{\partial p_k}\frac{\partial f}{\partial q_k}\right). \tag{6.5}$$

On the other hand, the convective derivative defined for three dimensions in (4.11, p. 21) may be generalized for $2n$ dimensions thus:

$$\frac{df}{dt} = \frac{\partial f}{\partial t} + \sum_k \left(\frac{\partial f}{\partial q_k}\dot{q}_k + \frac{\partial f}{\partial p_k}\dot{p}_k\right). \tag{6.6}$$

Then (6.4) says that in virtue of the mechanical equations

$$\frac{df}{dt} = 0. \tag{6.7}$$

The result expressed by the equivalent equations (6.4) and (6.7) is called Liouville's theorem. The density function is an integral of the canonical equations, i.e. $f =$ const. along any trajectory in phase space; in other words, the substance of the fluid is carried along by the motion in phase space, so that the integral

$$I = \int f\,dpdq \tag{6.8}$$

over any part of the substance moving in phase space is independent of time.

Any admissible distribution function, namely one for which the probabilities of a configuration at different times are compatible with the deterministic laws of mechanics, must be an integral of motion, satisfying the partial differential equation (6.4). For a closed system, i.e. one which is free from external disturbances (like a gas in a solid vessel), H is explicitly independent of time. The special case of statistical equilibrium corresponds to certain time-independent solutions of (6.4), i.e. functions f satisfying

$$[H,f] = 0. \tag{6.9}$$

An obvious integral of this equation is $f = \Phi(H)$, where Φ indicates an arbitrary function. This case plays a prominent part in statistical mechanics.

Yet before continuing with these very general considerations we had better return to the ideal gases and consider the kinetic theory in more detail. In an ideal gas, the particles (atoms, molecules) are supposed to move independently of one another. Hence the function $f(p,q)$ is a product of N functions $f(\mathbf{x},\boldsymbol{\xi},t)$ each belonging to a single particle and all formally identical; $\mathbf{x}$ is the position vector and $\boldsymbol{\xi} = (1/m)\mathbf{p}$ the velocity vector. Then $f\,d\mathbf{x}d\boldsymbol{\xi}$ is the probability of finding a particle at time t at a specified element of volume and velocity.

In the case where no external forces are present ($\partial H/\partial t = 0$, $\partial H/\partial \mathbf{x} = 0$) the Hamiltonian reduces to the kinetic energy,

$$H = \tfrac{1}{2}m\boldsymbol{\xi}^2 = (1/2m)\mathbf{p}^2.$$

The hypothesis of molecular chaos is expressed by assuming f to be a function of $\boldsymbol{\xi}^2$ alone. This is indeed a solution of (6.9), as it can be written in the form $f = \Phi(H)$ mentioned above. No other solution exists if the gas as a whole is homogeneous and isotropic (i.e. all positions and directions are physically equivalent; see Appendix, **12**).

The determination of the velocity distribution function $f(\boldsymbol{\xi}^2)$ was recognized by Maxwell as a fundamental problem of kinetic theory: it is the quantitative formulation of the 'law of chance' for this case. He gave several solutions; his first and simplest reasoning was this: Suppose the three components of velocity ξ_1, ξ_2, ξ_3 to be statistically independent, then

$$f(\boldsymbol{\xi}^2) = f(\xi_1^2+\xi_2^2+\xi_3^2) = \phi(\xi_1^2)\phi(\xi_2^2)\phi(\xi_3^2). \tag{6.10}$$

This functional equation has the only solution (see Appendix, **13**)

$$\begin{aligned} \phi &= e^{\alpha-\beta\xi^2}, \\ f &= e^{3\alpha-\beta(\xi_1^2+\xi_2^2+\xi_3^2)}, \end{aligned} \tag{6.11}$$

where α, β are constants.

This is Maxwell's celebrated law of velocity distribution. However, the derivation given is objectionable, as the supposed independence of the velocity components is not obvious at all. I have mentioned it because the latest proof (and as I think the most satisfactory and rigorous and of the widest possible generalization) of the distribution formula uses exactly this Maxwellian argument, only applied to more suitable variables—as we shall presently see.

Maxwell, being aware of this weakness, gave several other proofs which have been improved and modified by other authors. Eventually it appears that there are two main types of argument: the equilibrium proof and the dynamical proof. We shall first consider the equilibrium proof in some detail.

Assume each molecule to be a mechanical system with coordinates $q_1, q_2,\ldots$ and momenta $p_1, p_2,\ldots$, for which we write simply q, p, and with a Hamiltonian $H(p, q)$. The interaction between the molecules will be neglected. The total number n and the total energy U of the assembly of molecules are given.

In order to apply the laws of probability it is convenient to reduce the continuous set of points p, q in phase space to a discontinuous enumerable set of volume elements. One divides the phase space into N small cells of volumes $\omega_1 V, \omega_2 V,\ldots, \omega_N V$, where V is the total volume; hence

$$\omega_1+\omega_2+\ldots+\omega_N = 1. \tag{6.12}$$

To each cell a value of the energy $H(p, q)$ can be attached, say that corresponding to its centre; let these energies be $\epsilon_1, \epsilon_2,\ldots, \epsilon_N$. Now suppose the particles distributed over the cells so that there are n_1 in the first cell, n_2 in the second, etc., but of course with the restriction that the totals

$$n_1+n_2+...+n_N = n, \tag{6.13}$$

$$n_1\epsilon_1+n_2\epsilon_2+...+n_N\epsilon_N = U \tag{6.14}$$

are fixed. Liouville's theorem suggests that the probability of a single molecule being in a given cell is proportional to its volume. Making this assumption, one has to calculate the composite probability P for any distribution $n_1, n_2,..., n_N$ under the restrictions (6.13) and (6.14).

This is an elementary problem of the calculus of probability (see Appendix, **14**) which can be solved in this way: First the second condition (6.14) is omitted; then the probability of a given distribution $n_1, n_2,..., n_N$ is

$$P(n_1, n_2,..., n_N) = \frac{n!}{n_1!\, n_2!...\, n_N!}\, \omega_1^{n_1}\omega_2^{n_2},...\omega_N^{n_N}. \tag{6.15}$$

If this is summed over all $n_1, n_2,..., n_N$ satisfying (6.13), one obtains by the elementary polynomial theorem

$$\sum_{n_1, n_2,..., n_N} P(n_1, n_2,..., n_N) = (\omega_1+\omega_2+...+\omega_N)^n = 1, \tag{6.16}$$

because of (6.12)—as it must be if P is a properly normalized probability.

It is well known that the polynomial coefficients $n!/n_1!\, n_2!...n_N!$ have a sharp maximum for $n_1 = n_2 = ... = n_N$; that means, if all cells have equal volumes ($\omega_1 = \omega_2 = ... = \omega_N$) the uniform distribution would have an overwhelming probability. Yet this is modified by the second condition (6.14) which we have now to take into account. The simplest method of doing this proceeds in three approximations which seem to be crude, but are perfectly satisfactory for very large numbers of particles ($n \to \infty$). The first approximation consists in neglecting all distributions of comparatively small $n_1, n_2,..., n_N$; then the n_k can be treated as continuous variables. The second approximation consists in replacing the exact expression (6.15) by its asymptotic value for large n_k by using Stirling's formula $\log(n!) \rightarrow n(\log n - 1)$ (see Appendix, **14**), and the result is

$$\log P = -n_1 \log n_1 - n_2 \log n_2 - \ldots - n_N \log n_N + \text{const.} \tag{6.17}$$

The third approximation consists in the following assumption: the actual behaviour of a gas in statistical equilibrium is determined solely by the state of maximum probability; all other states have so little chance to appear that they can be neglected.

Hence one has to determine the maximum of $\log P$ given by (6.17) under the conditions (6.13) and (6.14). Using elementary calculus this leads at once to

$$n_k = e^{\alpha - \beta\epsilon_k}, \tag{6.18}$$

where α and β are two constants which are necessary in order to satisfy the conditions (6.13), (6.14). Yet these constants play a rather different part.

If one has to do with a mixture of two gases A and B with given numbers $n^{(A)}$ and $n^{(B)}$, one gets two conditions of the type (6.13) but only one of the type (6.14), expressing that the total energy is given.

Hence one obtains

$$n_k^{(A)} = e^{\alpha^{(A)} - \beta\epsilon_k^{(A)}}, \qquad n_k^{(B)} = e^{\alpha^{(B)} - \beta\epsilon_k^{(B)}}, \tag{6.19}$$

with two different constants $\alpha^{(A)}$ and $\alpha^{(B)}$, but only one β. Therefore β is the parameter of thermal equilibrium between the two constituents and must depend only on temperature.

Indeed, if one now calculates the mean energy U and the mean pressure p, one can apply thermodynamics and sees easily that the second law is satisfied if

$$\beta = \frac{1}{kT}, \tag{6.20}$$

where T is the absolute temperature and k a constant, called Boltzmann's constant. At the same time it appears that the entropy is given by

$$S = k \log P = -k \sum_{\alpha} n_\alpha \log n_\alpha. \tag{6.21}$$

All these results are mainly due to Boltzmann; in particular (6.18) is called Boltzmann's distribution law. It obviously contains Maxwell's law (6.11) as a special case, namely for mass points.

We have now to ask: Is this consideration which I called the equilibrium proof of the distribution law really satisfactory?

One objection can be easily dismissed, namely that the approximations made are too crude. They can be completely avoided. Darwin and Fowler have shown that one can give a rigorous expression for the mean value of any physical quantity in terms of complex integrals, containing the so-called 'partition function' (see Appendix **15**)

$$\omega_1 z^{\epsilon_1}+\omega_2 z^{\epsilon_2}+\ldots+\omega_N z^{\epsilon_N} = F(z). \qquad (6.22)$$

No distribution is neglected and no use is made of the Stirling formula. Yet in the limit $n \to \infty$, all results are exactly the same as given by the Boltzmann distribution function. Although this method is extremely elegant and powerful, it does not introduce any essential new feature in regard to the fundamental question of statistical mechanics.

Another objection is going deeper: can the molecules of a gas really be treated as independent?

There are numerous phenomena which show they are not, even if one considers only statistical equilibrium. For no real gas is 'ideal', i.e. satisfies Boyle's law rigorously, and the deviations increase with pressure, ending in a complete collapse, condensation. This proves the existence of long-range attractive forces between the molecules. The statistical method described above is unable to deal with them. The first attempt to correct this was the celebrated theory of van der Waals, which was followed by many others. I shall later describe in a few words the modern version of these theories, which is, from a certain standpoint, rigorous and satisfactory.

More serious are the interactions revealed by non-equilibrium phenomena: viscosity, conduction of heat, diffusion. They can all be qualitatively understood by supposing that each molecule has a finite volume, or more correctly that two molecules have a short-range repulsive interaction which prohibits a close approach. This assumption has the consequence that there exists an effective cross-section for a collision, hence a mean free path for the straight motion of a molecule. The coefficients of the three phenomena mentioned can be reduced, by elementary considerations, to the free path, and the results, as far as they go, are in good agreement with observations.

All this is very good physics producing in a simple and intuitive way formulae which give the correct order of magnitude of different correlated effects.

But for the problem of a rigorous kinetic theory, which takes account of the interactions and is valid not only for equilibria, but also for motion, these considerations have only the value of a preliminary reconnoitring. The question is: How can one derive the hydrodynamical equations of visible motion together with the phenomena of transformation and conduction of heat and, for a mixture, of diffusion?

This is an ambitious programme. For such a theory must include the result that a gas left to itself tends to equilibrium. Hence it must lead to irreversibility, although the laws of ordinary reversible mechanics are assumed to hold for the molecules. How is this possible? Further, is the equilibrium obtained in this way the same as that derived directly, say by the method of the most probable distribution?

To begin with the last question. Its answer represents what I have called above the dynamical proof of the distribution law for equilibrium.

The formulation of the non-equilibrium theory of gases is due to Boltzmann. One can obtain his fundamental equation by generalizing one of the equivalent formulae (6.4) or (6.7). These are based on the assumption that each molecule moves independently of the others according to the laws of mechanics, and they describe how the distribution f of an assembly of such particles develops in time. Now the assumption of independence is dropped, hence the expression on the left-hand side of (6.4) or (6.7) is not zero; denoting by $f(1)$ the probability density for a certain particle 1, one can write

$$\frac{df(1)}{dt} = \frac{\partial f(1)}{\partial t} - [H, f(1)] = C(1), \tag{6.23}$$

where $C(1)$ represents the influence of the other molecules on the particle 1; it is called the 'collision integral', as Boltzmann calculates it only for the case where the orbit of the centre of a particle can be described as straight and uniform motion interrupted by sudden collisions. For this purpose a new and independent application of the laws of probability is made by assuming that the probability of a collision between two particles 1 and 2 is proportional to the product of the probabilities of finding them in a given configuration, $f(1)f(2)$. If one then expresses that some molecules are thrown by a collision out of a given element of phase space, others into it, one obtains (see Appendix, **16**)

$$C(1) = \iint \{f'(1)f'(2)-f(1)f(2)\}|\boldsymbol{\xi}_1-\boldsymbol{\xi}_2|\, d\mathbf{b}d\boldsymbol{\xi}_2, \quad (6.24)$$

where $f(2)$ is the same function as $f(1)$, but taken for the particle 2 as argument. $f(1)$, $f(2)$ refer to the motion of two particles 'before' the collision, $f'(1)$, $f'(2)$ to that 'after' the collision; one has to integrate over all velocities of the particle 2, $(d\boldsymbol{\xi}_2)$, and over the 'cross-section' of the collision, $(d\mathbf{b})$, which I shall not define in detail. 'Before' and 'after' the collision mean the asymptotic straight and uniform motions of approach and separation; it is clear that if the former is given, the latter is completely determined for any law of interaction force—it is the two-body problem of mechanics. Hence the velocities of both particles $\boldsymbol{\xi}'_1$, $\boldsymbol{\xi}'_2$ after the collision are known functions of those before the collision $\boldsymbol{\xi}_1$, $\boldsymbol{\xi}_2$, and (6.23) assumes the form of an integro-differential equation for calculating f.

This equation has been the object of thorough mathematical investigations, first by Boltzmann and Maxwell, and later by modern writers. Hilbert has indicated a systematic method of solution in which each step of approximation leads to an integral equation of the normal (so-called Fredholm) type. Enskog and Chapman have developed this method, with some modifications, in detail. There is an admirable book by Chapman and Cowling which represents the whole theory of non-homogeneous gases as a consequence of the equation (6.23). I can only mention a few points of these important investigations.

The first is concerned with the question of equilibrium. Does the equation (6.23) really indicate an irreversible approach from any initial state to a homogeneous equilibrium? This is in fact the case, and a very strange result indeed: the metamorphosis of reversible mechanics into irreversible thermodynamics with the help of probability. But before discussing this difficult question, I shall indicate the mathematical proof.

From the statistics of equilibrium it is known how the entropy is connected with probability, namely by equation (6.21). Replace here the discontinuous n_k by the continuous f and summation by integration over the phase space, and you obtain

$$S = -k \int f(1) \log f(1)\, dq dp. \tag{6.25}$$

If one now calculates the time derivative dS/dt by substituting $\partial f(1)/\partial t$ from (6.23), and assuming no external interference, one finds (see Appendix, **17**)

$$\frac{dS}{dt} \geqslant 0, \tag{6.26}$$

where the $=$ sign holds only if $f(1)$ is independent of the space coordinates and satisfies, as a function of the velocities,

$$f(1)f(2) = f'(1)f'(2) \tag{6.27}$$

identically for any collision.

The result expressed by (6.26) is often quoted as Boltzmann's H-theorem (because he used the symbol H for $-S/k$). Boltzmann claimed that it gave the statistical explanation of thermodynamical irreversibility.

Equation (6.27) is a functional equation which determines f as a function of 'collision invariants', like total energy and total momentum. If the gas is at rest as a whole, the only solution of (6.27) is Maxwell's (or Boltzmann's) distribution law:

$$f = e^{\alpha - \beta \epsilon}, \qquad H(p,q) = \epsilon. \tag{6.28}$$

This is what I called the dynamical proof, and is a most remarkable result indeed; for it has been derived from the mechanism of collisions, which was completely neglected in the previous equilibrium methods. This point needs elucidation.

Before doing so, let me mention that the hydro-thermal equations of a gas, i.e. the equations of continuity, of motion and of conduction of heat, are obtained from Boltzmann's equation (6.23) by a simple formal process (multiplication with $1, \boldsymbol{\xi}$ and $\frac{1}{2}m\boldsymbol{\xi}^2$ followed by integration over all velocities) in terms of the stress tensor T—you will remember Cauchy's general formula (4.9)—which itself is expressed in terms of the distribution function f. To give these equations a real meaning, one has to expand f in terms of physical quantities, and this is the object of the theories contained in Chapman and Cowling's book. In this way a very satisfactory theory of hydro-thermodynamics of gases, including viscosity, conduction of heat, and diffusion, is obtained.

STATISTICAL MECHANICS

I remember that forty years ago when I began to read scientific literature there was a violent discussion raging about statistical methods in physics, especially the H-theorem. The objections raised have been classified into two types, one concerning reversibility, the other periodicity.

Loschmidt, like Boltzmann, a member of the Austrian school, formulated the reversibility objection in this way: by reversing all velocities you get from any solution of the mechanical equations another one—how can the integral S, which depends on the instantaneous situation, increase in both cases?

The periodicity objection is based on a theorem of the great French mathematician Henri Poincaré, which states that every mechanical system is, if not exactly periodic, at least quasi-periodic. This follows from Liouville's theorem according to which a given region in phase space moves without change of volume and describes therefore a tube-shaped region of ever increasing length. As the total volume available is finite (it is contained in the surface of maximum energy), this tube must somewhere intersect itself, which means that final and initial states come eventually near together.

Zermelo, a German mathematician, who worked on abstract problems like the theory of Cantor's sets and transfinite numbers, ventured into physics by translating Gibbs's work on statistical mechanics into German. But he was offended by the logical imperfections of this theory and attacked it violently. He used in particular Poincaré's theorem to show how scandalous the reasoning of the physicists was: they claimed to have proved the irreversible increase of a mechanical quantity for a system which returns after a finite time to its initial state with any desired accuracy.

These objections were not quite futile, as they led two distinguished physicists, Paul Ehrenfest and his wife Tatjana, to investigate and clear up the matter beyond doubt in their well-known article in vol. iv of the *Mathematical Encyclopedia*.

To-day we hardly need to follow all the logical finesses of this work. It suffices to point out that the objections are based on the following misunderstanding. If we describe the behaviour of the gas (we speak only of this simple case, as for no other case has the H-theorem been proved until recently) by the equation (6.4), taking for H the Hamiltonian of the whole system, a function of the coordinates and momenta of all particles, then f is indeed reversible and quasi-periodic, no H-theorem can be proved.

Boltzmann's proof is based not on this equation, but on (6.23), where now H is the Hamiltonian of one single molecule undisturbed by the others, and where the right-hand term is not zero but equal to the collision integral $C(1)$. The latter is taken as representing roughly the effect of all the other molecules; 'roughly', that means after some reasonable averaging. This averaging is the expression of our ignorance of the actual microscopic situation. Boltzmann's theorem says that this equation mixing mechanical knowledge with ignorance of detail leads to irreversibility. There is no contradiction between the two statements.

But there rises the other question whether such a modification of the fundamental equation is justified. We shall see presently that it is indeed, in a much wider sense than that claimed by Boltzmann, namely not only for a gas, but for any substance which can be described by a mechanical model. We have therefore now to take up the question of how statistical methods can be applied to general mechanical systems. Without such a theory, one cannot even treat the deviations from the so-called ideal behaviour of gases (Boyle's law), which appear at high pressure and low temperature, and which lead to condensation.

Theories like that of van der Waals have obviously only preliminary character. What is needed is a general and well-founded formalism covering the gaseous, liquid, and solid states, under all kind of external forces.

For the case of statistical equilibrium, this formalism was supplied by Willard Gibbs's celebrated book on *Statistical Mechanics* (1901), which has proved to be extremely successful in its applications (see Appendix, **18**). The gist of Gibbs's idea is to apply Boltzmann's results for a real assembly of many equal molecules to an imaginary or 'virtual' assembly of many copies of the system under consideration, and to postulate that the one system under observation will behave like the average calculated for the assembly. Before criticizing this assumption, let us have a glimpse of Gibbs's procedure. He starts from Liouville's theorem (6.4) and considers especially the case of equilibrium where the partition function f of this virtual assembly has to satisfy equation (6.9). He states that $f = \Phi(H)$ is a solution (as we have seen) and he chooses two particular forms of the function Φ. The first is

$$\begin{aligned} f = \Phi(H) &= \text{const.,} \quad \text{if} \quad E < H < E+\Delta E, \\ &= 0 \qquad\qquad \text{outside of this interval,} \end{aligned} \tag{6.29}$$

where E is a given energy and ΔE a small interval of energy. (In modern notation one could write $\Phi(H) = \delta(H-E)$, where δ is Dirac's symbolic function.) The corresponding distribution he calls micro-canonical.

The second form is just that of Maxwell–Boltzmann,

$$f = e^{\alpha-\beta E}, \qquad H(p,q) = E, \tag{6.30}$$

and the corresponding distribution is called canonical. Gibbs shows that both assumptions lead to the same results for the averages of physical quantities. But the canonical is preferable, as it is simpler to handle. β turns out again to be equal for systems in thermal equilibrium; if one puts $\beta = 1/kT$ the formal relations between the averages constructed with (6.30) are a true replica of thermodynamics. For instance, the normalization condition for the probability

$$\int f\,dpdq = \int e^{\alpha-\beta E}\,dpdq = 1 \tag{6.31}$$

can be written

$$F = \alpha/\beta = kT \log Z, \qquad Z = \iint e^{-E/kT}\, dpdq. \tag{6.32}$$

This F plays the part of Helmholtz's free energy. The integral Z, to-day usually called the 'partition function', depends, apart from the energy E, on molar parameters like the volume V. All physical properties can be obtained by differentiation, e.g. entropy S and pressure p by

$$S = -\frac{\partial F}{\partial T}, \qquad p = -\frac{\partial F}{\partial V}. \tag{6.33}$$

This formalism has been amazingly successful in treating thermo-mechanical and also thermo-chemical properties. For instance, the theory of real (non-ideal) gases is obtained by writing

$$E = H(p,q) = K(p)+U(q), \tag{6.34}$$

where K is the kinetic and U the potential energy; the latter depends on the mutual interactions of the molecules. As K is quadratic in the p, the corresponding integration in Z is easily performed and the whole problem reduces to calculating the multiple integral

$$Q = \int \dots \int e^{-U(q_1 q_2 \dots q_N)/kT}\, dq_1\, dq_2 \dots dq_N. \tag{6.35}$$

Still, this is a very formidable task, and much work has been spent on it. I shall mention only the investigations initiated by Ursell, and perfected by Mayer and others, the aim of which was to replace van der Waals's semi-empirical equation of state by an exact one. In fact one can expand Q into a series of powers of V^{-1} and, introducing this into (6.32) and (6.33), one obtains the pressure p as a similar series

$$p = \frac{RT}{V}\left(1-\frac{A}{V}+\frac{B}{V^2}-\dots\right), \tag{6.36}$$

where the coefficients $A, B, \dots$, called virial coefficients, are functions of T. One can even go further and discuss the process of condensation, but the mathematical difficulties in the treatment of the liquid state itself are prohibitive.

The range of application of Gibbs's theory is enormous. But reading his book again, I felt the lack of a deeper foundation.

A few years later (1902, 1903) there appeared a series of papers by Einstein in which the same formalism was developed, obviously quite independently, as Maxwell and Boltzmann are quoted, but not Gibbs; these papers contained two essential improvements: an attempt to justify the statistical assumptions, and an application to a case which at once transformed the kinetic theory of matter from a useful hypothesis into something very real and directly observable, namely, the theory of Brownian motion.

Concerning the foundation, Einstein used an argument which Boltzmann had already introduced to support his distribution law (6.18)—though this seems to be hardly necessary, as for a real assembly the method of enumerating distributions over cells is perfectly satisfactory. Curiously enough, this argument of Boltzmann is based on a theorem similar to Poincaré's considerations on quasi-periodicity with which Zermelo intended to smash statistical mechanics altogether. Einstein considers a distribution of the micro-canonical type, in Gibbs's nomenclature, where only one 'energy surface' $H(p,q) = E$ in the phase space is taken into account. The representative point in phase space moves always on this surface. It may happen that the whole surface is covered in such a way that the orbit passes through every point of the surface. Such systems are called ergodic; but it is rather doubtful whether they exist at all. Systems are called quasi-ergodic where the orbit comes near to every point of the energy surface; that this happens can be seen by an argument similar to that which leads to Poincaré's theorem of quasi-periodicity. Then it can be made plausible that the total time of sojourn of the moving point in a given part of the energy surface is proportional to its area; hence the time average of any function of p, q is obviously the same as that taken with the help of a micro-canonical virtual assembly. In this way quasi-periodicity is used to justify statistical mechanics, exactly reversing Zermelo's reasoning. This paradox is resolved by the remark that Zermelo believes the period to be large and macroscopic, while Einstein assumes it to be unobservably small. Who is right? You may find the obvious answer for yourselves (see Appendix, **19**).

Modern writers use other ways of establishing the foundations of statistical mechanics. They are mostly adaptations of the cell-method to the virtual assembly; one has then to explain why the average properties of a single real observed system can be obtained by averaging over a great many systems of the virtual assembly. Some say simply: As we do not know the real state, we have the right to expect the average provided exceptional situations are theoretically extremely rare—and this is of course the case. Others say we have not to do with a single isolated system, but with a system in thermal contact with its surroundings, as if it were in a thermostat or heat bath; we can then assume this heat bath to consist of a great many copies of the system considered, so that the virtual assembly is transformed into a real one. I think considerations of this kind are not very satisfactory.

There remains the fact that statistical mechanics has justified itself by explaining a great many actual phenomena. Among these are the fluctuations and the Brownian motion to which Einstein applied his theory (see Appendix, **20**). To appreciate the importance of this step one has to remember that at that time (about 1900) atoms and molecules were still far from being as real as they are to-day—there were still physicists who did not believe in them. After Einstein's work this was hardly possible any longer. Visible tiny particles suspended in a gas or a liquid (colloid solution) are test bodies small enough to reveal the granular structure of the surrounding medium by their irregular motion. Einstein showed that the statistical properties of this movement (mean density, mean square displacement in time, etc.) agree qualitatively with the predictions of kinetic theory. Perrin later confirmed these results by exact measurements and obtained the first reliable value of Avogadro's number N, the number of particles per mole. From now on kinetic theory and statistical mechanics were definitely established.

But beyond this physical result, Einstein's theory of Brownian motion had a most important consequence for scientific methodology in general. The accuracy of measurement depends on the sensitivity of the instruments, and this again on the size and weight of the mobile parts and the restoring forces acting on them. Before Einstein's work it was tacitly assumed that progress in this direction was limited only by experimental technique. Now it became obvious that this was not so. If an indicator, like the needle of a galvanometer, became too small or the suspending fibre too thin, it would never be at rest but perform a kind of Brownian movement. This has in fact been observed. Similar phenomena play a large part in modern electronic technique, where the limit of observation is given by irregular variations which can be heard as a 'noise' in a loud speaker. There is a limit of observability given by the laws of nature themselves.

This is a striking example that the code of rules for inference by induction, though perhaps metaphysical in some way, is certainly not *a priori*, but subject to reactions from the knowledge which it has helped to create. For those rules which taught the experimentalist how to obtain and improve the accuracy of his findings contained to begin with certainly no hint that there is a natural end to the process.

However, the idea of unlimited improvement of accuracy need not be given up yet. One had only to add the rule: make your measurements at as low a temperature as possible. For Brownian motion dies down with decreasing temperature.

Yet later developments in physics proved this rule also to be ineffective, and a much more trenchant change in the code had to be made.

But before dealing with this question we have to finish our review of statistical methods in classical mechanics.

GENERAL KINETIC THEORY *

Kinetic theory could only be regarded as complete if it applied to matter in (visible) motion as well as to equilibrium. But if you look through the literature you will find very little—a few simple cases. The most important of these, the theory of gases, has been dealt with in some detail. Two others must be mentioned: the theory of solids and of the Brownian motion.

Ideal solids are crystal lattices or gigantic periodic molecules.

* See Note 5 of Appendix Two, p. 213.

But only for zero temperature are the atoms in regularly spaced equilibrium positions; for higher temperatures they begin to vibrate. As long as the amplitudes are small, the mutual forces will be linear functions of them; then the vibrations can be analysed into 'normal modes', each of which is a wave running through the lattice with a definite frequency. These normal modes represent a system of independent harmonic oscillations to which Gibbs's method of statistical mechanics can be applied without any difficulty. If, however, the temperature rises, the amplitudes of the vibrations increase and higher terms appear in the interaction: the waves are scattering one another and are therefore strongly damped. Hence there exists a kind of free path for the transport of energy which can be used for explaining conduction of heat in crystals (Debye). Similar considerations, applied to the electrons in metallic crystals, are used for the explanation of transport phenomena like electric and thermal conduction in metals.

In the case of Brownian motion, I have already mentioned that Einstein calculated not only the mean density of a colloidal solution, say, under gravity, but also the mean square displacement of a single suspended particle in time (or, what amounts to the same, the dispersion of a colloid by diffusion as a function of time). The simplifying assumption which makes this possible is that the mass of the colloidal particle is large compared with the mass of the surrounding molecules, so that these impart only small impulses. Similar considerations have been applied to other fluctuation phenomena (see Appendix, **20**).

A great number of more or less isolated examples of non-equilibria have been treated by a semi-empirical method which uses the notion of relaxation time. You find a very complete account of such things related to solids and liquids in a book of J. Frenkel, *Kinetic Theory of Liquids*. But you must not expect to find in this work a systematic theory, based on a general idea, nor will you find it in any other book.

My collaborator Dr. Green and I have tried to fill this gap, and to develop the kinetic theory of matter in general. I hope you will not mind if I indulge a little in the pleasure of explaining the leading ideas. It will help the understanding of the interplay of cause and chance in the laws of nature.

We have to remember the general principles laid down by Gibbs which he, however, used only for the case of statistical equilibrium.

An arbitrary piece of matter, fluid or solid, is, from the atomistic standpoint, a mechanical system of particles (atoms, molecules) defined by a Hamiltonian H. Its state is completely determined if the initial values of coordinates and momenta are given. Actually this is not the case; but there is a probability (as yet unknown) $f^0(p,q)\,dpdq$ for the initial distribution. The causal laws of motion demand that the distribution $f(t,p,q)$ at a later time t is a solution of the Liouville equation (6.4) (p. 49)

$$\frac{df}{dt} = \frac{\partial f}{\partial t} - [H,f] = 0, \tag{6.37}$$

namely that solution which for $t = 0$ becomes f^0,

$$f(0,p,q) = f^0(p,q). \tag{6.38}$$

Let us assume for simplicity that all molecules are equal particles (point masses) with coordinates $\mathbf{x}^{(k)}$ and velocities $\boldsymbol{\xi}^{(k)} = \mathbf{p}^{(k)}/m$. We shall consider f to be a function of these and write $f(t,\mathbf{x},\boldsymbol{\xi})$. If we want to indicate that a function f depends on h particles, we do not write all arguments, but simply $f_h(1, 2,\ldots h)$ or shortly f_h. As all the particles are physically indistinguishable, we can assume all the functions f_h to be symmetrical in the particles.

Now the physicist is not directly interested in a symmetric solution f_N of (6.37). He wants to know such things as the number density (number of particles per unit volume) $n_1(t, \mathbf{x})$ at a given point $\mathbf{x}$ of space, or perhaps, in addition, the velocity distribution $f_1(t, \mathbf{x}, \boldsymbol{\xi})$, i.e. just those quantities which are familiar from the kinetic theory of gases, depending on one particle only.

One has therefore to reduce the function f_N for N particles step by step to the function f_1 of one particle.

This is done by integrating over the position and velocity of one particle, say the last one, with the help of the integral operator

$$\chi_q \cdots = \iint d\mathbf{x}^{(q)}\, d\xi^{(q)} \ldots. \tag{6.39}$$

If f_{q+1} is given, we obtain f_q by applying the operator χ_{q+1}; it is, however, convenient to add a normalizing factor and to write

$$(N-q)f_q = \chi_{q+1} f_{q+1}. \tag{6.40}$$

The physical meaning of the operation is this: we give up the pretence to know the whereabouts of one particle and declare frankly our ignorance. By repeated application of the operation, we obtain a chain of functions

$$f_N, \quad f_{N-1}, \quad ..., \quad f_2, \quad f_1, \tag{6.41}$$

to which one can add $f_0 = 1$; f_q means the probability of finding the system in a state where q particles have fixed positions (i.e. lie in given elements). The normalization is such that

$$\int f_1(t, \mathbf{x}^{(1)}, \boldsymbol{\xi}^{(1)})\, d\boldsymbol{\xi}^{(1)} = n_1(t, \mathbf{x}^{(1)}) \tag{6.42}$$

is the number density; for one has

$$\int n_1(t, \mathbf{x}^{(1)})\, d\mathbf{x}^{(1)} = \iint f_1\, d\mathbf{x}^{(1)} d\boldsymbol{\xi}^{(1)} = \chi_1 f_1 = N, \tag{6.43}$$

where the last equality follows from (6.40) for $q = 0$ (with $f_0 = 1$).

Now we have to reduce the fundamental equation (6.37) step by step by repeatedly applying the operator χ (see Appendix, **21**). Assuming that the atoms are acting on another with central forces, $\Phi^{(ij)}$ being the potential energy between two of them, the result of the reduction is a chain of equations of the form

$$\frac{\partial f_q}{\partial t} = [H_q, f_q] + S_q \quad (q = 1, 2, ..., N), \tag{6.44}$$

where

$$S_q = \sum_{i=1}^{q} \chi_{q+1}[\Phi^{(i,q+1)}, f_{q+1}]. \tag{6.45}$$

This quantity S_q will be called the statistical term. What is the advantage of this splitting up of the problem into the solution of a chain of equations? The first impression is that there is no advantage at all; for to determine f_1 you need to know S_1, but S_1 contains f_2, and this again depends on f_3, and so on, so that one eventually arrives at f_N, which satisfies the original equation. Yet this reasoning supposes the desire to get information about every detail of the motion, and that is just what we do not want.

We wish to obtain some observable and rather crude averages. Starting from f_1 and climbing up to $f_2, f_3, \ldots$, we can soon stop, as the chaos increases with the number of particles, and replace the rigorous connexion between f_q and f_{q+1} by an approximate one, according to the imperfection of observation.

Before explaining the application of this 'method of ignorance' to simple examples, I wish to mention that we have actually found the chain of equations (6.44) in quite a different way, starting with f_1 and using the calculus of probability for events not independent of one another (see Appendix, **22**).

This derivation is less formal than the first one and illuminates the physical meaning of the statistical term.

It would now be very attractive to show how from this general formula (6.44) the mechanical and thermal laws for continuous substances can be derived. But I have to restrict myself to a few indications concerning the general 'method of ignorance', to which I have already alluded.

The first example is the theory of gases. We have seen that this theory is based on Boltzmann's equation (6.23)

$$\frac{\partial f(1)}{\partial t} = [H, f(1)] + C(1), \tag{6.46}$$

where $C(1)$ is the collision integral (6.24);

$$C(1) = \int [f'(1)f'(2) - f(1)f(2)] |\xi_1 - \xi_2| \, d\mathbf{b} d\xi_2. \tag{6.47}$$

Now (6.46) has the same form as our general formula (6.44) for $q = 1$, provided $C(1)$ can be identified with S_1.

Green has shown that this is indeed the case, provided that the molecular forces have a small range r_0; then one can assume that in the gaseous state the probability of finding more than two particles in a distance smaller than r_0 is negligible. In other words, one can exclude all except 'binary' encounters. Two particles outside the sphere of interaction can be regarded as independent; hence one has there

$$f_2(1, 2) = f_1(1) f_1(2). \tag{6.48}$$

This holds also, in virtue of Liouville's theorem, if on the left-hand side the positions and velocities refer to a point in th interior of the sphere of action while on the right-hand side the values on its surface are used. With the help of this fact, the integration in S_1 can be performed (see Appendix, **23**), and leads exactly to the expression $C(1)$, in which only the 'boundary values' of the functions $f(1)$ and $f(2)$ on the surface of the sphere of action appear.

Hence the whole kinetic theory of gases is contained as a special case in our theory.

Concerning liquids, one must proceed in a different way, because triple and higher collisions cannot be handled with elementary formulae. We have adopted a method suggested by the American physicist Kirkwood. His formula is a generalization of (6.48), namely

$$f_3(1,2,3) = \frac{f_2(2,3)f_2(3,1)f_2(1,2)}{f_1(1)f_1(2)f_1(3)}, \tag{6.49}$$

and may be interpreted in different ways, e.g. by saying that the occurrences of three pairs of particles (2, 3), (3, 1), (1, 2) at given positions and with given velocities are almost independent events, because the mutual interactions decrease rapidly with the distance.

Substituting f_3 from (6.49) in S_2, one obtains from (6.44), (6.45) two integro-differential equations for f_1 and f_2 which form a closed system and can be solved by suitable approximations. (If then f_3 is calculated from the solution f_1, f_2, with the help of (6.49), the relation (6.40) for $q = 3$ is not necessarily satisfied; this is the sacrifice of accuracy introduced by the Kirkwood method.)

All physical properties of a liquid of the kind discussed here (particles with central forces) can be expressed in terms of $n_2(1,2)$, a function known to the experimenters in X-ray research on liquids as the radial distribution function. The method explained leads to explicit formulae for the equation of state and the energy; it allows also a discussion of the singularity which separates the gaseous and liquid states. But I cannot enter into a discussion of details.

Concerning non-equilibria, one can obtain the differential

equations for the mechanical and thermal flow in a rigorous way; the result has, of course, the form of Cauchy's equations (4.9) for continuous media, yet with a stress tensor $T_{\alpha\beta}$ which can be explicitly expressed in terms of the time derivatives of the strain tensor (or the space derivative of the velocity) and the gradient of temperature. In this way expressions for the coefficients of viscosity and thermal conductivity are obtained. They differ from the known formulae for gases by the great contribution of the mutual forces. Yet again I cannot dwell on this subject which would lead us far from the main topic of these lectures, to which I propose now to return (see Appendix, **33**).

VII

CHANCE AND ANTECEDENCE

WHAT can we learn from all this about the general problem of cause and chance? The example of gases has already shown us that the introduction of chance and probability into the laws of motion removes the reversibility inherent in them; or, in other words, it leads to a conception of time which has a definite direction and satisfies the principle of antecedence in the cause–effect relation.

The formal method consists in defining a certain quantity, the entropy

$$S = -k\frac{\int f\log f\,dpdq}{\int f\,dpdq}, \tag{7.1}$$

and showing that it never decreases in time: $dS/dt \geqslant 0$. In the case of a gas, the function f was the distribution function f_1 of one single molecule, a function of the point p, q of the phase space of this molecule.

The same integral represents also the entropy of an arbitrary system in statistical mechanics, if f is replaced by f_N, the distribution function in the $2N$-dimensional phase space; it satisfies all equilibrium relations of ordinary thermodynamics.

In the case of a gas, the time derivative of S could be determined with the help of Boltzmann's collision equation, and it was found that always

$$\frac{dS}{dt} \geqslant 0. \tag{7.2}$$

I have stressed the point that this is not in contradiction to the reversibility of mechanics; for this reversibility refers to a distribution function of non-interacting molecules, satisfying

$$\frac{\partial f}{\partial t} = [H, f], \tag{7.3}$$

while molecules colliding with one another satisfy

$$\frac{\partial f}{\partial t} = [H, f]+C, \tag{7.4}$$

where C is the collision integral. Irreversibility is therefore a consequence of the explicit introduction of ignorance into the fundamental laws.

Now the same considerations hold for any system. If we take for f the function f_N of a closed system of N particles, (7.3) is again satisfied, and if its solution is introduced into (7.1), it can be easily shown that $dS/dt = 0$.

Irreversibility can be understood only by explicitly exempting a part of the system from causality. One has to abandon the condition that the system is closed, or that the positions and velocities of all particles are under control. The remarkable thing is that it suffices to assume one single particle beyond control. Then we have to do with a system of $N+1$ particles, but concentrate our interest only on N of them. The partition function of these N particles satisfies the equation (6.44) for $q = N$:

$$\frac{\partial f_N}{\partial t} = [H_N, f_N] + S_N, \tag{7.5}$$

where S_N is a certain integral over f_{N+1} given by (6.45) for $q = N$. For a solution of this equation (7.5) the entropy is either constant or increasing. This is of course *a fortiori* the case if the system of N particles is coupled to more complicated systems out of control (see Appendix, **24**).

The increase of S continues until statistical equilibrium is reached, and it can be shown that the final distribution is the canonical one

$$f_N = e^{\alpha - \beta E}, \qquad H(p,q) = E. \tag{7.6}$$

This result is, in my opinion, the final answer of the age-old question how the reversibility of classical mechanics and the irreversibility of thermodynamics can be reconciled. The latter is due to a deliberate renunciation of the demand that in principle the fate of every single particle can be determined. You must violate mechanics in order to obtain a result in obvious contradiction to it. But one may say: this violation may be necessary from practical reasons because one can neither observe all particles nor solve the innumerable equations—in reality, however, the world is reversible, and thermodynamics only a trick for obtaining probable, not certain, results. This is the standpoint taken in many presentations of statistical mechanics. It is difficult to contradict if one accepts the axiom that the positions and velocities of all particles can, at least in principle, be determined—but can this really be maintained? We have seen that the Brownian motion sets a limit to all observations even on a macroscopic scale. One needs a spirit who can do things we could not even do with infinitely improved technical means. Further, the idea of a completely closed system is also almost fantastic.

I think that the statistical foundation of thermodynamics is quite satisfactory even on the ground of classical mechanics.

But in fact, classical mechanics has turned out to be defective just in the atomic domain where we have applied it. The whole situation has therefore to be re-examined in the light of quantum mechanics.

VIII

MATTER

MASS, ENERGY, AND RADIATION

In order not to lose sight of my main subject I have added to the heading of each section of these lectures words like 'cause', 'contiguity', 'antecedence', 'chance'. The one for the present section, 'matter', seems to be an intruder. For classical philosophy teaches that matter is a fundamental conception of a specific kind, entirely different from cause, though on the same level in the hierarchy of notions: another 'category' in Kant's terminology. This doctrine was generally accepted at the time before the great discoveries were made of which I have now to speak. It was the period when physics was governed by the dualism 'force and matter', *Kraft und Stoff* (the title of a popular book by Büchner). In modern physics this duality has become vague, almost obsolete. The first steps in this direction have been described in the preceding survey: the transition from Newton's distance forces to contact forces, first in mechanics, then in electromagnetism, and finally for gravitation; in other words, the victory of the idea of contiguity. If force is spreading in 'empty space' with finite velocity, space cannot be quite empty; there must be something which carries the forces. So space is filled with ether, a kind of substance akin to ordinary matter in many respects, in which strains and stresses can be produced. Though these contact forces obey different laws from those which govern elasticity, they are still forces in an ether, something different from the carrier. Yet this distinction vanishes more and more. Relativity showed that the ether does not share with ordinary matter the property of 'localization': you cannot say 'here I am'; there is no physical way of identifying a point in the ether, as you could recognize a point in running water by a little mark, a particle of dust. Electric and magnetic stresses are not something in the ether, they are 'the ether'. The question of a carrier becomes meaningless.

However, this is a question of interpretation. Physicists are very broad-minded in this respect; they will continue using obsolete expressions like ether, and no harm is done. For them a matter of terminology is not serious until a new quantitative law is involved. That has happened here indeed. I refer to the law connecting mass m, energy ϵ, and the velocity of light c (see Appendix, **25**),

$$\epsilon = mc^2, \tag{8.1}$$

which, after having been found to hold in special cases, was generally established by Einstein. His reasoning is based on the existence of the pressure of light, demonstrated experimentally and also derivable from Maxwell's equations of electrodynamics. If a body of mass M emits a well-defined quantity of light in a parallel beam which carries the total electromagnetic energy ϵ, it suffers a recoil corresponding to the momentum ϵ/c transferred. It therefore moves in the opposite direction, and to avoid a clash with the mechanical law that the centre of mass of a system cannot be accelerated by an internal process, one has to ascribe to the beam of light not only an energy ϵ and momentum ϵ/c but also a mass ϵ/c^2, and to assume that the mass M of the emitting body is reduced by the same amount $m = \epsilon/c^2$.†

The theory of relativity renders this result quite natural. It provides, moreover, an expression for the dependence of mass on velocity; one has

$$m = \frac{m_0}{\sqrt{(1-v^2/c^2)}}, \tag{8.2}$$

where m_0 is called the rest-mass. Energy ϵ and momentum $\mathbf{p}$ are then given by

$$\epsilon = mc^2, \qquad \mathbf{p} = m\mathbf{v}. \tag{8.3}$$

I need hardly to remind you how this result of 'purest science' has been lately confirmed by a terrifying, horrible, 'technical' application in New Mexico, Japan, and Bikini. There is no doubt, matter and energy are the same. The old duality between the force and the substance on which it acts, has to be abandoned, and hence also the original idea of force as the cause of motion. We see how old notions are dissolved by new experiences. It is this process which has led me to the abstract

† M. Born, *Atomic Physics* (Blackie), 4th ed., 1948, Ch. III. 2, p. 52; A. VII, p. 288. See Appendix, **25**.

definition of causality based only on the notion of physical dependence, but transcending special theories which change according to the experimental situation.

Returning to our immediate object, we learn from Einstein's law that the atomistic conception of matter is necessarily connected with the atomistic conception of energy. In fact the existence of quanta of energy was deduced by Planck from the laws of heat radiation five years before Einstein published his relation between mass and energy.

Planck's discovery opened the first chapter in the history of quantum theory, which corresponds to the years 1900 to 1913 and could be entitled 'Tracing the quantum by thermodynamical and statistical methods'. The next chapter deals with the period 1913–25 when spectroscopical and electronic methods were in the foreground, while the last chapter describes the birth and development of quantum mechanics.

I cannot possibly give an account of this long and tedious development, but I shall pick out a few points which are not so well known and hardly found in text-books, beginning with some remarks on the thermo-statistical quantum hunt.

The problem which Planck solved was the determination of the density of radiation ρ in equilibrium with matter of a given temperature T as function of T and of the frequency ν, so that $\rho(\nu, T)\,d\nu$ is the energy per unit volume in the frequency interval $d\nu$. By purely thermodynamical methods several properties of this function were known: the temperature dependence of the total radiation $\int \rho\, d\nu = \sigma T^4$ (law of Stefan and Boltzmann) and the specification that ρ/ν^3 is only a function of the quotient ν/T.† The problem remained to determine this function, and here statistical methods had to be used.

One can proceed in two ways. Either one regards the radiation as being in equilibrium with a set of atoms which in their interaction with radiation can be replaced by harmonic oscillators; then the mean energy of these can be calculated in terms of the radiation density and turns out to be proportional to it. This was the method preferred by Planck. Or one regards the radia-

† Law of Wien; see *Atomic Physics*, Ch. VII. 1, p. 198; A. XXVII, p. 343.

tion itself as a system of oscillators, each of these representing the amplitude of a plane wave. This method was used by Rayleigh and later by Jeans. In both cases the relation between the mean energy $u(\nu)$ of the oscillators of frequency ν and the radiation density ρ is given by†

$$\rho = \frac{8\pi\nu^2}{c^3}u, \tag{8.4}$$

and it suffices to determine u.

This can be done with the help of the so-called equipartition law of statistical mechanics. Suppose the Hamiltonian H of a system has the form

$$H = \frac{a}{2}\xi^2+H', \tag{8.5}$$

where ξ is any coordinate or momentum and H' contains all the other coordinates and momenta but not ξ. Then the mean value of the contribution to the energy of this variable ξ is (see Appendix, **26**)

$$\overline{\frac{a}{2}\xi^2} = \frac{k}{2}T, \tag{8.6}$$

independent of the constant a—hence the same for all variables of that description.

Applied to a set of oscillators of frequency ν, where

$$H = \frac{1}{2m}(p^2+4\pi^2\nu^2q^2), \tag{8.7}$$

one obtains for the average energy

$$u = kT, \tag{8.8}$$

hence, from (8.4),

$$\rho = \frac{8\pi\nu^2}{c^3}kT. \tag{8.9}$$

This is called the Rayleigh–Jeans radiation formula. It is a rigorous consequence of classical statistical mechanics, but nevertheless in obvious contradiction to facts. It does not even lead to a finite total radiation, since ρ increases as ν^2 with frequency. The law is, however, not quite absurd as it agrees well with measurements for small frequencies (long waves) or high temperatures. At the other end of the spectrum, the observed

† See *Atomic Physics*, Ch. VII. 1, p. 201; A. XXVIII, p. 347.

energy density decreases again, and Wien has proposed for this region an experimental law which would correspond to the assumption that in (8.4) the oscillator energy is of the form

$$u = u_0 e^{-\epsilon_0/kT}. \tag{8.10}$$

This looks very much like a Boltzmann distribution. According to Wien's displacement law it holds for high values of the

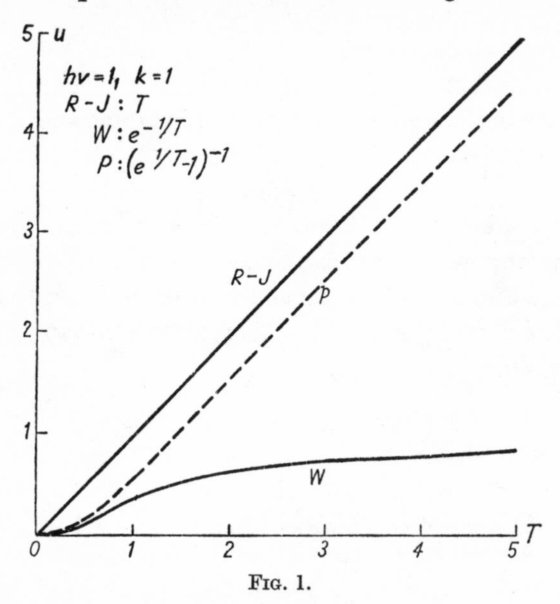

FIG. 1.

quotient ν/T, and both constants u_0 and ϵ_0 must be proportional to ν; but their meaning is obscure.

This was the situation which Planck encountered: two limiting cases given by the formulae (8.8) and (8.10), the first valid for large T, the second for small T. Planck set out to discover a bridging formula; the difficulty of this task can be visualized by looking at the two mathematical expressions or the corresponding graphs in Fig. 1. Planck decided that the energy was a variable unsuited for interpolation, and he looked for another one. He found it in the entropy S. I shall give here his reasoning in a little different form (due to Einstein, 1905), where the entropy does not appear explicitly but the formulae of statistical mechanics are used. Starting from Boltzmann's distribution law, according to which the probability of finding a system in a state with energy ϵ is proportional to $e^{-\beta\epsilon}$, where $\beta = 1/kT$, one can express the mean square fluctuation of the energy

$$\overline{(\Delta\epsilon)^2} = \overline{(\epsilon-\bar{\epsilon})^2} = \overline{\epsilon^2}-\bar{\epsilon}^2$$

in terms of the average energy $\bar{\epsilon} = u$ itself if the latter is given as function of temperature or of β (see Appendix, **20**.10):

$$\overline{(\Delta\epsilon)^2} = -\frac{du}{d\beta}. \tag{8.11}$$

Now this function $u(\beta)$ is known for the two limiting cases: T large or β small, and T small or β large, from (8.8) and (8.10),

$$u = \begin{cases} \beta^{-1} \text{ for small } \beta, \\ u_0 \, e^{-\beta\epsilon_0} \text{ for large } \beta. \end{cases} \tag{8.12}$$

Hence one has

$$\overline{(\Delta\epsilon)^2} = -\frac{du}{d\beta} = \begin{cases} \beta^{-2} = u^2, \text{ small } \beta; \\ u_0 \, \epsilon_0 \, e^{-\beta\epsilon_0} = \epsilon_0 \, u, \text{ large } \beta. \end{cases} \tag{8.13}$$

Now Planck argues like this: the two limiting cases will correspond to the preponderance of two different causes, whatever they may be. A well-known theorem of statistics says that the mean square fluctuations due to independent causes are additive. Let us assume that the condition of independence is here satisfied. Hence, if both causes act simultaneously, we should have

$$\overline{(\Delta\epsilon)^2} = -\frac{du}{d\beta} = \epsilon_0 \, u + u^2. \tag{8.14}$$

This is a differential equation for u, with the general solution

$$u = \frac{\epsilon_0}{e^{\alpha+\beta\epsilon_0}-1}. \tag{8.15}$$

The constant of integration α must vanish in order to have the limiting cases (8.13) all right. Wien's displacement law, according to which $\rho/\nu^3 = 8\pi u/c^3\nu$ depends only on T/ν, leads then to $\epsilon_0 = h\nu$, where h is a constant, known as Planck's constant.

The result is Planck's formula for the mean oscillator energy

$$u = \frac{h\nu}{e^{\beta h\nu}-1}, \qquad \beta = \frac{1}{kT}, \tag{8.16}$$

from which the radiation density follows according to (8.9); a refined interpolation which turned out to be in so excellent agreement with experiment that Planck looked for a deeper explanation and discovered it in the assumption of energy quanta of finite size $\epsilon_0 = h\nu$. If the energy is a multiple of ϵ_0, the integral (6.32) has to be replaced by the sum

$$Z = \sum_{n=0}^{\infty} e^{-\beta\epsilon_0 n} = \frac{1}{1-e^{-\beta\epsilon_0}}, \tag{8.17}$$

and then the usual procedure outlined in section 6 leads at once to the expression (8.16) for the oscillator energy u.

Planck believed that the discontinuity of energy was a property of the atoms, represented by oscillators in their interaction with radiation, which itself behaved quite normally. Seven years later Einstein showed that indeed wherever oscillations occur in atomic systems, their energy follows Planck's formula (8.16); I refer to his theory of specific heat of molecules and solids which opened more than one new chapter of physics. But this is outside the scope of these lectures.†

Einstein had, however, arrived already in 1905 at the conclusion that radiation itself was not as innocent as Planck assumed, that the quanta were an intrinsic property of radiation and ought to be imagined to be a kind of particles flying about. In text-books this revival of Newton's corpuscular theory of light is connected with Einstein's explanation of the photoelectric effect and similar phenomena where kinetic energy of electrons is produced by light or vice versa. This is quite correct, but not the whole story. For it was again a statistical argument which led Einstein to the hypothesis of quanta of light, or photons, as we say to-day.

He considered the two limiting cases (8.13) from a different point of view. Suppose the wave theory of light is correct, then heat radiation is a statistical mixture of harmonic waves of all directions, frequencies, and amplitudes. Then one can determine the mean energy of the radiation and its fluctuation in a given section of a large volume. This calculation has been performed by the Dutch physicist, H. A. Lorentz, with the result

† See *Atomic Physics*, Ch. VII. 2, p. 207.

that $\overline{(\Delta\rho)^2} = \bar{\rho}^2$ for any frequency, or expressed in terms of the equivalent oscillators, $\overline{(\Delta\epsilon)^2} = u^2$, in agreement with the Rayleigh–Jeans case (small β, large T) in (8.13). Hence there must be something else going on besides the waves, for which $\overline{(\Delta\epsilon)^2} = \epsilon_0 u$; what can this be?

Suppose Planck's quanta exist really in the radiation and let n be their number per unit volume and unit frequency interval. As each quantum has the energy $\epsilon_0 = h\nu$, one has $\bar{\epsilon} = u = \bar{n}\epsilon_0$, and $\overline{(\Delta\epsilon)^2} = \epsilon_0^2\overline{(\Delta n)^2}$. Hence the fluctuation law in Wien's case (large β, small T) of (8.13) can be written as

$$\overline{(\Delta n)^2} = \bar{n}. \tag{8.18}$$

This is a well-known formula of statistics referring to the following situation: a great number of objects are distributed at random in a big volume and n is the number contained in a part. Then one has just the relation (8.18) between the average $\bar{n}$ and its mean square fluctuation (see Appendix, **20**). So Einstein was led to the conclusion that the Wien part of the fluctuation of energy is accounted for by quanta behaving like independent particles, and he corroborated it by taking into account, besides the energy, also the momentum $h\nu/c$ of the quantum and the recoil of an atom produced by it. It was this result which encouraged him to look for experimental evidence and led him to the well-known interpretation of the photo-electric effect as a bombardment of photons which knock out electrons from the metal transferring their energy to them.

Expressed in terms of photon numbers the combined fluctuation law (8.14) reads

$$\overline{(\Delta n)^2} = -\frac{1}{\epsilon_0}\frac{d\bar{n}}{d\beta} = \bar{n}+\bar{n}^2 = \bar{n}(\bar{n}+1), \tag{8.19}$$

with the general solution

$$\bar{n} = \frac{1}{e^{\alpha+\beta\epsilon_0}-1}, \tag{8.20}$$

where $\alpha = 0$ leads to the correct value for large T. But what if $\alpha \neq 0$?

Every physicist glancing at the last formula will recognize it as the so-called Bose–Einstein distribution law for an ideal gas of indistinguishable particles according to quantum theory. It is most remarkable that at this early stage of quantum theory Planck and Einstein have already hit on a result which was rediscovered much later (Einstein again participating) (see Appendix, **25, 32**). In fact Planck's interpolation can be interpreted in modern terms as the first and completely successful attempt to bridge the gulf between the wave aspect and the particle aspect of a system of equal and independent components whatever they may be—photons or atoms.

I shall conclude this section by giving a short account of another consideration of Einstein's which belongs to a later period of quantum theory, when Bohr's theory of atoms was already well established, namely the existence of stationary states in the atoms which differ by finite amounts of energy content. Suppose the atom can exist in a lower state 1 and a higher state 2; transitions are possible by emission or absorption of a light quantum of energy $\epsilon_2-\epsilon_1 = \epsilon_0$, hence of frequency $\nu = \epsilon_0/h$. On the other hand, according to Boltzmann's law the relative number of atoms in the two states will be

$$\frac{N_2}{N_1} = e^{-\beta\epsilon_0}. \tag{8.21}$$

Now one can write (8.20), with $\alpha = 0$, in the form

$$(\bar{n}+1)e^{-\beta\epsilon_0} = \bar{n},$$

or, using (8.21),

$$\bar{n}N_2+N_2 = \bar{n}N_1. \tag{8.22}$$

For this equation Einstein gave the following interpretation: the left-hand side represents the number of quanta emitted per unit of time from the N_2 atoms in the higher state, the right-hand side those absorbed by the N_1 atoms in the lower state, two processes which in equilibrium must of course cancel one another.

The absorption is obviously proportional to the number of atoms in the lower state, N_1, and to the number $\bar{n}$ of photons present, i.e. to $\bar{n}N_1$. Concerning the emission the term N_2 signifies a spontaneous process, independent of the presence of radiation; it corresponds to the well-known emission of electromagnetic waves by a vibrating system of charges. The other term $\bar{n}N_2$ is a new phenomenon which was signalled the first time in this paper of Einstein (later confirmed experimentally), namely a forced or induced emission proportional to the number of photons present.*

If we denote the number of spontaneous emissions by AN_2, of induced emissions by $B_{21}N_2\bar{n}$, of absorptions $B_{12}N_1\bar{n}$, we learn from (8.22) that the probability coefficients (probabilities per unit time, per atom, and per light-quantum) are all equal:

$$A = B_{12} = B_{21}. \tag{8.23}$$

This result had far-reaching consequences. The first is the existence of a symmetric probability coefficient $B_{12} = B_{21}$ for transition between two states induced by radiation. This became one of the clues for the discovery of the matrix form of quantum mechanics.

The second point is seen if one considers, not equilibrium, but a process in time; Einstein's consideration leads at once to the equation

$$\frac{d\bar{n}}{dt} = \frac{dN_1}{dt} = -\frac{dN_2}{dt} = A\{\bar{n}(N_2-N_1)+N_2\}, \tag{8.24}$$

which is of the type used by the chemists for the calculation of reaction velocities. One has, in their terminology, three competing reactions, namely two diatomic ones and one monatomic one. Now genuine monatomic reactions are rare in ordinary chemistry, but abundant in nuclear chemistry; they were in fact until recently the only known ones, namely the natural radioactive disintegrations. If the radiation density is zero, $\bar{n} = 0$, one has

$$-\frac{dN_2}{dt} = AN_2, \tag{8.25}$$

which is exactly the elementary law of radioactive decay, according to Rutherford and Soddy. It expresses the assumption that the disintegrations are purely accidental and completely independent of one another.

Thus Einstein's interpretation means the abandonment of causal description and the introduction of the laws of chance for the interaction of matter and radiation.

* See Note 6 of Appendix Two, p. 213.

ELECTRONS AND QUANTA

Although my programme takes me through the whole history of physics, I am well aware that it is a very one-sided account of what really has happened. It will not have escaped you that I believe progress in physics essentially due to the inductive method (of which I hope to say a little more later), yet the experimentalist may rightly complain that his efforts and achievements are hardly mentioned. Yet as I am concerned with the development of ideas and conceptions, I may be permitted to take the skill and inventive genius of the experimenters for granted and to use their results for my purpose without detailed acknowledgement.

The period about 1900, when quantum theory sprang from the investigations of radiation, was also full of experimental discoveries: radioactivity, X-rays, and the electron, are the major ones.

In regard to the role of chance in physics, radioactivity was of special importance. As I said before, the law of decay is the expression of independent accidental events. Moreover, the decay constant turned out to be perfectly insensitive to all physical influences. There might be, of course, some internal parameters of the atom which determine when it will explode. Yet the situation is different from that in gas theory: there we know the internal parameters, or believe we know them, they are supposed to be ordinary coordinates and momenta; what we do not know are their actual values at any time, and we are compelled to take refuge in statistics because of this lack of detailed knowledge. In radioactivity, on the other hand, nobody had an idea what these parameters might be, their nature itself was unknown. However, one might have kindled the hope that this question would be solved and radioactive statistics reduced to ordinary statistical mechanics. In fact, just the opposite has happened.

Radioactivity is also important for our problem because it provided the means of investigating the internal structure of the atom. You know how Rutherford used α-particles as projectiles to penetrate into the interior of the atom, and found the nucleus.

This result, together with J. J. Thomson's discovery of the electron, led to the planetary model of the atom: a number of electrons surrounding the nucleus, bound to it by electric forces. The fundamental difficulty of this model is its mechanical instability.

As long as nothing was known about the forces which keep the elementary particles in an atom together one could assume a law of force which allowed stable equilibrium states. An ingenious model of this kind is due to J. J. Thomson. But now one knew that the forces were electrostatic ones, following Coulomb's law, and these could never guarantee the extraordinary stability of the actual atoms which survive billions of collisions without any change of structure. Bohr connected this difficulty with the facts of spectroscopy, and the result was his well-known model of the atom consisting of 'quantized' electronic orbits.

Mentioning spectroscopy, I feel again sadly how I have to skip over great fields of research with a few words.

The discovery of simple laws in line spectra was in fact a great achievement. Still more important than numerical formulae, like the one discovered by the Swiss schoolmaster Balmer for the hydrogen spectrum, was the rule found by Ritz (also a Swiss, who unfortunately died quite young), the so-called combination principle; it says that the frequencies of the spectral lines of gases can be obtained by forming differences of a single row of quantities $T_1, T_2, T_3,\ldots$, which are called terms:

$$\nu_{nm} = T_n - T_m, \tag{8.26}$$

though not all of these differences appear as lines in the spectrum. Balmer's formula for hydrogen is a special case where $T_n = R/n^2$, namely

$$\nu_{2m} = R\left(\frac{1}{4} - \frac{1}{m^2}\right) \quad (m = 3, 4,\ldots).$$

The formula (8.26) gave Bohr the clue to the application of quantum theory. Multiplying it by Planck's constant h he interpreted it as the energy difference $\epsilon_{nm} = h\nu_{nm}$ between any two stationary states having the energies $\epsilon_n = hT_n$ $(n = 1, 2,\ldots)$. This interpretation is a sweeping generalization of Planck's original conception of discrete energy-levels of oscillators. It explained at once the stability of atoms against impacts with an energy smaller than a certain threshold, the difference between emission and absorption spectra (the latter being of the form $h\nu_{n1} = \epsilon_n - \epsilon_1$, where 1 means the ground state), and was in detail confirmed by the well-known experiments of Franck and Hertz (excitation of spectra by electron bombardment).

However, I cannot continue to describe the whole development of quantum theory because that would mean writing an encyclopaedia of physics of the last thirty-five years. I have given this short account of the initial period because it is fashionable to-day to regard physics as the product of pure reason. Now I am not so unreasonable as to say that physics could proceed by experiment only, without some hard thinking, nor do I deny that the forming of new concepts is guided to some degree by general philosophical principles. But I know from my own experience, and I could call on Heisenberg for confirmation, that the laws of quantum mechanics were found by a slow and tedious process of interpreting experimental results. I shall try to describe the main steps of this process in the shortest possible way.

Yet it must be remembered that these steps do not form a straight staircase upwards, but a tangle of interconnected alleys. However, I must begin somewhere.

There was first the question whether the stationary states are certain selected mechanical orbits, and if so, which. Proceeding from example to example (oscillator, rotator, hydrogen atom), 'quantum conditions' were found (Bohr, Wilson, Sommerfeld) which for every periodic coordinate q of the motion can be expressed in the form

$$I = \oint p\,dq = hn, \tag{8.27}$$

where p is the momentum corresponding to q and the integration extended over a period. The most convincing theoretical argument for choosing these integrals I was given by Ehrenfest, who showed that if the system is subject to a slow external perturbation, I is an invariant and therefore well suited to be equated to a discontinuous 'jumping' quantity hn.

Among these 'adiabatic invariants' I there is in particular the angular momentum of a rotating system and its component in a given direction; if both are to be integer multiples of h, the strange conclusion is obtained that an atom could not exist in all orientations but only in a selected finite set. This was confirmed by Stern and Gerlach's celebrated experiment (deflecting an atomic beam in an inhomogeneous magnetic field). I am proud that this work was done in my department in Frankfort-on-Main. There is hardly any other effect which demonstrates the deviations from classical mechanics in so striking a manner.

A signpost for further progress was Bohr's correspondence principle. It says that, though ordinary mechanics does not apply to atomic processes, we must expect that it holds at least approximately for large quantum numbers. This was not so much philosophy as common sense. Yet in the hands of Bohr and his school it yielded a rich harvest of results, beginning with the calculation of the constant R in the Balmer formula.† The mysterious laws of spectroscopy were reduced to a few general rules about the energy-levels and the transitions between them. The most important of these rules was Pauli's exclusion principle, derived from a careful discussion of simple spectra; it says that two or more electrons are never in the same quantum state, described by fixed values of the quantum numbers (8.27) belonging to all periods, including the electronic spin (Uhlenbeck and Goudsmit). With the help of these simple principles the periodic system of the elements could be explained in terms of electronic states. But all these great achievements of Bohr's theory are outside the scope of our present interest. I have, however, to mention Bohr's considerations about the correspondence between the amplitudes of the harmonic components of a mechanical orbit and the intensity of certain spectral lines. Consider an atom in the quantum state n with energy ϵ_n and suppose the orbit can be, for large n, approximately described by giving the coordinates q as functions of time. As these will be periodic, one can represent q as a harmonic (Fourier) series, of the type

$$q(t) = \sum_{m=1}^{\infty} a_m(n)\cos[2\pi\nu(n)(mt+\delta_m)], \tag{8.28}$$

† See *Atomic Physics*, Ch. V. 1, p. 98; A. XIV, p. 300.

where the fundamental frequency $\nu(n)$ and the amplitudes $a_m(n)$ depend on the number n of the orbit considered. In reality, the frequencies observed are not $\nu(n), 2\nu(n), 3\nu(n),...$ but

$$\nu_{nm} = \frac{1}{\hbar}(\epsilon_n - \epsilon_m);$$

and what about the amplitudes? It was clear that the squares $|a_m(n)|^2$ should correspond in some way to the transition probabilities $B_{nm} = B_{mn}$ introduced by Einstein in his derivation of Planck's radiation law (8.16). But how could the mth overtone of the nth orbit be associated with the symmetric relation between two states m, n?

This was the central problem of quantum physics in the years between 1913 and 1925. In particular there arose a great interest in measuring intensities of spectral lines, with the help of newly-invented recording micro-photometers. Simple laws for the intensities of the component lines of multiplets were discovered (Ornstein, Moll), and presented in quadratic tables which look so much like matrices that it is hard to understand why this association of ideas did not happen in some brain.

It did not happen because the mind of the physicist was still working on classical lines, and it needed a special effort to get rid of this bias. One had to give up the idea of a coordinate being a function of time, represented by a Fourier series like (8.28); one had to omit the summation in this formula and to take the set of unconnected terms as representative of the coordinate. Then it became possible to replace the Fourier amplitudes $a_m(n)$ by quantum amplitudes $a(m, n)$ with two equivalent indices m, n, and to generalize the multiplication law for Fourier-coefficients into that for matrices†

$$c_m(n) = \sum_k a_k(n) b_{k-m}(n) \rightarrow c(m, n) = \sum_k a(m, k) b(k, n). \quad (8.29)$$

Heisenberg justified the rejection of traditional concepts by a general methodological principle: a satisfactory theory should use no quantities which do not correspond to anything observable. The classical frequencies $m\nu(n)$ and the whole idea of orbits have this doubtful character. Therefore one should

† See *Atomic Physics*, Ch. V. 3, p. 123; A. XV, p. 305.

eliminate them from the theory and introduce instead the quantum frequencies $\nu_{nm} = h^{-1}(\epsilon_n - \epsilon_m)$, while the orbits should be completely abandoned.

This suggestion of Heisenberg has been much admired as the root of the success of quantum mechanics. Attempts have been made to use it as a guide in overcoming the difficulties which have meanwhile turned up in physics (in the application of quantum methods to field theories and ultimate particles); yet with little success. Now quantum mechanics itself is not free from unobservable quantities. (The wave-function of Schrödinger, for instance, is not observable, only the square of its modulus.) To rid a theory of all traces of such redundant concepts would lead to unbearable clumsiness. I think, though there is much to be said for cleaning a theory in the way recommended by Heisenberg, the success depends entirely on scientific experience, intuition, and tact.

The essence of the new quantum mechanics is the representation of physical quantities by matrices, i.e. by mathematical entities which can be added and multiplied according to well-known rules just like simple numbers, with the only difference that the product is non-commutative. For instance, the quantum conditions (8.27) can be transcribed as the commutation law

$$qp - pq = i\hbar \qquad \left(\hbar = \frac{h}{2\pi}\right). \tag{8.30}$$

The Hamiltonian form of mechanics can be preserved by replacing all quantities by the corresponding matrices. In particular the determination of stationary states can be reduced to finding matrices q, p for which the Hamiltonian $H(p, q)$ as a matrix has only diagonal elements which are then the energy-levels of the states. In order to obtain the connexion with Planck's theory of radiation, the squares $|q(m,n)|^2$ have to be interpreted as Einstein's coefficients B_{mn}. In this way a few simple examples could be satisfactorily treated. But matrix mechanics applies obviously only to closed systems with discrete energy-levels, not to free particles and collision problems.

This restriction was removed by Schrödinger's wave mechanics which sprang quite independently from an idea of de Broglie about the application of quantum theory to free particles. It is widely held that de Broglie's work is a striking example of the power of the human mind to find natural laws by pure reason, without recourse to observation. I have not taken part in the beginnings of wave mechanics, as I have in matrix mechanics, and cannot speak therefore from my own experience. Yet I think that not a single step would have been possible if some necessary foothold in facts had been missing. To deny this would mean to maintain that Planck's discovery of the quantum and Einstein's theory of relativity were products of pure thinking. They were interpretations of facts of observation, solutions of riddles given by Nature—difficult riddles indeed, which only great thinkers could solve.

De Broglie observed that in relativity the energy ϵ of a particle is not a scalar, but the fourth component of a vector in space-time, whose other components represent the momentum $\mathbf{p}$; on the other hand, the frequency ν of a plane harmonic wave is also the fourth component of a space-time vector, whose other components represent the wave vector $\mathbf{k}$ (having the direction of the wave normal and the length λ^{-1}, where λ is the wave-length). Now if Planck postulates that $\epsilon = h\nu$, one is compelled to assume also $\mathbf{p} = h\mathbf{k}$. For light waves where $\lambda\nu = c$, this had already been done by Einstein, who spoke of photons behaving like darts with the momentum $p = \epsilon/c = h\nu/c$. De Broglie applied it to electrons where the relation between ϵ and p is more complicated, namely obtained from (8.3) by eliminating the velocity $\mathbf{v}$:

$$\left(\frac{\epsilon}{c}\right)^2 = \mathbf{p}^2 + m_0^2 c^2. \tag{8.31}$$

If a particle $(\epsilon, \mathbf{p})$ is always accompanied by a wave $(\nu, \mathbf{k})$ the phase velocity of the wave would be (using $\epsilon = mc^2$, $p = mv$)

$$\nu\lambda = \nu/k = \epsilon/p = c^2/v \geqslant c, \tag{8.32}$$

apparently an impossible result, as the principle of relativity excludes velocities larger than that of light. But de Broglie was not deterred by this; he observed that the prohibition of velocities larger than c refers only to such motions which can be used for sending time-signals. That is impossible by means of a monochromatic wave. For a signal one must have a small group of waves, the velocity of which can be obtained, according to Rayleigh, by differentiating frequency with respect to wave number. Thus, from (8.31) and (8.32),†

$$\frac{d\nu}{dk} = \frac{d\epsilon}{dp} = \frac{pc^2}{\epsilon} = v, \tag{8.33}$$

a most satisfactory result which completely justifies the formal connexion of particles and waves, though the physical meaning of this connexion was still mysterious.

This reasoning is indeed a stroke of genius, yet not a triumph of *a priori* principles, but of an extraordinary capacity for combining and unifying remote subjects.

I should say the same about the work of Schrödinger and Dirac, but you could better ask them directly what they think about the roots of their discoveries. I shall not describe them here in detail, but indicate some threads to other facts or theories. Schrödinger says that he was stimulated by a remark of de Broglie that any periodic motion of an electron must correspond to a whole number of waves of the corresponding wave motion. This led him to his wave equation whose eigenvalues are the energy-levels of stationary states. He was further guided by the analogy of mechanics and optics known from Hamilton's investigations; the relation of wave mechanics to ordinary mechanics is the same as that of undulating optics to geometrical optics. Then, looking out for a connexion of wave mechanics with matrix mechanics, Schrödinger recognized as the essential feature of a matrix that it represents a linear operator acting on a vector (one-column matrix), and came in this way to his operator calculus (see Appendix, **27**); if a coordinate q is taken as an ordinary variable and the corresponding momentum as the operator

$$p = \frac{\hbar}{i}\frac{\partial}{\partial q},$$

the commutation law (8.30) becomes a trivial identity. Applying the theory of sets of ortho-normal functions, he could then establish the exact relation between matrix and wave mechanics.

† See *Atomic Physics*, Ch. IV. 5, p. 84; A. XI, p. 295.

It is most remarkable that the whole story has been developed by Dirac from Heisenberg's first idea by an independent and formally more general method based on the abstract concept of non-commuting quantities (q-numbers).

The growth of quantum mechanics out of three independent roots uniting to a single trunk is strong evidence for the inevitability of its concepts in view of the experimental situation.

From the standpoint of these lectures on cause and chance it is not the formalism of quantum mechanics but its interpretation which is of importance. Yet the formalism came first, and was well secured before it became clear what it really meant: nothing more or less than a complete turning away from the predominance of cause (in the traditional sense, meaning essentially determinism) to the predominance of chance.

This revolution of outlook goes back to a tentative interpretation which Einstein gave of the coexistence of light waves and photons. He spoke of the waves being a 'ghost field' which has no ordinary physical meaning but whose intensity determines the probability of the appearance of photons. This idea could be transferred to the relation of electrons (and of material particles in general) to de Broglie's waves. With the help of Schrödinger's wave equation, the scattering of particles by obstacles, the excitation laws of atoms under electron bombardment, and other similar phenomena could be calculated with results which confirmed the assumption.

I shall now describe the present situation of the theory in a formulation due to Dirac which is well adapted to comparing the new statistical physics with the old deterministic one.

IX

CHANCE

QUANTUM MECHANICS

In quantum mechanics physical quantities or observables are not represented by ordinary variables, but by symbols which have no numerical values but determine the possible values of the observable in a definite way to be described presently. These symbols can be added and multiplied with the proviso that multiplication is non-commutative: AB is in general different from BA. I cannot deal with the most general aspect of this symbolic calculus, but shall consider a special representation, namely that where the coordinates $q_1, q_2,...$, of the particles are regarded as ordinary numbers. Then a definite state of a system is defined by a function $\psi(q_1, q_2,...)$, and an observable A can be represented by a linear operator: $A\psi(q)$ means a new function $\phi(q)$, the result of operating with A on ψ. If this result is, apart from a factor, identical with ψ,

$$A\psi = a\psi, \tag{9.1}$$

ψ is called an eigenfunction of A and the constant a an eigenvalue. The whole set of eigenvalues is characteristic for the operator A and represents the possible numerical values of the observable, which may be continuous or discontinuous.

The coordinates q themselves can be considered to be operators, namely multiplication operators: q_α operating on ψ means multiplying ψ by q_α. Operators whose eigenvalues are all real numbers are called real (or 'Hermitian') operators. It is clear that all physical quantities have to be represented by real operators, as the eigenvalues are supposed to represent the possible results of measuring a physical quantity. One can easily see that not only the multiplication operators q_α but also the momenta $p_\alpha = \frac{\hbar}{i}\frac{\partial}{\partial q_\alpha}$ are real. But for the formal argument one can also use complex operators, of the form $C = A+iB$ (where $i = \sqrt{-1}$), and its conjugate $C^* = A-iB$; then CC^* can be shown to be a real operator with only positive (or zero) eigenvalues.

If two observables are represented by non-commuting operators, A and B, their eigenfunctions are not all identical; if a is an eigenvalue of A belonging to such an eigenfunction, there is no state of the system for which a measurement can result in finding simultaneously for A and B sharp numerical values a and b.

The theory cannot therefore in general predict definite values of all physical properties, but only probability laws. The same experiment, repeated under identical and controllable conditions, may result in finding for a quantity A so many times a_1, so many times a_2, etc., and for B in the same way b_1 or b_2, etc. But the average of repeated measurements must be predictable. Whatever the rule for constructing the number which represents the average $\bar{A}$ of the measurements of A, it must, by common sense, have the properties that $\overline{A+B} = \bar{A}+\bar{B}$ and $\overline{cA} = c\bar{A}$, if c is any number.

From this alone there follows an important result. Consider apart from the averages $\bar{A}, \bar{B}$ of two operators A, B also their mean square deviations, or the 'spreadings' of the measurements,

$$\delta A = \sqrt{\{\overline{(A-\bar{A})^2}\}}, \qquad \delta B = \sqrt{\{\overline{(B-\bar{B})^2}\}}, \tag{9.2}$$

then by a simple algebraic reasoning (see Appendix, **28**), which uses nothing other than the fact stated above that CC^* has no negative eigenvalues, hence $\overline{CC^*} \geqslant 0$, it is found that

$$\delta A . \delta B \geqslant \frac{\hbar}{2} |\overline{[A, B]}|, \tag{9.3}$$

where
$$[A, B] = \frac{1}{i\hbar}(AB-BA) \tag{9.4}$$

is the so-called 'commutator' of the two operators A, B. If this is specially applied to a coordinate and its momentum, $A = p$, $B = q$, one has $[q, p] = 1$, therefore

$$\delta p . \delta q \geqslant \frac{\hbar}{2}. \tag{9.5}$$

This is Heisenberg's celebrated uncertainty principle which is a quantitative expression for the effect of non-commutation on measurements, but independent of the exact definition of averages. It shows how a narrowing of the range for the measured q-values widens the range for p. The same holds, according to (9.3), for any two non-commuting observables with the difference that the 'uncertainty' depends on the mean of the commutator.

These general considerations are, so to speak, the kinematical part of quantum mechanics. Now we turn to the dynamical part.

Just as in classical mechanics, the dynamical behaviour of a system of particles is described by a Hamiltonian

$$H(q_1, q_2, ...; p_1, p_2, ...)$$

which is a (differential) operator. It is usually just taken over from classical mechanics (where, if necessary, products like pq have to be 'symmetrized' into $\frac{1}{2}(pq+qp)$). In Dirac's relativistic theory of the electron there are, apart from the space coordinates, observables representing the spin (and similar quantities in meson theory); they lead to no fundamental difficulty and will not be considered here.

Yet one remark about the Hamiltonian H has to be made, bearing on our general theme of cause and chance: H contains in the potential energy (and in corresponding electromagnetic interaction terms) the last vestiges of Newton's conception of force, or, using the traditional expression, of causation. We have to remember this point later.

In classical mechanics we have used a formulation of the laws of motion which applies just as well to a simple system, where all details of the motion are of interest, as to a system of numerous particles, where only statistical results are desired (and possible). A function $f(t, p, q)$ of time and of all coordinates and momenta was considered; if p, q change with time according to the equations of motion, the total change of f is given by

$$\frac{df}{dt} = \frac{\partial f}{\partial t} - [H, f], \tag{9.6}$$

where $[H,f]$ is the Poisson bracket

$$[H,f] = \sum_k \left(\frac{\partial H}{\partial q_k}\frac{\partial f}{\partial p_k} - \frac{\partial H}{\partial p_k}\frac{\partial f}{\partial q_k}\right). \tag{9.7}$$

One recovers the canonical equations by taking for f simply q_k or p_k respectively. On the other hand, if one puts $df/dt = 0$, any solution of this equation is an integral of the equations of motion, and from a sufficient number of such integrals $f_k(t,p,q) = c_k$ one can obtain the complete solution giving all p, q as functions of t.

But if this is not required, the same equation is also the means for obtaining statistical information in terms of a solution f, called the 'distribution function', as I have described in detail. f is that integral of

$$\frac{\partial f}{\partial t} = [H,f], \tag{9.8}$$

which for $t = 0$ goes over into a given initial distribution $f_0(p,q)$. If, in particular, this latter function vanishes except in the neighbourhood of a given point p_0, q_0 in phase space, or, in Dirac's notation, if $f_0 = \delta(p-p_0)\delta(q-q_0)$, one falls back to the case of complete knowledge, q_0 and p_0 being the initial values of q and p.

This procedure cannot be transferred without alteration to quantum mechanics for the simple reason that p and q cannot be simultaneously given fixed values. The uncertainty relation (9.5) forbids the prescribing of sharp initial values for all p and q. Hence the first part of the programme, namely a complete knowledge of the motion in the same sense as in classical mechanics, breaks down right from the beginning. Yet the second part, statistical prediction, remains possible. Following Dirac, we ask which quantities have to replace the Poisson brackets (9.7) in quantum theory, where all quantities are in general non-commuting. These brackets $[\alpha, \beta]$ have a number of algebraic properties; the most important of them being

$$\begin{aligned} [\alpha, \beta_1+\beta_2] &= [\alpha, \beta_1]+[\alpha, \beta_2], \\ [\alpha, \beta_1\beta_2] &= \beta_1[\alpha, \beta_2]+[\alpha, \beta_1]\beta_2. \end{aligned} \tag{9.9}$$

If one postulates that these shall hold also for non-commuting quantities α and β, provided the order of factors is always preserved (as it is in (9.9)), then it can be shown (Appendix, **29**) that $[\alpha, \beta]$ is exactly the commutator as defined by (9.4).

Now one has to replace the function f in (9.8) by a time-dependent operator ρ, called the statistical operator, and to determine ρ from the equation (formally identical with (9.8)):

$$\frac{\partial \rho}{\partial t} = [H, \rho] \tag{9.10}$$

with suitable initial conditions. To express these in a simple way it is convenient to represent all operators by matrices in the q-space; A operating on a function $\psi(q)$ is defined by

$$A\psi(q) = \int A(q, q')\psi(q')\, dq' \tag{9.11}$$

(q stands for all coordinates $q_1, q_2, \ldots$, and q' for another set of values $q_1', q_2', \ldots$), where $A(q, q')$ is called the matrix representing A.

The product AB is represented by the matrix

$$AB(q, q') = \int A(q, q'')B(q'', q')\, dq''. \tag{9.12}$$

If now ρ and H are taken as such matrices, where the elements of ρ depend also on time, (9.10) is a differential equation for $\rho(t, q, q')$, and the initial conditions are simply

$$\rho(0, q, q') = \rho_0(q, q'), \tag{9.13}$$

where ρ_0 is a given function of the two sets of variables.

The number of vector arguments in ρ for a system of N particles is $2N$, exactly as in the case of classical theory in the function $f(p, q)$. But while the meaning of f depending on p, q is obvious, that of ρ depending on two sets q, q' is not, except in one case, namely when the two sets are identical, $q = q'$; then the function

$$\rho(t, q, q) = n(t, q) \tag{9.14}$$

is the number density, corresponding to the classical

$$\int f(t, q, p)\, dp = n(t, q).$$

Quite generally, the classical operation of integrating over the p's is replaced by the simpler operation of equating the two sets of q's, $q = q'$, or in matrix language, taking the diagonal elements of ρ.

The average of an observable A for a configuration q must be a real number $\bar{A}$ formed from ρ and A so that $n\bar{A}$ is linear in both operators. The simplest expression of this kind is

$$n\bar{A} = \tfrac{1}{2}(\rho A + A\rho)_{q=q'}, \tag{9.15}$$

and this gives, in fact, all results of quantum mechanics usually obtained with the help of the wave function. For instance, the statistical matrix describing a stationary state where A has a sharp value a, belonging to the eigenfunction $\psi(a,q)$, is

$$\rho = \psi(a,q)\psi^*(a,q'). \tag{9.16}$$

Then, from the definition (9.12) it follows easily that for this ρ and any real operator A one has

$$A\rho = \rho A = a\rho, \tag{9.17}$$

hence for $q = q'$, with (9.14),

$$n(a,q) = |\psi(a,q)|^2, \quad \bar{A} = a. \tag{9.18}$$

Thus we have obtained the usual assumption that $|\psi(a,q)|^2$ is the 'probability' (if normalized to 1) or 'number density' (if normalized to N) at the point q for the state a. (It must, however, be noted that for systems of numerous particles, like liquids in motion, other ways of averaging are useful, for instance for the square of a momentum instead of $n\overline{p^2} = \frac{1}{2}(\rho p^2 + p^2\rho)_{q=q'}$ the expression $\frac{1}{4}(\rho p^2 + p^2\rho + 2p\rho p)_{q=q'}$, which, however, for uniform conditions coincides with the former.)

Let us consider the general stationary case where ρ is independent of time and therefore satisfies

$$[H, \rho] = 0. \tag{9.19}$$

Any solution of this equation, i.e. any quantity Λ which commutes with H, is called an integral of the motion, in analogy to the corresponding classical conception. H itself is, of course, an integral. All integrals $\Lambda_1, \Lambda_2,\ldots,$ have different eigenvalues $\lambda_1, \lambda_2,\ldots,$ for one and the same eigenfunction $\psi(\lambda_1, \lambda_2,\ldots; q_1, q_2,\ldots)$, or shortly $\psi(\lambda, q)$:

$$\Lambda_1\psi = \lambda_1\psi, \qquad \Lambda_2\psi = \lambda_2\psi, \qquad \ldots . \tag{9.20}$$

ρ can be taken as any function of the Λ's; its matrix representation is given by

$$\rho(q,q') = \sum P(\lambda)\psi(\lambda,q)\psi^*(\lambda,q'), \tag{9.21}$$

from which one obtains, with (9.18),

$$n(q) = \rho(q,q) = \sum_{\lambda} P(\lambda)|\psi(\lambda,q)|^2 = \sum_{\lambda} P(\lambda)n(\lambda,q). \quad (9.22)$$

This shows that the arbitrary coefficient $P(\lambda)$ is the probability of finding the system in the stationary state λ.

Dynamical problems arise in a somewhat different way from those in classical theory. There it has a definite meaning to speak about the motion of particles in a closed system, for instance of the orbit of Jupiter in the planetary system. In quantum theory a closed system settles down in a definite stationary state, or a mixture of such states as given by (9.21). But then nothing is changing in time; one cannot even make an observation without interfering with the state of the system. In classical physics it is supposed that we have to do with an objective and always observable situation; the process of measuring is assumed to have no influence on the object of observation. I have, however, drawn your attention to the point that even in classical physics this postulate is practically never fulfilled because of the Brownian motion which affects the instruments. We are therefore quite prepared to find that the assumption of 'harmless' observations is impossible.

The most general way of formulating a dynamical problem is to split the Hamiltonian in two parts

$$H = H_0 + V, \quad (9.23)$$

where H_0 describes what is of interest while V is of minor importance, a so-called perturbation. V may also include external influences and depend explicitly on the time. This partition is, of course, arbitrary to a high degree; but it corresponds to the actual situation. If a water molecule H_2O is assembled from its atoms, one can either ask what the stationary states of the whole system are, or one can consider the parts H_2 and O and ask how the states of the hydrogen molecule H_2 are changed by the approaching oxygen atom, or one can ask the same question for the HO radical and the H atom. The latter two are dynamical problems.

Dynamical problems in quantum theory therefore, in contrast to those in classical theory, cannot be defined without a subjective, more or less arbitrary decision about what you are interested in. In other words, quantum mechanics does not describe an objective state in an independent external world, but the aspect of this world gained by considering it from a certain subjective standpoint, or with certain experimental means and arrangements. This statement has produced much controversy, and though it is generally accepted by the present generation of physicists it has been decidedly rejected by just those two men who have done more for the creation of quantum physics than anybody else, Planck and Einstein. Yet, with all respect, I cannot agree with them. In fact, the assumption of absolute observability which is the root of the classical concepts seems to me only to exist in imagination, as a postulate which cannot be satisfied in reality.

Assuming the partition (9.23) one has to describe the system in terms of the integrals of motion $\Lambda_1, \Lambda_2,\ldots$ of H_0 which are, however, not integrals of motion of H. All operators are then to be expressed as matrices in the eigenvalues λ $(\lambda_1, \lambda_2,\ldots)$ of $\Lambda_1, \Lambda_2,\ldots$; for instance, the statistical operator ρ by the matrix $\rho(t;\lambda,\lambda')$. The diagonal elements of this matrix

$$P(t;\lambda) = \rho(t;\lambda,\lambda) \tag{9.24}$$

represent the probability of a state λ at time t, and they go over for $t = 0$ into the coefficients $P(\lambda)$ which appear in the expansion (9.21) and represent the initial probabilities. The function $\rho(t;\lambda,\lambda')$ can be determined from the differential equation (9.10) by a method of successive approximations. My collaborator, Green, has even found an elegant formula representing the complete solution. To a second approximation one finds

$$P(t,\lambda) = P(\lambda)+\sum_{\lambda'} J(\lambda,\lambda')\{P(\lambda')-P(\lambda)\}+\ldots; \tag{9.25}$$

the coefficients are given by

$$J(\lambda,\lambda') = \frac{1}{\hbar^2}\left|\int_0^t V(t;\lambda,\lambda')e^{-(i/\hbar)(E-E')t}\,dt\right|^2, \tag{9.26}$$

where E is the energy of the unperturbed system in the state λ, E' that in the state λ' (see Appendix, **30**).

Now equation (9.25) has precisely the form of the laws of radioactive decay, or of a set of competing mono-molecular reactions. The matrix $J(\lambda, \lambda')$ obviously represents the probability of a transition or jump from the state λ to the state λ'. This interpretation becomes still more evident if one assumes that the λ-values are practically continuous, as would be the case if the system allowed particles to fly freely about (for instance in radioactivity one has to take account of the emitted α-particles; in the theory of optical properties of an atom of the photons emitted and absorbed). If external influences are excluded, so that V does not depend on time, the integral (9.26) can be worked out with the result that J becomes proportional to the time

$$J(\lambda, \lambda') = j(\lambda, \lambda')t, \tag{9.27}$$

where

$$j(\lambda, \lambda') = \frac{2\pi}{\hbar}|V(\lambda, \lambda')|^2\delta(E-E'). \tag{9.28}$$

The last factor $\delta(E-E')$ says that $j(\lambda, \lambda')$ differs from zero for two states λ and λ' only if their energy is equal. $j'(\lambda, \lambda')$ is obviously the transition probability per unit time, precisely the quantity used in radioactivity.

By applying the formula (9.25) to the case of the interaction of an atom with an electromagnetic field one obtains the formula (8.24) which was used by Einstein in his derivation of Planck's radiation law. There are innumerable similar applications, such as the calculation of the effective cross-sections of various kinds of collision processes, which have provided ample confirmation of the formula (9.25).

INDETERMINISTIC PHYSICS

There is no doubt that the formalism of quantum mechanics and its statistical interpretation are extremely successful in ordering and predicting physical experiences. But can our desire of understanding, our wish to explain things, be satisfied by a theory which is frankly and shamelessly statistical and indeterministic? Can we be content with accepting chance, not cause, as the supreme law of the physical world?

To this last question I answer that not causality, properly understood, is eliminated, but only a traditional interpretation of it, consisting in its identification with determinism. I have taken pains to show that these two concepts are not identical. Causality in my definition is the postulate that one physical situation depends on the other, and causal research means the discovery of such dependence. This is still true in quantum physics, though the objects of observation for which a dependence is claimed are different: they are the probabilities of elementary events, not those single events themselves.

In fact, the statistical matrix ρ, from which these probabilities are derived, satisfied a differential equation which is essentially of the same type as the classical field equations for elastic or electromagnetic waves. For instance, if one multiplies the eigenfunction $\psi(q)$ of the Hamiltonian H, $H\psi = E\psi$, by $e^{iEt/\hbar}$, the new function satisfies

$$-\frac{\hbar}{i}\frac{\partial\phi}{\partial t} = H\phi. \tag{9.29}$$

For a free particle, where $H = \frac{1}{2m}(p_x^2+p_y^2+p_z^2) = -\frac{\hbar^2}{2m}\Delta$, (9.29) goes over into the wave equation

$$\frac{2mi}{\hbar}\frac{\partial\phi}{\partial t} = \Delta\phi. \tag{9.30}$$

Although here only the first derivative with respect to time appears, it does not differ essentially from the ordinary wave equation $\left(\text{where the left-hand side is } \frac{1}{c^2}\frac{\partial^2\phi}{\partial t^2}\right)$. One must remember that only $\phi\phi^* = |\phi|^2$ has a physical meaning (as a probability), where ϕ^* satisfies the conjugate complex equation

$$-\frac{2mi}{\hbar}\frac{\partial\phi^*}{\partial t} = \Delta\phi^*.$$

For this pair of equations a change in the time direction ($t \rightarrow -t$) can be compensated by exchanging ϕ and ϕ^*, which has no influence on $\phi\phi^*$.

The same holds in the general case (9.29), and we see that the differential equations of the wave function share the property of all classical field equations that the principle of antecedence is violated: there is no distinction between past and future for the spreading of the probability density. On the other hand, the principle of contiguity is obviously satisfied.

The differential equation itself is constructed in a way very similar to the classical equations of motion. It contains in the potential energy, which is part of the Hamiltonian, the classical idea of force, or in other words, the Newtonian quantitative expression for causation. If, for instance, particles are acting on one another with a Coulomb force (as the nucleus and the electrons in an atom), there appears in H the same timeless action over finite distance as in Newtonian mechanics. Yet one has the feeling that these vestiges of classical causality are provisional and will be replaced in a future theory by something more satisfactory; in fact, the difficulties which the application of quantum mechanics to elementary particles encounters are connected with the interaction terms in the Hamiltonian; they are obviously still too 'classical'. But these questions are outside the scope of my lectures.

We have the paradoxical situation that observable events obey laws of chance, but that the probability for these events itself spreads according to laws which are in all essential features causal laws.

Here the question of reality cannot be avoided. What really are those particles which, as it is often said, can just as well appear as waves? It would lead me far from my subject to discuss this very difficult problem. I think that the concept of reality is too much connected with emotions to allow a generally acceptable definition. For most people the real things are those things which are important for them. The reality of an artist or a poet is not comparable with that of a saint or prophet, nor with that of a business man or administrator, nor with that of the natural philosopher or scientist. So let me cling to the latter kind of special reality, which can be described in fairly precise terms. It presupposes that our sense impressions are not a permanent hallucination, but the indications of, or signals from, an external world which exists independently of us. Although these signals change and move in a most bewildering way, we are aware of objects with invariant properties. The set of these invariants of our sense impressions is the physical reality which our mind constructs in a perfectly unconscious way. This chair here looks different with each movement of my head, each twinkle of my eye, yet I perceive it as the same chair. Science is nothing else than the endeavour to construct these invariants where they are not obvious. If you are not a trained scientist and look through a microscope you see nothing other than specks of light and colour, not objects; you have to apply the technique of biological science, consisting in altering conditions, observing correlations, etc., to learn that what you see is a tissue with cancer cells, or something like that. The words denoting things are applied to permanent features of observation or observational invariants.

In physics this method has been made precise by using mathematics. There the invariant against transformation is an exact notion. Felix Klein in his celebrated *Erlanger Programm* has classified the whole of mathematics according to this idea, and the same could be done for physics.

From this standpoint I maintain that the particles are real, as they represent invariants of observation. We believe in the 'existence' of the electron because it has a definite charge e and a definite mass m and a definite spin s; that means in whatever circumstances and experimental conditions you observe an effect which theory ascribes to the presence of electrons you find for these quantities, e, m, s, the same numerical values.

Whether you can now, on account of these results, imagine the electron like a tiny grain of sand, having a definite position in space, that is another matter. In fact you can, even in quantum theory. What you cannot do is to suppose it also to have a definite velocity at the same time; that is impossible according to the uncertainty relation. Though in our everyday experience we can ascribe to ordinary bodies definite positions and velocities, there is no reason to assume the same for dimensions which are below the limits of everyday experience.

Position and velocity are not invariants of observation. But they are attributes of the idea of a particle, and we must use them as soon as we have made up our minds to describe certain phenomena in terms of particles. Bohr has stressed the point that our language is adapted to our intuitional concepts. We cannot avoid using these even where they fail to have all the properties of ordinary experience. Though an electron does not behave like a grain of sand in every respect, it has enough invariant properties to be regarded as just as real.

The fact expressed by the uncertainty relation was first discovered by interpreting the formalism of the theory. An explanation appealing to intuition was given afterwards, namely that the laws of nature themselves prohibit the measurement with infinite accuracy because of the atomic structure of matter: the most delicate instruments of observation are atoms or photons or electrons, hence of the same order of magnitude as the objects observed. Niels Bohr has applied this idea with great success to illustrate the restrictions on simultaneous measurements of quantities subject to an uncertainty rule, which he calls 'complementary' quantities.

One can describe one and the same experimental situation about particles either in terms of accurate positions or in terms of accurate momenta, but not both at the same time. The two descriptions are complementary for a complete intuitive understanding. You find these things explained in many text-books so that I need not dwell upon them.

The adjective complementary is sometimes also applied to the particle aspect and the wave aspect of phenomena—I think quite wrongly. One can call these 'dual aspects' and speak of a 'duality' of description, but there is nothing complementary as both pictures are necessary for every real quantum phenomenon. Only in limiting cases is an interpretation using particles alone or waves alone possible. The particle case is that of classical mechanics and is applicable only to the case of large masses, e.g. to the centre of mass of an almost closed system. The wave case is that of very large numbers of independent particles, as illustrated by ordinary optics.

The question of whether the waves are something 'real' or a fiction to describe and predict phenomena in a convenient way is a matter of taste. I personally like to regard a probability wave, even in $3N$-dimensional space, as a real thing, certainly as more than a tool for mathematical calculations. For it has the character of an invariant of observation; that means it predicts the results of counting experiments, and we expect to find the same average numbers, the same mean deviations, etc., if we actually perform the experiment many times under the same experimental condition. Quite generally, how could we rely on probability predictions if by this notion we do not refer to something real and objective? This consideration applies just as much to the classical distribution function $f(t; p, q)$ as to the quantum-mechanical density matrix $\rho(t; q, q')$.

The difference between f and ρ lies only in the law of propagation, a difference which can be described as analogous to that between geometrical optics and undulatory optics. In the latter case there is the possibility of interference. The eigenfunctions of quantum mechanics can be superposed like light waves and produce what is often called 'interference of probability'.

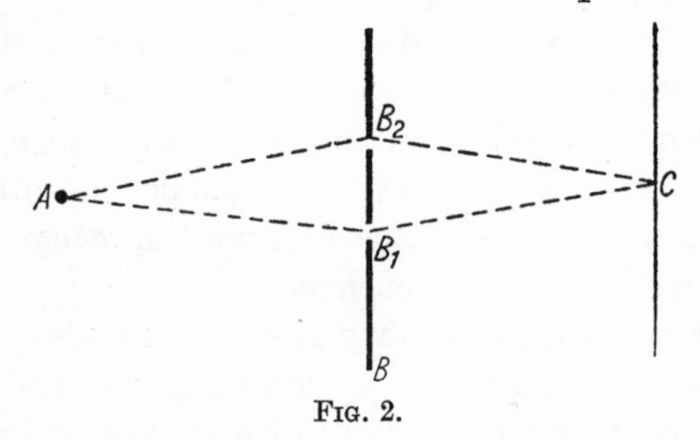

FIG. 2.

This leads sometimes to puzzling situations if one tries to express the observations only in terms of particles. Simple optical experiments can be used as examples. Assume a source A of light illuminating a screen B with two slits B_1, B_2 and the light penetrating these observed on a parallel screen C. If only one of the slits B_1 is open, one sees a diffraction pattern around the point where the straight line AB_1 hits the screen, with a bright central maximum surrounded by small fringes. When both slits are open and the central maxima of the diffraction pattern overlap, there appear in this region new interference fringes, depending on the distance of the two slits.

The intensity, i.e. the probability of finding photons on the screen, in the case of both slits open, is therefore not a simple superposition of those obtained when only one of the slits is open. This is at once understandable if you use the picture of probability waves determining the appearance of photons. For the spreading of the waves depends on the whole arrangement, and there is no miracle in the effect of shutting one slit. Yet if you try to use the particles alone you get into trouble; for then a particle must have passed one slit or the other and it is perfectly mysterious how a slit at a finite distance can have an influence on the diffraction pattern. Reichenbach, who has published a very thorough book on the philosophical foundations of quantum mechanics, speaks in such cases of 'causal anomalies'. To avoid the perplexity produced by them he distinguishes between phenomena, i.e. things really observable, such as the appearance of the photons on the screen, and 'inter-phenomena', i.e. theoretical constructions about what has happened to a photon on its way, whether it has passed through one slit or the other. He states rightly that the difficulties arise only from discussing inter-phenomena. 'That a photon has passed through the slit B_1 is meaningless as a statement of a physical fact.' If we want to make it a physical fact we have to change the arrangement in such a way that the passing of a photon through the slit B_1 can be really registered; but then it would not fly on undisturbed, and the phenomenon on the screen would be changed. Reichenbach's whole book is devoted to the discussion of this type of difficulty. I agree with many of his discussions, though I object to others. For instance, he treats the interference phenomenon of two slits also in what he calls the wave interpretation; but here he seems to me to have misunderstood the optical question. In order to formulate the permitted and forbidden (or meaningless) statements he suggests the use of a three-valued logic, where the law of the 'excluded middle' (*tertium non datur*) does not hold. I have the feeling that this goes too far. The problem is not one of logic or logistic but of common sense. For the mathematical theory, which is perfectly capable of accounting for the actual observations, makes use only of ordinary two-valued logics.

Difficulties arise solely if one transcends actual observations and insists on using a special restricted range of intuitive images and corresponding terms. Most physicists prefer to adapt their imagination to the observations. Concerning the logical problem itself, I had the impression when reading Reichenbach's book that in explaining three-valued logic he constantly used ordinary logic. This may be avoidable or justifiable. I remember the days when I was in daily contact with Hilbert, who was working on the logical foundations of mathematics. He distinguished two stages of logics: intuitive logic dealing with finite sets of statements, and formal logic (logistics), which he described as a game with meaningless symbols invented to deal with the infinite sets of mathematics avoiding contradictions (like that revealed in Russell's paradox). But Gödel showed that these contradictions crop up again, and Hilbert's attempt is to-day generally considered a failure. I presume that three-valued logic is another example of such a game with symbols. It is certainly entertaining, but I doubt that natural philosophy will gain much by playing it.

Thinking in terms of quantum theory needs some effort and considerable practice. The clue is the point which I have stressed above, that quantum mechanics does not describe a situation in an objective external world, but a definite experimental arrangement for observing a section of the external world. Without this idea even the formulation of a dynamical problem in quantum theory is impossible. But if it is accepted, the fundamental indeterminacy in physical predictions becomes natural, as no experimental arrangement can ever be absolutely precise.

I think that even the most fervent determinist cannot deny that present quantum mechanics has served us well in actual research. Yet he may still hope that one day it will be replaced by a deterministic theory of the classical type.

Allow me to discuss briefly what the chances of such a counter-revolution are, and how I expect physics to develop in future.

It would be silly and arrogant to deny any possibility of a return to determinism. For no physical theory is final; new experiences may force us to alterations and even reversions. Yet scanning the history of physics in the way we have done we see fluctuations and vacillations, but hardly a reversion to more primitive conceptions. I expect that our present theory will be profoundly modified. For it is full of difficulties which I have not mentioned at all—the self-energies of particles in interaction and many other quantities, like collision cross-sections, lead to divergent integrals. But I should never expect that these difficulties could be solved by a return to classical concepts. I expect just the opposite, that we shall have to sacrifice some current ideas and use still more abstract methods. However, these are only opinions. A more concrete contribution to this question has been made by J. v. Neumann in his brilliant book, *Mathematische Grundlagen der Quantenmechanik.* He puts the theory on an axiomatic basis by deriving it from a few postulates of a very plausible and general character, about the properties of 'expectation values' (averages) and their representation by mathematical symbols. The result is that the formalism of quantum mechanics is uniquely determined by these axioms; in particular, no concealed parameters can be introduced with the help of which the indeterministic description could be transformed into a deterministic one. Hence if a future theory should be deterministic, it cannot be a modification of the present one but must be essentially different. How this should be possible without sacrificing a whole treasure of well-established results I leave to the determinists to worry about.

I for my part do not believe in the possibility of such a turn of things. Though I am very much aware of the shortcomings of quantum mechanics, I think that its indeterministic foundations will be permanent, and this is what interests us from the standpoint of these lectures on cause and chance. There remains now only to show how the ordinary, apparently deterministic laws of physics can be obtained from these foundations.

QUANTUM KINETIC THEORY OF MATTER

The main problem of the classical kinetic theory of matter was how to reconcile the reversibility of the mechanical motion of the ultimate particles with the irreversibility of the thermodynamical laws of matter in bulk. This was achieved by proclaiming a distinction between the true laws which are strictly deterministic and reversible but of no use for us poor mortals with our restricted means of observation and experimentation, and the apparent laws which are the result of our ignorance and obtained by a deliberate act of averaging, a kind of fraud or falsification from the rigorous standpoint of determinism.

Quantum theory can appear with a cleaner conscience. It has no deterministic bias and is statistical throughout. It has accepted partial ignorance already on a lower level and need not doctor the final laws.

In order to define a dynamical phenomenon one has, as we have seen, to split the system in two parts, one being the interesting one, the other a 'perturbation'; and this separation is highly arbitrary and adaptable to the experimental arrangement to be described. Now this circumstance can be exploited for the problem of thermodynamics. There one considers two (or more) bodies first separated and in equilibrium, then brought into contact and left to themselves until equilibrium is again attained.

Let $H^{(1)}$ be the Hamiltonian of the first body, $H^{(2)}$ that of the second, and write

$$H_0 = H^{(1)}+H^{(2)}. \tag{9.31}$$

Then this is the combined Hamiltonian of the separated bodies. If they are brought into contact the Hamiltonian will be different, namely

$$H = H_0+V, \tag{9.32}$$

where V is the interaction, which for ordinary matter in bulk will consist of surface forces. Now (9.32) has exactly the form of the Hamiltonian of the fundamental dynamical problem, if we are 'interested' in H_0: and that is just the case.

Hence we describe the behaviour of the combined system by the proper variables of the unperturbed system, i.e. by the integrals of motion $\Lambda_1^{(1)}$, $\Lambda_2^{(1)}$,..., of the first body, and the integrals of motion $\Lambda_1^{(2)}$, $\Lambda_2^{(2)}$,..., of the second body, which all together form the integrals of motion of the separated bodies, represented by H_0. Hence we can use the solution of the dynamical problem given before, namely (9.25),

$$P(t,\lambda) = P(\lambda) + \sum_{\lambda'} J(\lambda,\lambda')\{P(\lambda') - P(\lambda)\} + \dots, \qquad (9.33)$$

where now λ represents the sets of eigenvalues $\lambda^{(1)} = (\lambda_1^{(1)}, \lambda_2^{(1)},\dots)$ of $\Lambda_1^{(1)}, \Lambda_2^{(1)},\dots$, and $\lambda^{(2)} = (\lambda_1^{(2)}, \lambda_2^{(2)},\dots)$ of $\Lambda_1^{(2)}, \Lambda_2^{(2)},\dots$.

Let us consider first statistical equilibrium. Then

$$P(t,\lambda) = P(\lambda);$$

hence the sum must vanish, and one must have

$$P(\lambda') = P(\lambda) \qquad (9.34)$$

for any two states λ, λ' for which the transition probability $J(\lambda,\lambda')$ is not zero. But we have seen further that these quantities $J(\lambda,\lambda')$ are in all practical cases proportional to the time and vanish unless the energy is conserved, $E = E'$ (see formulae 9.27, 9.28). If we disregard cases where other constants of motion exist for which a conservation law holds (like angular momentum for systems free to rotate), one can replace $P(\lambda)$ by $P(E)$. But as the total system consists of two parts which are practically independent, one has

$$P(E) = P(\lambda) = P_1(\lambda^{(1)})P_2(\lambda^{(2)}), \qquad (9.35)$$

where the two factors represent the probabilities of finding the separated parts initially in the states $\lambda^{(1)}$ and $\lambda^{(2)}$. This factorization need not be taken from the axioms of the calculus of probability; it is a consequence of quantum mechanics itself. For if the energy is a sum of the form (9.31), the exact solution of the fundamental equation for the density operator

$$\frac{\partial \rho}{\partial t} = [H, \rho] \qquad (9.36)$$

is $\rho = \rho_1 \rho_2$, where ρ_1 refers to the first system $H^{(1)}$, ρ_2 to the second $H^{(2)}$; as according to (9.24) $P(t,\lambda) = \rho(t; \lambda, \lambda)$, the product formula (9.35) holds not only for the stationary case (as long as the interactions can be neglected). If now $E^{(1)}(\lambda^{(1)})$ and $E^{(2)}(\lambda^{(2)})$ are the energies of the separated parts, one obtains from (9.35)

$$P(E^{(1)} + E^{(2)}) = P_1(\lambda^{(1)})P_2(\lambda^{(2)}), \qquad (9.37)$$

which is a functional equation for the three functions P, P_1, P_2. The solution is easily found to be (see Appendix, **31**)

$$P = e^{\alpha-\beta E}, \qquad P_1 = e^{\alpha_1-\beta E_1}, \qquad P_2 = e^{\alpha_2-\beta E_2}, \tag{9.38}$$

with

$$\alpha = \alpha_1+\alpha_2, \qquad E = E_1+E_2 \tag{9.39}$$

and the same β in all three expressions.

Thus we have found again the canonical distribution of Gibbs, with the modification that the energies appearing are not explicit functions of q and p (Hamiltonians) but of the eigenvalues $\lambda, \lambda^{(1)}, \lambda^{(2)}$ of the integrals of motion.

This derivation is obviously a direct descendant of Maxwell's first proof of his velocity distribution law which we discussed previously, p. 51. But while the argument of independence is not justifiable with regard to the three components of velocity, it is perfectly legitimate for the constants of motion Λ. The fact that the multiplication law of probabilities and the additivity of energies for independent systems leads to the exponential distribution law has, of course, been noticed and used by many authors, beginning with Gibbs himself. This reasoning becomes, with the help of quantum mechanics, an exact proof which shows the limits of validity of the results. For if there exist constants of motion other than the energy, the distribution law has to be modified, and therefore the whole of thermodynamics. This happens for instance for bodies moving freely in space, like stars, where the quantity $\beta = 1/kT$ is no longer a scalar but the time component of a relativistic four-vector, the other components representing $\beta\mathbf{v}$, where $\mathbf{v}$ is the mean velocity of the body. Yet this is outside the scope of these lectures.

The simplest and much discussed application of quantum statistics is that to the ideal gases. It was Einstein who first noticed that for very low temperatures deviations from the classical laws should appear. The Indian physicist, Bose, had shown that one can obtain Planck's law of radiation by regarding the radiation as a 'photon gas' provided one did not treat the photons as individual recognizable particles but as completely indistinguishable. Einstein transferred this idea to material atoms. Later it was recognized that this so-called Bose–

Einstein statistics was a straightforward consequence of quantum mechanics; about the same time Fermi and Dirac discovered another similar case which applies to electrons and other particles with spin.

In the language used here the two 'statistics' can be simply characterized by the symmetry of the density function

$$\rho(\mathbf{x}_1, \mathbf{x}_2,..., \mathbf{x}_N; \mathbf{x}'_1, \mathbf{x}'_2,..., \mathbf{x}'_N).$$

It is always symmetric, for indistinguishable particles, in both sets of arguments, i.e. it remains unchanged if both sets are subject to the same permutation. If, however, only one set is permuted, ρ remains also unchanged in the Bose–Einstein case for all permutations, while in the Fermi–Dirac case it does so only for even permutations, and changes sign for odd permutations.

Applied to a system of free particles of equal structure, one obtains at once from the canonical distribution law the properties of so-called degenerate gases. But as these are treated in many text-books, I shall not discuss them here (see Appendix, **32**).

After having considered statistical equilibrium we have now to ask whether quantum mechanics accounts for the fact that every system approaches equilibrium in time by the dissipation of visible energy into heat, or, in other words, whether the H-theorem of Boltzmann holds.

This is the case indeed, and not difficult to prove. One defines the total entropy, just as in classical theory, by

$$S = -k\frac{\sum_\lambda P(t,\lambda)\log P(t,\lambda)}{\sum_\lambda P(t,\lambda)}, \tag{9.40}$$

where the summations are to be extended over all values of the $\lambda_1, \lambda_2,...$; i.e. for each separate part of a coupled system over $\lambda_1^{(1)}, \lambda_2^{(1)},...$ and $\lambda_1^{(2)}, \lambda_2^{(2)},...$, respectively, and for the whole system over both sets. For loosely coupled systems the probabilities are, as we have seen, multiplicative at any time:

$$P(t; \lambda^{(1)}, \lambda^{(2)}) = P_1(t, \lambda^{(1)})P_2(t, \lambda^{(2)}). \tag{9.41}$$

From this it follows easily that the entropies are additive,

$$S = S_1 + S_2. \tag{9.42}$$

Now substitute into (9.40) the explicit expression for $P(t, \lambda)$ from (9.33) which holds for weak coupling; then by neglecting higher powers of the small quantities $J(\lambda, \lambda')$ one obtains

$$S = S_0 + \frac{k}{2} \frac{\sum_{\lambda, \lambda'} J(\lambda, \lambda') Q(\lambda, \lambda')}{\sum_{\lambda} P(\lambda)}, \tag{9.43}$$

where
$$Q(\lambda, \lambda') = \{P(\lambda) - P(\lambda')\} \log \frac{P(\lambda)}{P(\lambda')}. \tag{9.44}$$

The transition probabilities $J(\lambda, \lambda')$ are, as we have seen, in all practical cases proportional to time and vanish for transitions, for which energy is not conserved; one has, according to (9.27) and (9.28),

$$J(\lambda, \lambda') = t \frac{2\pi}{\hbar} |V(\lambda, \lambda')|^2 \delta(E - E'), \tag{9.45}$$

where V is the interaction potential. These quantities $J(\lambda, \lambda')$ are always positive. So is the denominator $\sum_{\lambda} P(\lambda)$, while $Q(\lambda, \lambda')$ is positive as long as $P(\lambda)$ differs from $P(\lambda')$.

Hence S increases with time and will continue to do so, until statistical equilibrium is reached. For only then no further increase of S will happen, as is seen by taking equilibrium as the initial state (where according to (9.34) $Q(\lambda, \lambda') = 0$ for all non-vanishing transitions).

It remains now to investigate whether quantum kinetics leads, for matter in bulk, to the ordinary laws of motion and thermal conduction as formulated by Cauchy. This is indeed the case, as far as these laws are expressed in terms of stress, energy, and flux of matter and heat. Yet, as we have seen, this is only half the story, since Cauchy's equations are rather void of meaning as long as the dependence of these quantities on strain, temperature, and the rate of their changes in space and time are not given. Now in these latter relations the difference between quantum theory and classical theory appears and can reach vast proportions under favourable circumstances, chiefly for low temperatures. The theory sketched in the following is mainly due to my collaborator, Green.

The formal method of obtaining the hydrothermal equations is very similar to that used in classical theory. Starting from the fundamental equation for N particles

$$\frac{\partial \rho_N}{\partial t} = [H_N, \rho_N], \tag{9.46}$$

a reduction process is applied to obtain similar equations for $N-1, N-2,...,$ particles, until the laws of motion for one particle are reached.

The reduction consists, as in classical theory, in averaging over one, say the last, particle of a set. The coordinates of each particle appear twice as arguments of a matrix

$$\rho_n = \rho_n(\mathbf{x}^{(1)}, \mathbf{x}^{(2)},..., \mathbf{x}^{(n)}; \mathbf{x}^{(1)'}, \mathbf{x}^{(2)'},..., \mathbf{x}^{(n)'}).$$

Put here $\mathbf{x}^{(n)} = \mathbf{x}^{(n)'}$ and integrate over $\mathbf{x}^{(n)}$; the result is $\chi_n \rho_n$, a matrix which depends only on $\mathbf{x}^{(1)},..., \mathbf{x}^{(n-1)}; \mathbf{x}^{(1)'},..., \mathbf{x}^{(n-1)'}$. With the same normalization as in classical theory, (6.40), p. 67, we write

$$\chi_{q+1} \rho_{q+1} = (N-q)\rho_q. \tag{9.47}$$

By applying this operation several times to (9.46) one obtains (see Appendix, **33**)

$$\frac{\partial \rho_q}{\partial t} = [H_q, \rho_q]+S_q \quad (q = 1, 2,..., N), \tag{9.48}$$

where
$$S_q = \sum_{i=1}^{q} \chi_{q+1}[\Phi^{(i,q+1)}, \rho_{q+1}], \tag{9.49}$$

in full analogy with the corresponding classical equations (6.44), (6.45). Here H_q means the Hamiltonian of q particles, $\Phi^{(i,q+1)}$ the interaction between one of these (i) and a further particle ($q+1$), and S_q is called, as before, the statistical term.

The quantity $\rho_q(\mathbf{x}, \mathbf{x}) = n_q(\mathbf{x})$ represents the generalized number density for a 'cluster' of q particles, and in particular $n_1(\mathbf{x})$ is the ordinary number density.

Now one can obtain generalized hydro-thermodynamical equations from (9.47) by a similar process to that employed in classical theory. Instead of integrating over the velocities one has to take the diagonal terms of the matrices (putting $\mathbf{x} = \mathbf{x}'$), and one has to take some precautions in regard to non-commutativity by symmetrizing products, e.g. replacing $\alpha\beta$ by $\frac{1}{2}(\alpha\beta+\beta\alpha)$ (see Appendix, **33**). Exactly as in the classical equations of motion there appears the average kinetic energy of the particle (i) in a cluster of q particles which, divided by $\frac{1}{2}k$, may be called a kinetic temperature of the particle (i) in the cluster of q particles. One might expect that the quantity T_1 corresponds to the ordinary temperature; but this is not the case.

It is well known from simple examples (e.g. the harmonic oscillator) that in quantum theory for statistical equilibrium the thermodynamic temperature T, defined as the integrating denominator of entropy, is not equal to the mean square momentum. Here in the case of non-equilibrium it turns out that not only this happens, but that a similar deviation occurs with regard to pressure. The thermodynamical pressure p is defined as the work done by compression for unit change of volume; the kinetic pressure p_1 is the isotropic part of the stress tensor in the equations of motion. These two quantities differ in quantum theory.

Observable effects produced by this difference occur only for extremely low temperatures. For gases these are so low that they cannot be reached at all because condensation takes place long before. Most substances are solid crystals in this region of temperature; for these one has a relatively simple quantum theory, initiated by Einstein, where the vibrating lattice is regarded as equivalent to a set of oscillators (the 'normal modes'). This theory represents the quantum effects in equilibrium (specific heat, thermal expansion) fairly well down to zero temperature, while the phenomena of flow are practically unobservable.

There are only two cases where quantum phenomena of flow at very low temperatures are conspicuous. One is liquid helium which, owing to its small mass and weak cohesion, does not crystallize under normal pressure even for the lowest temperatures and becomes supra-fluid at about 2° absolute. The other case is that of the electrons in metals which, though not an ordinary fluid, behave in many respects like one and, owing to their tiny mass, exhibit quantum properties, the strangest of which is supra-conductivity.*

In order to confirm the principles of quantum statistics, investigations of these two cases are of great interest. Both have been studied theoretically in my department in Edinburgh, and I wish to say a few words about our results.

In the supra-fluid state helium behaves very differently from a normal liquid. It appears to lose its viscosity almost completely; it flows through capillaries or narrow slits with a fixed velocity almost independent of the pressure, creeps along the walls of the container, and so on. A metal in the supra-conductive state has, as the name says, no measurable electrical resistance and behaves abnormally in other ways. A common and very conspicuous feature of both phenomena is the sharpness of the transition point which is accompanied by an anomaly of the specific heat: it rises steeply if the temperature approaches the critical value T_c from below, and drops suddenly for $T = T_c$, so that the graph looks like the Greek letter λ; hence the expression λ-point for T_c. However, this similarity cannot be very deeply rooted. Where has one to expect, from the theoretical standpoint, the beginning of quantum phenomena? Evidently when the momentum p of the particles and some characteristic length l are reaching the limit stated by the uncertainty principle, $pl \sim \hbar$. If we equate the kinetic energy $p^2/2m$ to the thermal energy kT, the critical temperature will be given by $kT_c \sim \hbar^2/2ml^2$. If one substitutes here for k and $\hbar$ the well-known numerical values and for m the mass of a hydrogen atom times the atomic mass number μ, one finds, in degrees absolute,

$$T_c \sim \frac{23}{\mu l^2}, \tag{9.50}$$

where l is measured in Ångström units (10^{-8} cm.).

For a helium atom one has $\mu = 4$, and if l is the mean distance of two atoms (order 1 Å) one obtains for T_c a few degrees, which agrees with the observed transition at about 2°. But for electrons in metals one has $\mu = 1/1840$. If one now assumes one

* See Note 7 of Appendix Two, p. 214.

electron per atom and interprets l as their mean distance it would be again of the order 1 Å, hence the expression (9.50) would become some thousand degrees and has therefore nothing to do with the λ-point of supra-conductivity. This temperature has, in fact, another meaning; it is the so-called 'degeneration temperature' T_g of the electronic fluid; below T_g, for instance at ordinary temperatures, there are already strong deviations from classical behaviour (e.g. the extremely small contribution of the electrons to the specific heat), though not of the extreme character of supra-conductivity. In order to explain the λ-point of supra-conductivity which lies for all metals at a few degrees absolute, one has to take l about 200 times larger ($\sim$ 200 Å). As the interpretation of this length is still controversial, I shall not discuss supra-conductivity any further (see Appendix, **34**).

Nor do I intend in the case of supra-fluidity of helium to give a full explanation of the λ-discontinuity, but I wish to direct your attention to the thermo-mechanical properties of the supra-liquid below the λ-point, called He II.

I have already mentioned that in quantum liquids one has to distinguish the ordinary thermodynamic temperature T and pressure p from the kinetic temperature T_1 and pressure p_1. The hydro-thermal equations contain only T_1 and p_1, and these quantities are constant in equilibrium, i.e. for a state where no change in time takes place. But T_1 and p_1 are not simple functions of T and p but depend also on the velocity and its gradient. Therefore in such a state permanent currents of mass and of energy may flow as if no viscosity existed. This is reflected in the energy balance which can be derived from the hydro-thermal equations. One obtains a curious result which looks like a violation of the first law of thermodynamics; for the change of heat is given by

$$dQ = T\,dS = dU+p\,dV-V\,d\pi, \tag{9.51}$$

where all symbols have the usual meaning, and $\pi = p_1-p$ is the difference of the kinetic and thermodynamic pressures. This equation differs from the ordinary thermodynamical expression (5.12) by the term $-V\,d\pi$; how is this possible if thermodynamics claims rightly universal validity? This claim is quite legitimate, but the usual form of the expression for dQ depends on the assumption that a quasi-static, i.e. very slow, process can be regarded as a sequence of equilibria each determined by the instantaneous values of pressure and volume. This is correct in the classical domain, because if the rate of change of external action (compression, heat supply, etc.) is slowed down, all velocities in the fluid tend to disappear. Not so in quantum mechanics. In consequence of the indeterminacy condition the momenta or the velocities cannot decrease indefinitely if the coordinates of the particles are restricted to very small regions. An investigation of the hydro-thermal equations shows that this effect is preserved, to some degree, even for the visible velocities; it is true there can exist a genuine statistical equilibrium where the density is uniform and the currents of mass and energy vanish, but there are also those states possible where certain combinations of currents of mass (velocities) and of energy (heat) permanently exist. The production of these depends entirely on the way in which the heat dQ is supplied to the system and cannot be suppressed by just making the rate of change of volume very small. We have therefore not a breakdown of the law of conservation of energy but of its traditional thermodynamical formulation.

The consequences of that extra term in (9.51) are easily seen by introducing instead of the internal energy the quantity

$$E = U - \pi V \tag{9.52}$$

in the expression (9.51) for dQ, which then reads

$$dQ = dE + p_1 dV, \tag{9.53}$$

where $p_1 = p + \pi$ is the kinetic pressure. This shows that the specific heat at constant volume is

$$c_v = \left(\frac{dQ}{dT}\right)_v = \left(\frac{dE}{dT}\right)_v, \tag{9.54}$$

not $(dU/dT)_v$, as in classical thermodynamics. Now as p_1, and therefore $\pi = p_1 - p$, is very large at $T = 0$ and decreases with increasing T to reach the value 0 at the λ-point, one obtains for

$c_v(T)$ a curve exactly of the form actually observed. Hence the λ-anomaly is due to the coupling of heat currents with the mass motion characteristic of quantum liquids. It is a molar, macroscopic motion, the shape of which depends on the geometrical conditions, presumably consisting of tiny closed threads of fast-moving liquid, or groups of density waves.

A similar conception has been derived by several authors (Tisza, Mendelssohn, Landau) from the experiments; they speak of the liquid being a mixture of ordinary atoms and special degenerate atoms (z-particles) which are in the lowest quantum state and carry neither energy nor entropy. Yet in a liquid one cannot attribute a quantum state to single atoms.

These considerations are also the clue to the understanding of other anomalous phenomena, as the flow through narrow capillaries or slits, the so-called fountain effect, the 'second sound', etc. Green has studied the properties of He II in detail and arrived at the conclusion that the quantum theory of liquids can account for the strange behaviour of this substance.

I have dwelt on this special problem in some detail as it reveals in a striking way that quantum phenomena are not confined to atomic physics or microphysics where one aims at observing single particles, but appear also in molar physics which deals with matter in bulk. From the fundamental standpoint this distinction, so essential in classical physics, loses much of its meaning in quantum theory. The ultimate laws are statistical, and the deterministic form of the molar equations holds for certain averages which for large numbers of particles or quanta are all one wants to know.

Now these molar laws satisfy all postulates of classical causality: they are deterministic and conform to the principles of contiguity and antecedence.

With this statement the circle of our considerations about cause and chance in physics is closed. We have seen how classical physics struggled in vain to reconcile growing quantitative observations with preconceived ideas on causality, derived from everyday experience but raised to the level of metaphysical postulates, and how it fought a losing battle against the intrusion of chance. To-day the order of ideas has been reversed: chance has become the primary notion, mechanics an expression of its quantitative laws, and the overwhelming evidence of causality with all its attributes in the realm of ordinary experience is satisfactorily explained by the statistical laws of large numbers.

X

METAPHYSICAL CONCLUSIONS

The statistical interpretation which I have presented in the last section is now generally accepted by physicists all over the world, with a few exceptions, amongst them a most remarkable one. As I have mentioned before, Einstein does not accept it, but still believes in and works on a return to a deterministic theory. To illustrate his opinion, let me quote passages from two letters. The first is dated 7 November 1944, and contains these lines:

'In unserer wissenschaftlichen Erwartung haben wir uns zu Antipoden entwickelt. Du glaubst an den würfelnden Gott und ich an volle Gesetzlichkeit in einer Welt von etwas objektiv Seiendem, das ich auf wild spekulativem Weg zu erhaschen suche. Ich hoffe, dass einer einen mehr realistischen Weg, bezw. eine mehr greifbare Unterlage für eine solche Auffassung finden wird, als es mir gegeben ist. Der grosse anfängliche Erfolg der Quantentheorie kann mich doch nicht zum Glauben an das fundamentale Würfelspiel bringen.'

(In our scientific expectations we have progressed towards antipodes. You believe in the dice-playing god, and I in the perfect rule of law in a world of something objectively existing which I try to catch in a wildly speculative way. I hope that somebody will find a more realistic way, or a more tangible foundation for such a conception than that which is given to me. The great initial success of quantum theory cannot convert me to believe in that fundamental game of dice.)

The second letter, which arrived just when I was writing these pages (dated 3 December 1947), contains this passage:

'Meine physikalische Haltung kann ich Dir nicht so begründen, dass Du sie irgendwie vernünftig finden würdest. Ich sehe natürlich ein, dass die principiell statistische Behandlungsweise, deren Notwendigkeit im Rahmen des bestehenden Formalismus ja zuerst von Dir klar erkannt wurde, einen bedeutenden Wahrheitsgehalt hat. Ich kann aber deshalb nicht ernsthaft daran glauben, weil die Theorie mit dem Grundsatz unvereinbar ist, dass die Physik eine Wirklichkeit in Zeit und Raum darstellen soll, ohne spukhafte Fernwirkungen. . . . Davon bin ich fest überzeugt, dass man schliesslich bei einer Theorie landen wird, deren gesetzmässig verbundene Dinge nicht Wahrscheinlichkeiten, sondern gedachte Tatbestände sind, wie man es bis vor kurzem als selbstverständlich betrachtet hat. Zur Begründung dieser Überzeugung kann ich aber nicht logische Gründe, sondern nur meinen kleinen Finger als Zeugen beibringen, also keine Autorität, die ausserhalb meiner Haut irgendwelchen Respekt einflössen kann.'

(I cannot substantiate my attitude to physics in such a manner that you would find it in any way rational. I see of course that the statistical interpretation (the necessity of which in the frame of the existing formalism has been first clearly recognized by yourself) has a considerable content of truth. Yet I cannot seriously believe it because the theory is inconsistent with the principle that physics has to represent a reality in space and time without phantom actions over distances. . . . I am absolutely convinced that one will eventually arrive at a theory in which the objects connected by laws are not probabilities, but conceived facts, as one took for granted only a short time ago. However, I cannot provide logical arguments for my conviction, but can only call on my little finger as a witness, which cannot claim any authority to be respected outside my own skin.)

I have quoted these letters because I think that the opinion of the greatest living physicist, who has done more than anybody else to establish modern ideas, must not be by-passed. Einstein does not share the opinion held by most of us that there is overwhelming evidence for quantum mechanics. Yet he concedes 'initial success' and 'a considerable degree of truth'. He obviously agrees that we have at present nothing better, but he hopes that this will be achieved later, for he rejects the 'dice-playing god'. I have discussed the chances of a return to determinism and found them slight. I have tried to show that classical physics is involved in no less formidable conceptional difficulties and had eventually to incorporate chance in its system. We mortals have to play dice anyhow if we wish to deal with atomic systems. Einstein's principle of the existence of an objective real world is therefore rather academic. On the other hand, his contention that quantum theory has given up this principle is not justified, if the conception of reality is properly understood. Of this I shall say more presently.

Einstein's letters teach us impressively the fact that even an exact science like physics is based on fundamental beliefs. The words *ich glaube* appear repeatedly, and once they are underlined. I shall not further discuss the difference between Einstein's principles and those which I have tried to extract from the history of physics up to the present day. But I wish to collect some of the fundamental assumptions which cannot be further reduced but have to be accepted by an act of faith.

Causality is such a principle, if it is defined as the belief in the existence of mutual physical dependence of observable situations. However, all specifications of this dependence in regard to space and time (contiguity, antecedence) and to the infinite sharpness of observation (determinism) seem to me not fundamental, but consequences of the actual empirical laws.

Another metaphysical principle is incorporated in the notion of probability. It is the belief that the predictions of statistical calculations are more than an exercise of the brain, that they can be trusted in the real world. This holds just as well for ordinary probability as for the more refined mixture of probability and mechanics formulated by quantum theory.

The two metaphysical conceptions of causality and probability have been our main theme. Others, concerning logic, arithmetic, space, and time, are quite beyond the frame of these lectures. But let me add a few more which have occasionally occurred, though I am sure that my list will be quite incomplete. One is the belief in harmony in nature, which is something distinct from causality, as it can be circumscribed by words like beauty, elegance, simplicity applied to certain formulations of natural laws. This belief has played a considerable part in the development of theoretical physics—remember Maxwell's equations of the electromagnetic field, or Einstein's relativity—but how far it is a real guide in the search of the unknown or just the expression of our satisfaction to have discovered a significant relation, I do not venture to say. For I have on occasion made the sad discovery that a theory which seemed to me very lovely nevertheless did not work. And in regard to simplicity, opinions will differ in many cases. Is Einstein's law of gravitation simpler than Newton's? Trained mathematicians will answer Yes, meaning the logical simplicity of the foundations, while others will say emphatically No, because of the horrible complication of the formalism. However this may be, this kind of belief may help some specially gifted men in their research; for the validity of the result it has little importance (see Appendix, **35**).

The last belief I wish to discuss may be called the principle of objectivity. It provides a criterion to distinguish subjective impressions from objective facts, namely by substituting for given sense-data others which can be checked by other individuals. I have spoken about this method when I had to define temperature: the subjective feeling of hot and cold is replaced by the reading of a thermometer, which can be done by any person without a sensation of hot or cold. It is perhaps the most important rule of the code of natural science of which innumerable examples can be given, and it is obviously closely related to the conception of scientific reality. For if reality is understood to mean the sum of observational invariants—and I cannot see any other reasonable interpretation of this word in physics—the elimination of sense qualities is a necessary step to discover them.

Here I must refer to the previous Waynflete Lectures given by Professor E. D. Adrian, on *The Physical Background of Perception*, because the results of physiological investigations seem to me in perfect agreement with my suggestion about the meaning of reality in physics. The messages which the brain receives have not the least similarity with the stimuli. They consist in pulses of given intensities and frequencies, characteristic for the transmitting nerve-fibre, which ends at a definite place of the cortex. All the brain 'learns' (I use here the objectionable language of the 'disquieting figure of a little hobgoblin sitting up aloft in the cerebral hemisphere') is a distribution or 'map' of pulses. From this information it produces the image of the world by a process which can metaphorically be called a consummate piece of combinatorial mathematics: it sorts out of the maze of indifferent and varying signals invariant shapes and relations which form the world of ordinary experience.

This unconscious process breaks down for scientific ultra-experience, obtained by magnifying instruments. But then it is continued in the full light of consciousness, by mathematical reasoning. The result is the reality offered by theoretical physics.

The principle of objectivity can, I think, be applied to every human experience, but is often quite out of place. For instance: what is a fugue by Bach? Is it the invariant cross-section, or the common content of all printed or written copies, gramophone records, sound waves at performances, etc., of this piece of music? As a lover of music I say No! that is not what I mean by a fugue. It is something of another sphere where other notions apply, and the essence of it is not 'notions' at all, but the immediate impact on my soul of its beauty and greatness.

In cases like this, the idea of scientific objective reality is obviously inadequate, almost absurd.

This is trivial, but I have to refer to it if I have to make good my promise to discuss the bearing of modern physical thought on philosophical problems, in particular on the problem of free will. Since ancient times philosophers have been worried how free will can be reconciled with causality, and after the tremendous success of Newton's deterministic theory of nature, this problem seemed to be still more acute. Therefore, the advent of indeterministic quantum theory was welcomed as opening a possibility for the autonomy of the mind without a clash with the laws of nature. Free will is primarily a subjective phenomenon, the interpretation of a sensation which we experience, similar to a sense impression. We can and do, of course, project it into the minds of our fellow beings just as we do in the case of music. We can also correlate it with other phenomena in order to transform it into an objective relation, as the moralists, sociologists, lawyers do—but then it resembles the original sensation no more than an intensity curve in a spectral diagram resembles a colour which I see. After this transformation into a sociological concept, free will is a symbolic expression to describe the fact that the actions and reactions of human beings are conditioned by their internal mental structure and depend on their whole and unaccountable history. Whether we believe theoretically in strict determinism or not, we can make no use of this theory since a human being is too complicated, and we have to be content with a working hypothesis like that of spontaneity of decision and responsibility of action. If you feel that this clashes with determinism, you have now at your disposal the modern indeterministic philosophy of nature, you can assume a certain 'freedom', i.e. deviation from the deterministic laws, because these are only apparent and refer to averages. Yet if you believe in perfect freedom you will get into difficulties again, because you cannot neglect the laws of statistics which are laws of nature.

I think that the philosophical treatment of the problem of free will suffers often (see Appendix, **36**) from an insufficient distinction between the subjective and objective aspect. It is doubtless more difficult to keep these apart in the case of such sensations as free will, than in the case of colours, sounds, or temperatures. But the application of scientific conceptions to a subjective experience is an inadequate procedure in all such cases.

You may call this an evasion of the problem, by means of dividing all experience into two categories, instead of trying to form one all-embracing picture of the world. This division is indeed what I suggest and consider to be unavoidable. If quantum theory has any philosophical importance at all, it lies in the fact that it demonstrates for a single, sharply defined science the necessity of dual aspects and complementary considerations. Niels Bohr has discussed this question with respect to many applications in physiology, psychology, and philosophy in general. According to the rule of indeterminacy, you cannot measure simultaneously position and velocity of particles, but you have to make your choice. The situation is similar if you wish, for instance, to determine the physico-chemical processes in the brain connected with a mental process: it cannot be done because the latter would be decidedly disturbed by the physical investigation. Complete knowledge of the physical situation is only obtainable by a dissection which would mean the death of the living organ or the whole creature, the destruction of the mental situation. This example may suffice; you can find more and subtler ones in Bohr's writings. They illustrate the limits of human understanding and direct the attention to the question of fixing the boundary line, as physics has done in a narrow field by discovering the quantum constant $\hbar$. Much futile controversy could be avoided in this way. To show this by a final example, I wish to refer to these lectures themselves which deal only with one aspect of science, the theoretical one. There is a powerful school of eminent scientists who consider such things to be a futile and snobbish sport, and the people who spend their time on it drones. Science has undoubtedly two aspects: it can be regarded from the social standpoint as a practical collective endeavour for the improvement of human conditions, but it can also be regarded from the individualistic standpoint, as a pursuit of mental desires, the hunger for knowledge and understanding, a sister of art, philosophy, and religion. Both aspects are justified, necessary, and complementary. The collective enterprise of practical science consists in the end of individuals and cannot thrive without their devotion. But devotion does not suffice; nothing great can be achieved without the elementary curiosity of the philosopher. A proper balance is needed. I have chosen the way which seemed to me to harmonize best with the spirit of this ancient place of learning.

APPENDIX ONE

1. (II. p. 8.) Multiple causes

Any event may have several causes. This possibility is not excluded by my definition (given explicitly on p. 9), though I speak there of A being 'the' cause of the effect B. Actually the 'number' of causes, i.e. of conditions on which an effect B depends, seems to me a rather meaningless notion. One often finds the idea of a 'causal chain' $A_1, A_2, \ldots$, where B depends directly on A_1, A_1 on A_2, etc., so that B depends indirectly on any of the A_n. As the series may never end—where is a 'first cause' to be found?—the number of causes may be, and will be in general, infinite. But there seems to be not the slightest reason to assume only one such chain, or even a number of chains; for the causes may be interlocked in a complicated way, and a 'network' of causes (even in a multi-dimensional space) seems to be a more appropriate picture. Yet why should it be enumerable at all? The 'set of all causes' of an event seems to me a notion just as dangerous as the notions which lead to logical paradoxes of the type discovered by Russell. It is a metaphysical idea which has produced much futile controversy. Therefore I have tried to formulate my definition in such a way that this question can be completely avoided.

2. (III. p. 13.) Derivation of Newton's law from Kepler's laws

The fact that Newton's law is a logical consequence of Kepler's laws is the basis on which my whole conception of causality in physics rests. For it is, apart from Galileo's simple demonstration the first and foremost example of a timeless cause–effect relation derived from observations. In most text-books of mechanics the opposite way (deduction of Kepler's laws from Newton's) is followed. Therefore it may be useful to give the full proof in modern terms.

We begin with formulating Kepler's laws, splitting the first one in two parts:

I *a*. The orbit of a planet is a plane curve.

I *b*. It has the shape of an ellipse, one focus of which is the sun.

II. The area A swept by the radius vector increases proportionally to time.

III. The ratio of the cube of the semi-axis a of the ellipse to the square of the period T is the same for all planets.

From Ia it follows that it suffices to consider a plane, introducing rectangular coordinates x, y, polar coordinates r, ϕ, so that

$$x = r\cos\phi, \qquad y = r\sin\phi.$$

Indicating differentiation with respect to time by a dot, one obtains for the velocity

$$\dot{x} = \dot{r}\cos\phi - r\dot{\phi}\sin\phi, \qquad \dot{y} = \dot{r}\sin\phi + r\dot{\phi}\cos\phi,$$

and for the acceleration

$$\ddot{x} = a_r\cos\phi - a_\phi\sin\phi, \qquad \ddot{y} = a_r\sin\phi + a_\phi\cos\phi,$$

where

$$a_r = \ddot{r} - r\dot{\phi}^2, \tag{1}$$

$$a_\phi = 2\dot{r}\dot{\phi} + r\ddot{\phi} \tag{2}$$

are the radial and tangential components of the acceleration.

Next we use II. The element of the area in polar coordinates is obviously

$$dA = \tfrac{1}{2}r^2 d\phi.$$

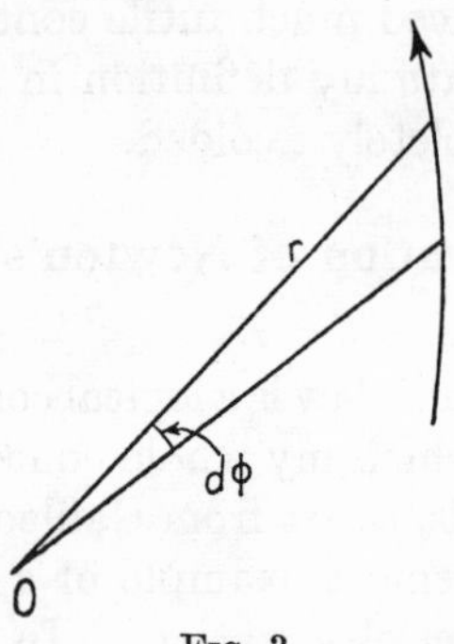

FIG. 3.

If the origin is taken at the centre of the sun, the rate of increase of A is constant, say $\frac{1}{2}h$, $dA = \frac{1}{2}h\,dt$, or

$$2\dot{A} = r^2\dot{\phi} = h. \tag{3}$$

Now it is convenient to use the variable

$$u = \frac{1}{r}$$

instead of r and to describe the orbit by expressing u as a function of ϕ, $u(\phi)$. Then

$$\dot{\phi} = \frac{h}{r^2} = hu^2, \tag{4}$$

$$\ddot{\phi} = \frac{d}{d\phi}(hu^2).\dot{\phi} = 2h^2u^3\frac{du}{d\phi}. \tag{5}$$

Further,
$$\dot{r} = \frac{dr}{d\phi}\dot{\phi} = -\frac{1}{u^2}\frac{du}{d\phi}\dot{\phi} = -h\frac{du}{d\phi}. \tag{6}$$

Substituting (4), (5), (6) into (2), one finds

$$a_\phi = 0.$$

Hence the acceleration has only a radial component a_r with respect to the sun. To obtain the value of a_r we calculate, with the help of (4),

$$\dot{r} = \frac{dr}{d\phi}\dot{\phi} = \frac{h}{r^2}\frac{dr}{d\phi} = -h\frac{du}{d\phi},$$

$$\ddot{r} = \frac{d}{d\phi}\left(-h\frac{du}{d\phi}\right)\dot{\phi} = -h^2u^2\frac{d^2u}{d\phi^2}, \tag{7}$$

and substitute this in (1):

$$a_r = -h^2u^2\left(\frac{d^2u}{d\phi^2}+u\right). \tag{8}$$

Now we use I*b*. The polar equation of an ellipse is

$$r = \frac{q}{1+\epsilon\cos\phi}, \tag{9}$$

where q is the semi-latus rectum and ϵ the numerical eccentricity;

or
$$u = \frac{1}{q}(1+\epsilon\cos\phi).$$

From this, one obtains

$$\frac{du}{d\phi} = -\frac{\epsilon}{q}\sin\phi, \qquad \frac{d^2u}{d\phi^2} = -\frac{\epsilon}{q}\cos\phi,$$

hence from (8)
$$a_r = -\frac{h^2}{q}u^2 = -\frac{h^2}{q}\frac{1}{r^2}. \tag{10}$$

The acceleration is directed to the sun (centripetal) and is inversely proportional to the square of the distance.

According to *the third law* III one can write

$$\frac{a^3}{T^2} = \frac{\mu}{4\pi^2}, \tag{11}$$

where the constant μ is the same for all planets.

Now integrating (3) for a full revolution one has

$$2A = hT. \tag{12}$$

On the other hand, the area of an ellipse is given by

$$A = \pi ab, \tag{13}$$

where a and b are the major and minor semi-axes.

Taking in (9) $\phi = 0$ and $\phi = \pi$ one gets the aphelion and perihelion distances; half of the sum of those is the semi-major axis:

$$a = \frac{1}{2}\left(\frac{q}{1+\epsilon}+\frac{q}{1-\epsilon}\right) = \frac{q}{1-\epsilon^2},$$

while the semi-minor axis is given by

$$b = a\sqrt{(1-\epsilon^2)} = \frac{q}{\sqrt{(1-\epsilon^2)}};$$

hence $$aq = b^2.$$

Substituting this in (13), one gets from (12)

$$T^2 = \left(\frac{2}{h}A\right)^2 = \left(\frac{2\pi}{h}\right)^2 a^2b^2 = \left(\frac{2\pi}{h}\right)^2 a^3q;$$

solving with respect to h^2/q and using (11):

$$\frac{h^2}{q} = 4\pi^2\frac{a^3}{T^2} = \mu. \tag{14}$$

Therefore the law of acceleration (10) becomes

$$a_r = -\frac{\mu}{r^2}, \tag{15}$$

where μ is the same for all planets, hence a property of the sun, called the gravitational mass.

This demonstrates the statement of the text that Newton's derivation of his law of force is purely deductive, based on the inductive work of Tycho Brahe and Kepler. The new feature due to Newton is the theoretical interpretation of the deduced formula for the acceleration, as representing the 'cause' of the motion, or the force determining the motion, which then led him to the fundamental idea of general gravitation (each body attracts each other one). In the text-books this situation is not always clear; this may be due to Newton's own representation in his *Principia* where he uses only geometrical constructions in the classical style of the Greeks. Yet it is known that he possessed the methods of infinitesimal calculus (theory of fluxions) for many years. I do not know whether he actually discovered his results with the help of the calculus; it seems to me incredible that he should not. He was obviously keen to avoid new mathematical methods in order to comply with the taste of his contemporaries. But it is known also that he liked to conceal his real ideas by dressing them up. This tendency is found in Gauss and other great mathematicians as well and has survived to our time, much to the disadvantage of science.

Newton regarded the calculation of terrestrial gravity from astronomical data as the crucial test of his theory, and he withheld publication for years as the available data about the radius of the earth were not satisfactory. The formula (3.3) of the text is simply obtained by regarding the earth as central body and the moon as 'planet'. Then μ is the gravitational mass of the earth which can be obtained from (11) by inserting for a the mean distance R of the centre of the moon from that of the earth, and for T the length of the month. Substituting $\mu = 4\pi^2R^3/T^2$ into (15), where r is the radius of the earth, one obtains for the acceleration on the earth's surface g ($= -a_r$) the formula (3.3) of the text,

$$g = \frac{4\pi^2R}{T^2}\left(\frac{R}{r}\right)^2. \tag{16}$$

If here the values $R/r = 60$, $R = 3{\cdot}84\times10^{10}$ cm., and $T = 27^{\text{d}}\ 7^{\text{h}}\ 43^{\text{m}}\ 11{\cdot}5^{\text{s}} = 2{\cdot}361\times10^6$ sec. are substituted, one finds $g = 980{\cdot}2$ cm. sec.$^{-2}$, while the observed value (extrapolated to the pole) is $g = 980{\cdot}6$ cm. sec.$^{-2}$

This reasoning is based on the plausible assumption that the acceleration produced by a material sphere at a point outside is independent of the radial distribution of density and the mass of the sphere can therefore be regarded as concentrated in the centre. The rigorous proof of this lemma forms an important part of Newton's considerations and was presumably achieved with the help of his theory of fluxions.

3. (IV. p. 20.) Cauchy's mechanics of continuous media

The mathematical tool for handling continuous substances is the following theorem of Gauss (also attributed to Green).

If a vector field **A** is defined inside and on the surface S of a volume V, one has

$$\int_V \operatorname{div} \mathbf{A}\, dV = \int_S \mathbf{A}.\mathbf{n}\, dS, \tag{1}$$

where **n** is the unit vector in the direction of the outer normal of the surface element dS and

$$\operatorname{div} \mathbf{A} = \frac{\partial A_x}{\partial x} + \frac{\partial A_y}{\partial y} + \frac{\partial A_z}{\partial z} = \frac{\partial}{\partial \mathbf{x}}.\mathbf{A}. \tag{2}$$

If ρ is the density, the total mass inside V is

$$m = \int \rho\, dV. \tag{3}$$

The amount of mass leaving the volume through the surface is

$$\int_S \mathbf{u}.\mathbf{n}\, dS,$$

where $\mathbf{u} = \rho\mathbf{v}$ is the current, $\mathbf{v}$ the velocity.

The indestructibility of mass is then expressed by

$$\dot{m} + \int \mathbf{u}.\mathbf{n}\, dS = 0.$$

Substituting (3) and applying (1), one obtains a volume integral, which vanishes for any surface; hence its integrand must be zero:

$$\dot{\rho} + \operatorname{div} \mathbf{u} = 0. \tag{4}$$

This is the continuity equation (4.5) of the text.

Consider now the forces acting on the volume V. Neglecting those forces which act on each volume element (like Newton's gravitation), we assume with Cauchy that there are surface forces or tensions, acting on each element dS of the surface S, and proportional to dS. They will also depend on the orientation of dS, i.e. on the normal vector **n**, and can therefore be written $\mathbf{T}_n\, dS$. If **n** coincides with one of the three axes of coordinates x, y, z, the corresponding forces per unit area may be represented by the vectors $\mathbf{T}_x, \mathbf{T}_y, \mathbf{T}_z$. Now the projections of an element dS on the coordinate planes are

$$dS_x = n_x\, dS, \qquad dS_y = n_y\, dS, \qquad dS_z = n_z\, dS.$$

The equilibrium of the tetrahedron with the sides dS, dS_x, dS_y, dS_z then leads to the equation

$$\mathbf{T}_n dS = \mathbf{T}_x dS_x + \mathbf{T}_y dS_y + \mathbf{T}_z dS_z,$$

or

$$\mathbf{T}_n = \mathbf{T}_x n_x + \mathbf{T}_y n_y + \mathbf{T}_z n_z, \tag{5}$$

which is the formula (4.6) of the text.

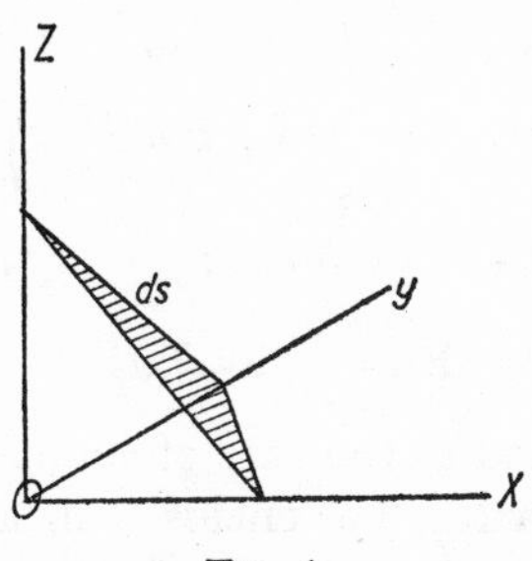

FIG. 4.

Consider further the equilibrium of a rectangular volume element, and in particular its cross-section $z = 0$, with the sides dx, dy. The components of $\mathbf{T}_x$ in this plane may be denoted by T_{xx} and T_{xy}, those of $\mathbf{T}_y$ by T_{yx}, T_{yy}. Then the tangential com-

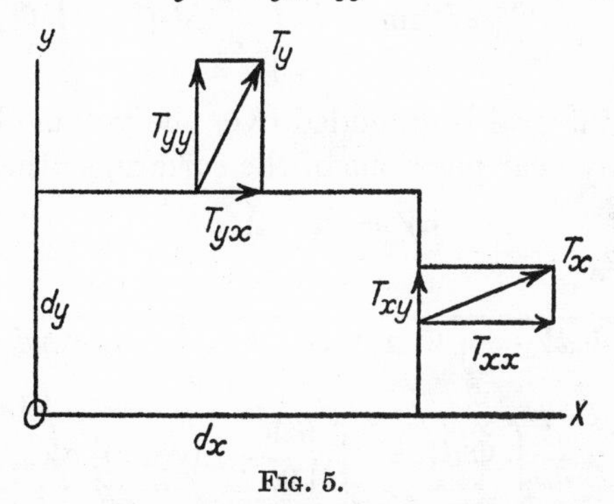

FIG. 5.

ponents on the surfaces $dydz$ and $dxdz$ produce a couple about the origin O with the moment

$$(T_{xy}\, dydz)dx - (T_{yx}\, dxdz)dy.$$

This must vanish in equilibrium; therefore one has

$$T_{xy} = T_{yx},$$

and the corresponding equations obtained by cyclic permutation of the indices, (4.7) of the text. Hence the stress tensor T defined by (4.8) is symmetrical. One can express this, with the help of (5), in the form

$$(\mathbf{T}_n)_x = T_{xx}n_x + T_{yx}n_y + T_{zx}n_z = \mathbf{T}_x \cdot \mathbf{n},$$

where $\mathbf{T}_x$ is the vector (T_{xx}, T_{xy}, T_{xz}).

The x-component of the total force $\mathbf{F} = \int \mathbf{T}_n \, dS$ can now be transformed with the help of formula (1) into a volume integral

$$F_x = \int_S (\mathbf{T}_n)_x \, dS = \int_S \mathbf{T}_x \cdot \mathbf{n} \, dS = \int_V \operatorname{div} \mathbf{T}_x \, dV.$$

Using the tensor notation of the text, (4.10), one can write this

$$\mathbf{F} = \int \operatorname{div} \mathsf{T} \, dV. \tag{6}$$

This has to be equated to the rate of change of momentum of a given amount of matter, i.e. enclosed in a volume moving in time. One has for any function Φ of space

$$\frac{d}{dt}\int \Phi \, dV = \lim_{\Delta t \to 0} \frac{1}{\Delta t}\left\{\int_{V(t+\Delta t)} \Phi \, dV - \int_{V(t)} \Phi \, dV\right\}$$

$$= \lim_{\Delta t \to 0} \frac{1}{\Delta t}\left\{\int_{V(t)} \frac{\partial \Phi}{\partial t} \Delta t \, dV + \int_{\Delta V} \Phi \, dV\right\}.$$

The second integral is extended over the volume between two infinitesimally near positions of the surface, so that

$$dV = \mathbf{n} \cdot \mathbf{v} \, \Delta t \, dS$$

and therefore

$$\int_{\Delta V} \Phi \, dV = \int_S \Phi \, \mathbf{n} \cdot \mathbf{v} \, dS \, \Delta t = \int_V \operatorname{div}(\Phi \mathbf{v}) \, dV \, \Delta t.$$

Hence

$$\frac{d}{dt}\int \Phi \, dV = \int_V \left\{\frac{\partial \Phi}{\partial t} + \operatorname{div}(\Phi \mathbf{v})\right\} dV. \tag{7}$$

If this is applied to the components of the momentum density $\rho \mathbf{v}$ one obtains for the rate of change of the total momentum $\mathbf{P}$:

$$\frac{d\mathbf{P}}{dt} = \frac{d}{dt}\int_V \rho \mathbf{v} \, dV = \int_V \left\{\frac{\partial(\rho \mathbf{v})}{\partial t} + \operatorname{div}(\rho \mathbf{v}\mathbf{v})\right\} dV$$

$$= \int_V \left[\rho\left\{\frac{\partial \mathbf{v}}{\partial t} + \left(\mathbf{v} \cdot \frac{\partial}{\partial \mathbf{x}}\right)\mathbf{v}\right\} + \mathbf{v}\left\{\frac{\partial \rho}{\partial t} + \operatorname{div}(\rho \mathbf{v})\right\}\right] dV.$$

Here the second integral vanishes in consequence of the continuity equation (4), with $\mathbf{u} = \rho\mathbf{v}$. In the first integral appears the convective derivative, defined by (4.11) of the text,

$$\frac{d\mathbf{v}}{dt} = \frac{\partial\mathbf{v}}{\partial t} + \left(\mathbf{v}\cdot\frac{\partial}{\partial\mathbf{x}}\right)\mathbf{v}.$$

Hence
$$\frac{d\mathbf{P}}{dt} = \int \rho\frac{d\mathbf{v}}{dt}\,dV. \tag{8}$$

Now the equation of motion

$$\frac{d\mathbf{P}}{dt} = \mathbf{F}$$

reduces in virtue of (6) and (8) to (4.9) of the text:

$$\rho\frac{d\mathbf{v}}{dt} = \operatorname{div}\mathsf{T}. \tag{9}$$

Consider in particular an elastic fluid where

$$T_{xx} = T_{yy} = T_{zz} = -p, \qquad T_{yz} = T_{zx} = T_{xy} = 0,$$

and the pressure p is a function of ρ alone. Then the continuity equation and the equations of motion

$$\frac{\partial\rho}{\partial t} + \operatorname{div}(\rho\mathbf{v}) = 0,$$

$$\rho\left\{\frac{\partial\mathbf{v}}{\partial t} + \left(\mathbf{v}\cdot\frac{\partial}{\partial\mathbf{x}}\right)\cdot\mathbf{v}\right\} + \frac{dp}{d\rho}\frac{\partial\rho}{\partial\mathbf{x}} = 0$$

are four differential equations for the four functions ρ, v_x, v_y, v_z.

If one wishes to determine small deviations from equilibrium, then $\mathbf{v}$ and $\phi = \rho - \rho_0$ are small and ρ_0 constant with regard to space and time. Then the last two equations reduce in first approximation to

$$\frac{\partial\phi}{\partial t} + \rho_0 \operatorname{div}\mathbf{v} = 0,$$

$$\rho_0\frac{\partial\mathbf{v}}{\partial t} + \left(\frac{dp}{d\rho}\right)_0\frac{\partial\phi}{\partial\mathbf{x}} = 0.$$

By differentiating the first of these with respect to time and substituting $\rho_0\frac{\partial\mathbf{v}}{\partial t}$ from the second, one finds

$$\frac{\partial^2\phi}{\partial t^2} - \left(\frac{dp}{d\rho}\right)_0 \operatorname{div}\left(\frac{\partial\phi}{\partial\mathbf{x}}\right) = 0,$$

or with
$$\operatorname{div}\frac{\partial}{\partial \mathbf{x}} = \frac{\partial}{\partial \mathbf{x}}\cdot\frac{\partial}{\partial \mathbf{x}} = \Delta$$

and
$$\left(\frac{dp}{d\rho}\right)_0 = c^2, \tag{10}$$

$$\frac{1}{c^2}\frac{\partial^2\phi}{\partial t^2} = \Delta\phi. \tag{11}$$

This is the equation (4.13) of the text applied to the variation of density ϕ. Each of the velocity components satisfies the same equation, which is the prototype of all laws of wave propagation.

4. (IV. p. 24.) **Maxwell's equations of the electromagnetic field**

The mathematical part of Maxwell's work consisted in condensing the experimental laws, mentioned in the text, in a set of differential equations which, with the usual notation, are

$$\begin{gathered} \operatorname{div}\mathbf{D} = 4\pi\rho, \qquad \operatorname{curl}\mathbf{H} = \frac{4\pi}{c}\mathbf{u}, \\ \operatorname{div}\mathbf{B} = 0, \qquad \operatorname{curl}\mathbf{E} + \frac{1}{c}\dot{\mathbf{B}} = 0, \\ \mathbf{D} = \epsilon\mathbf{E}, \qquad \mathbf{B} = \mu\mathbf{H}. \end{gathered} \tag{1}$$

To give a simple example, Coulomb's law for the electrostatic field is obtained by putting $\mathbf{B} = 0$, $\mathbf{H} = 0$, $\mathbf{u} = 0$; then there remains
$$\operatorname{div}\mathbf{D} = 4\pi\rho, \qquad \operatorname{curl}\mathbf{E} = 0.$$

The second equation implies that there is a potential ϕ, such that
$$\mathbf{E} = -\frac{\partial\phi}{\partial\mathbf{x}}.$$

In vacuo, where $\mathbf{D} = \mathbf{E}$, one obtains therefore Poisson's equation
$$-\operatorname{div}\mathbf{E} = \Delta\phi = -4\pi\rho.$$

The solution is
$$\phi = \int \frac{\rho}{r}\,dV, \tag{2}$$

provided singularities are excluded; this formula expresses Coulomb's law for a continuous distribution of density. In a similar way one obtains for stationary states ($\dot{\mathbf{B}} = 0$) the law of Biot and Savart for the magnetic field of a current of density $\mathbf{u}$.

Maxwell's physical idea consisted in discovering the asymmetry in the equations (1) which, in our style of writing, is obvious even to the untrained eye: the missing term $\frac{1}{c}\dot{\mathbf{D}}$ in the second equation. The logical necessity of this term follows from the fact of the existence of open currents, e.g. discharges of condensers through wires. In this case the charge on the condenser changes in time, hence $\dot{\rho} \neq 0$; on the other hand, the equations (1) imply $\operatorname{div}\mathbf{u} = \frac{c}{4\pi}\operatorname{div}\operatorname{curl}\mathbf{H} = 0$. Therefore the continuity equation $\dot{\rho}+\operatorname{div}\mathbf{u} = 0$ is violated.

To amend this Maxwell postulated a new type of current bridging the gap between the conductors in the condenser, with a certain density $\mathbf{w}$, so that

$$\operatorname{curl}\mathbf{H} = \frac{4\pi}{c}(\mathbf{u}+\mathbf{w}). \tag{3}$$

Then taking the div operation one has

$$\operatorname{div}\mathbf{w} = -\operatorname{div}\mathbf{u} = \dot{\rho} = \frac{1}{4\pi}\operatorname{div}\dot{\mathbf{D}}.$$

The simplest way of satisfying this equation is putting

$$\mathbf{w} = \frac{1}{4\pi}\dot{\mathbf{D}}, \tag{4}$$

so that the corresponding equation in Maxwell's set becomes

$$\operatorname{curl}\mathbf{H}-\frac{1}{c}\dot{\mathbf{D}} = \frac{4\pi}{c}\mathbf{u} \tag{5}$$

and complete symmetry between electric and magnetic quantities is obtained (apart from the fact that the latter have no true charge and current).

The modified system of field equations permits the prediction of waves with finite velocity. In an isotropic substance free of charges and currents ($\rho = 0$, $\mathbf{u} = 0$, $\mathbf{D} = \epsilon\mathbf{E}$, $\mathbf{B} = \mu\mathbf{H}$) one has

$$\operatorname{curl}\mathbf{H}-\frac{\epsilon}{c}\dot{\mathbf{E}} = 0, \qquad \operatorname{curl}\mathbf{E}+\frac{\mu}{c}\dot{\mathbf{H}} = 0;$$

taking the curl of one of them, and using the formula that for a vector with vanishing div one has curl curl $= -\Delta$, one obtains for each component of **E** and **H** the wave equation

$$\Delta\Phi - \frac{1}{c_1^2}\frac{\partial^2\Phi}{\partial t^2} = 0, \qquad c_1 = \frac{c}{\sqrt{(\epsilon\mu)}}. \tag{6}$$

For vacuum ($\epsilon = \mu = 1$) the velocity of propagation should therefore be equal to the electromagnetic constant c. As stated in the text, this constant has the dimensions of a velocity and can be measured by determining the magnetic field of a current produced by a condenser discharge (measured therefore electrostatically). Such experiments had been performed by Kohlrausch and Weber, and their result for c agreed with the velocity of light *in vacuo*. This evidence for the electromagnetic theory of light was strongly enhanced by experiments carried out by Boltzmann, which showed that the velocity of light in simple substances (rare gases, which are monatomic) can be calculated from their dielectric constant ϵ (μ being practically $= 1$) with the help of Maxwell's formula $c_1 = c/\sqrt{\epsilon}$.

Maxwell's formulation satisfies contiguity, but its relation to Cauchy's form of the dynamical laws has still to be established. The electric and magnetic field vectors, though originally defined by the forces on point charges and magnetic poles (which actually do not exist), are defined by the equations also in places where neither charges nor currents exist. Yet they are not stresses themselves; they are analogous to strains, on which the stresses depend. The law of this connexion has also been found by Maxwell; it is a mathematical formulation of Faraday's intuitive interpretation of the mechanical reactions between electrified and magnetized bodies. A short indication must here suffice.

Apart from the electric force on a point charge e, $\mathbf{F} = e\mathbf{E}$, there exists a mechanical force on the element of a linear current $\mathbf{u}$, produced by a magnetic field $\mathbf{H}$; this force is perpendicular to $\mathbf{H}$ and to the current $\mathbf{u}$ and therefore does no work. It is not quite uniquely determined, as one can obviously add any force whose line integral over a closed circuit vanishes. The simplest expression is:

$$\mathbf{F} = \frac{1}{c}\mathbf{u}\wedge\mathbf{B},$$

as can be seen by considering the change of magnetic energy $\frac{1}{8}\pi\int \mathbf{H}.\mathbf{B}\,dV$ produced by a virtual displacement of an element of the current.

To illustrate Maxwell's procedure it suffices to consider charge distributions *in vacuo* with density ρ and current $\mathbf{u} = \rho\mathbf{v}$. Combining the two forces $\mathbf{F} = e\mathbf{E}$ and $\mathbf{F} = \frac{1}{c}\mathbf{u}\wedge\mathbf{B}$ into one expression, one has for the density of force

$$\mathbf{f} = \rho\left\{\mathbf{E}+\frac{1}{c}(\mathbf{v}\wedge\mathbf{H})\right\}, \tag{7}$$

the so-called Lorentz force.

Substituting here for ρ and $\rho\mathbf{v}$ the expressions from Maxwell's equations one can, by elementary transformations, bring $\mathbf{f}$ into the form of Cauchy,

$$\mathbf{f} = \operatorname{div} \mathsf{T},$$

where

$$T_{xx} = \frac{1}{8\pi}(E_x^2-E_y^2-E_z^2)+\frac{1}{8\pi}(H_x^2-H_y^2-H_z^2), \quad \ldots,$$

$$T_{yz} = \frac{1}{4\pi}(E_y E_z+H_y H_z), \quad \ldots.$$

These are the celebrated formulae of Maxwell's tensions. They can be easily generalized for material bodies with dielectric constant and permeability, and they have become the prototype for similar expressions in other field theories, e.g. gravitation (Einstein), electronic field (Dirac), meson field (Yukawa).

5. (IV. p. 27.) **Relativity**

It is impossible to give a short sketch of the theory of relativity, and the reader is referred to the text-books. The best representation seems to me still the article in vol. v of the *Mathematical Encyclopaedia* written by W. Pauli when he was a student, about twenty years of age. There one finds a clear statement of the experimental facts which led to the mathematical theory almost unambiguously. Eddington's treatment gives the impression that the results could have been obtained—or even have been obtained—by pure reason, using epistemological principles. I need not say that this is wrong and misleading. There was, of course, a philosophical urge behind Einstein's relentless effort; in particular the violation of contiguity in Newton's theory seemed to him unacceptable. Yet the greatness of his achievement was just that he based his own theory not on preconceived notions but on hard facts, facts which were obvious to everybody, but noticed by nobody. The main fact was the identity of inertial and gravitational mass, which he expressed as the principle of equivalence between acceleration and gravitation. An observer in a closed box cannot decide by any experiment whether an observed acceleration of a body in the box is due to gravity produced by external bodies or to an acceleration of the box in the opposite direction. This principle means that arbitrary, non-linear transformations of time must be admitted. But the formal symmetry between space-coordinates and time discovered by Minkowski made it very improbable that the transformations of space should be linear, and this was corroborated by considering rotating bodies: a volume element on the periphery should undergo a peripheral contraction according to the results of special relativity, but remain unchanged in the radial direction. Hence acceleration was necessarily connected with deformation. This led to the postulate that all laws of nature ought to be unchanged (covariant) with respect to arbitrary space-time transformations. But as special relativity must be preserved in small domains, the postulate of invariance of the line element had to be made.

The long struggle of Einstein to find the general covariant field equations was due to the difficulty for a physicist to assimilate the mathematical ideas necessary, ideas which were in fact completely worked out by Riemann and his successors, Levi-Civita, Ricci, and others.

I wish to add here only one remark. The physical significance of the line element seems to me rather mystical in a genuinely continuous space-time. If it is replaced by the assumption of parallel displacement (affine connexion), this impression of mystery is still further enhanced. On the other hand, the appearance of a *finite* length in the ultimate equations of physics can be expected. Quantum theory is the first step in this direction; it introduces not a universal length but a constant, Planck's $\hbar$, of the dimension length times momentum into the laws of physics. There are numerous indications that the further development of physics will lead to a separate appearance of these two factors, $\hbar = q \, . \, p$, in the ultimate laws. The difficulties of present-day physics are centred about the problem of introducing this length q in a way which satisfies the principle of relativity. This fact seems to indicate that relativity itself needs a generalization where the infinitesimal element ds is replaced by a finite length.

The papers quoted in the text are: A. Einstein, L. Infeld, and B. Hoffmann, *Ann. of Math.*, **39,** no. 1, p. 65 (Princeton, 1938); V. A. Fock, *Journ. of Phys. U.S.S.R.* **1,** no. 2, p. 81 (1939).

6. (V. p. 38.) **On classical and modern thermodynamics**

It is often said that the classical derivation of the second law of thermodynamics is much simpler than Carathéodory's as it needs less abstract conceptions than Pfaffian equations. But this objection is quite wrong. For what one has to show is the existence of an integrating denominator of dQ. This is trivial for a Pfaffian of two variables (representing, for example, a single fluid with V, ϑ); it must be shown not to be trivial and even, in general, wrong for Pfaffians with more than two variables (e.g. two fluids in thermal contact with V_1, V_2, ϑ). Otherwise, the student cannot possibly understand what the fuss is all about. But that means explaining to him the difference between the two classes of Pfaffians of three variables, the integrable ones and the non-integrable ones. Without that all talk about Carnot cycles is just empty verbiage. But as soon as one has this difference, why not then use the simple criterion of accessibility from neighbouring points, instead of invoking quite new ideas borrowed from engineering? I think a satisfactory lecture or text-book should bring this classical reasoning as a corollary of historical interest, as I have suggested long ago in a series of papers (*Phys. Zeitschr.* **22,** pp. 218, 249, 282 (1921)).

Since writing the text I have come across one book which gives a short account of Carathéodory's theory, H. Margenau and G. M. Murphy, *The Mathematics of Physics and Chemistry* (D. van Nostrand Co., New York, 1943), § 1.15, p. 26. But though the mathematics is correct, it does not do justice to the idea. For it says on p. 28: 'This formal mathematical consequence of the properties of the Pfaff equation [namely the theorem proved in the next section of the appendix] is known as the principle of Carathéodory. It is exactly what we need for thermodynamics.' Carathéodory's principle is, of course, not that formal mathematical theorem but the induction from observation that there are inaccessible states in any neighbourhood of a given state.

7. (V. p. 39.) Theorem of accessibility

An example of a Pfaffian which has no integrating denominator (by the way, the same example as described in geometrical terms in the text) is this:

$$dQ = -y\,dx + x\,dy + k\,dz,$$

where k is a constant. If it were possible to write dQ in the form $\lambda\,d\phi$, where λ and ϕ are functions of x, y, z, one would have

$$\frac{\partial\phi}{\partial x} = -\frac{y}{\lambda}, \qquad \frac{\partial\phi}{\partial y} = \frac{x}{\lambda}, \qquad \frac{\partial\phi}{\partial z} = \frac{k}{\lambda},$$

hence

$$\frac{\partial^2\phi}{\partial y\partial z} = \frac{\partial}{\partial z}\left(\frac{x}{\lambda}\right) = \frac{\partial}{\partial y}\left(\frac{k}{\lambda}\right), \qquad \frac{\partial^2\phi}{\partial z\partial x} = -\frac{\partial}{\partial z}\left(\frac{y}{\lambda}\right) = \frac{\partial}{\partial x}\left(\frac{k}{\lambda}\right),$$

$$\frac{\partial^2\phi}{\partial x\partial y} = -\frac{\partial}{\partial y}\left(\frac{y}{\lambda}\right) = \frac{\partial}{\partial x}\left(\frac{x}{\lambda}\right),$$

or

$$x\frac{\partial\lambda}{\partial z} = k\frac{\partial\lambda}{\partial y}, \qquad -y\frac{\partial\lambda}{\partial z} = k\frac{\partial\lambda}{\partial x}, \qquad 2\lambda = x\frac{\partial\lambda}{\partial x} + y\frac{\partial\lambda}{\partial y}.$$

By substituting $\partial\lambda/\partial x$ and $\partial\lambda/\partial y$ from the first two equations in the third one finds

$$\lambda = 0.$$

Examples like this show clearly that the existence of an integrating denominator is an exception.

We now give the proof of the theorem of accessibility. Consider the solutions of the Pfaffian

$$dQ = X\,dx + Y\,dy + Z\,dz = 0, \tag{1}$$

which lie in a given surface S,

$$x = x(u,v), \qquad y = y(u,v), \qquad z = z(u,v).$$

They satisfy a Pfaffian

$$dQ = U\,du + V\,dv = 0, \tag{2}$$

where

$$U = X\frac{\partial x}{\partial u} + Y\frac{\partial y}{\partial u} + Z\frac{\partial z}{\partial u},$$

$$V = X\frac{\partial x}{\partial v} + Y\frac{\partial y}{\partial v} + Z\frac{\partial z}{\partial v}.$$

Hence through every point P of S there passes one curve, because (2) is equivalent to the ordinary differential equation

$$\frac{du}{dv} = -\frac{V}{U},$$

which has a one-parameter set of solutions $\phi(u,v) = \text{const.}$, covering the surface S.

Let us now suppose that, in the neighbourhood of a point P, there are inaccessible points; let Q be one of these. Construct through

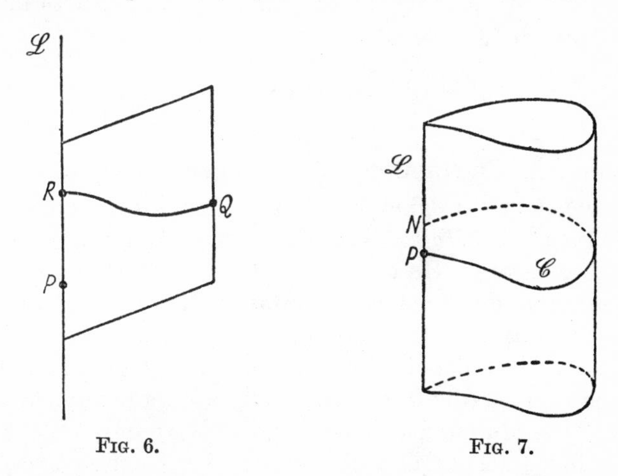

FIG. 6. FIG. 7.

P a straight line $\mathscr{L}$, which is not a solution of (1), and the plane π through Q and $\mathscr{L}$. In π there is just one curve satisfying (1) and going through Q; this curve will meet the line $\mathscr{L}$ at a point R. Then R must be inaccessible from P; for if there should exist a solution leading from P to R, then one could also reach Q from P by a continuous (though kinked) solution curve, which contradicts the assumption that Q is inaccessible from P. The point R can be made to lie as near to P as one wishes by choosing Q near enough to P.

Now we move the straight line $\mathscr{L}$ parallel to itself in a cyclic way so that it describes a closed cylinder. Then there exists on this cylinder a solution curve $\mathscr{C}$ which starts from P on $\mathscr{L}$ and meets $\mathscr{L}$ again at a point N. It follows that N and P must coincide. For otherwise one could, by deforming the cylinder, make N sweep along the line $\mathscr{L}$ towards P and beyond P. Hence there would be an interval of accessible points (like N) around P, while it has been proved before that there are inaccessible points Q in any neighbourhood of P.

As N now coincides with P the connecting curve $\mathscr{C}$ can be made, by steady deformation of the cylinder, to describe a surface which contains obviously all solutions starting from P. If this surface is given by $\phi(x, y, z) = 0$, one has

$$dQ = \lambda\, d\phi,$$

which is the theorem to be proved.

The function ϕ and the factor λ are not uniquely determined; if ϕ is replaced by $\Phi(\phi)$ one has

$$\lambda\, d\phi = \Lambda d\Phi \text{ with } \lambda = \Lambda \frac{d\Phi}{d\phi}.$$

8. (V. p. 43.) Thermodynamics of chemical equilibria

Carathéodory's original publication on his foundation of thermodynamics (*Math. Ann.* **61**, p. 355, 1909) is written in a very abstract way. He considers a type of systems which are called simple and defined by the property that of the parameters necessary to fix a state of equilibrium all except one are configurational variables, i.e. such that their values can be arbitrarily prescribed (like volumes). In my own presentation of the theory, of 1921 (quoted in Appendix, **6**), there is only a hint at the end (§ 9) how such variables can be introduced in more complicated cases, as for instance for chemical equilibria where the concentrations of the constituents can be changed. I hoped at that time that this might be worked out by the chemists themselves, for it needs nothing more than the usual method of semi-permeable walls with a slight modification of the wording. As this has not happened, I shall give here a short indication how to do it.

I consider first a simple fluid (without decomposition), but arrange it in such a way that volume V and mass M are both independently changeable. For this purpose one has to imagine a cylinder with a piston attached to the volume V, connected by a valve, through which substance can be pressed into the volume V considered. The position of the auxiliary piston determines uniquely the mass M contained in V; hence M can be regarded as a configuration variable in Carathéodory's sense. If the valve is closed, V can be changed, by moving the 'main' piston, without altering M. Hence M and V are both independent configuration variables, and the work done for any change of them must be regarded as measurable. If this work is determined adiabatically one obtains the energy function, say in terms of V, M and the empirical temperature ϑ, $U(V,M,\vartheta)$.

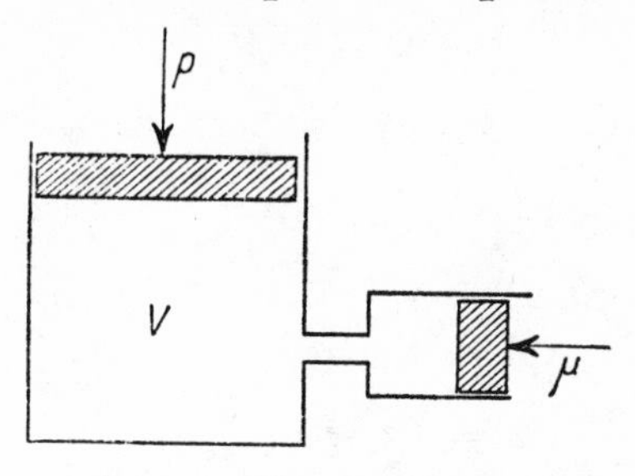

FIG. 8.

When this is known the differential of heat is defined by the difference

$$dQ = dU + p\,dV - \mu\,dM, \tag{1}$$

where p and μ are functions of the state (V,M,ϑ) like U, which can be regarded as empirically known.

Now one has in (1) a Pfaffian of three variables and can apply the same considerations as before which lead to the result that dQ is integrable and can be equated to $T\,dS$. Hence one can write

$$dU = T\,dS - p\,dV + \mu\,dM. \tag{2}$$

But U must be a homogeneous function of the first order in the variables S, V, M. If one introduces the specific variables u, s, v by

$$U = Mu, \qquad S = Ms, \qquad V = Mv, \tag{3}$$

one has according to Euler's theorem

$$u = Ts - pv + \mu, \tag{4}$$

where

$$T = \frac{\partial u}{\partial s}, \qquad p = -\frac{\partial u}{\partial v}, \tag{5}$$

and then, from (2),

$$du = T\,ds - p\,dv. \tag{6}$$

If the substance inside V is a chemical compound and one wishes to investigate its decomposition into n components, one assumes n cylinders with pistons attached to V, separated from V by semi-permeable walls, each of which allows the passage of only one of the components. Then one has in the same way

$$dU = T\,dS - p\,dV + \sum_{i=1}^{n} \mu_i\,dM_i, \tag{7}$$

where $V, M_1, M_2, \ldots, M_n$ can be regarded as configuration variables and $U, p, \mu_1, \mu_2, \ldots, \mu_n$ as known functions of these. Now, as above, the specific energy, entropy, and volume are introduced and further the concentrations c_i by

$$M_i = c_i M, \tag{8}$$

where M is the total mass: $M = \sum_i M_i$, hence

$$\sum_{i=1}^{n} c_i = 1. \tag{9}$$

One obtains from Euler's theorem

$$u = Ts - pv + \sum_i \mu_i c_i, \tag{10}$$

with
$$T = \frac{\partial u}{\partial s}, \qquad p = -\frac{\partial u}{\partial v}, \qquad \mu_i = \frac{\partial u}{\partial c_i}, \tag{11}$$

where the differentiation with respect to the c_i is performed as if they were independent; and

$$du = T\,ds - p\,dv + \sum_{i=1}^{n} \mu_i\,dc_i. \tag{12}$$

The formalism of thermodynamics consists in deriving relations between the variables by differentiating the equations (11), e.g.

$$\frac{\partial T}{\partial v} = -\frac{\partial p}{\partial s}, \qquad \frac{\partial \mu_i}{\partial v} = -\frac{\partial p}{\partial c_i}, \text{ etc.}$$

As experiments are often performed at constant pressure or temperature or both, one uses instead of $u(s, v, c_1, \ldots, c_n)$, the functions free energy $u - Ts = f$, enthalpy $u + pv = w$, or free enthalpy $\mu = u + pv - Ts$ (defined by (4)). For the latter, for example, it follows from (12) that

$$d\mu = -s\,dT + v\,dp + \sum_i \mu_i\,dc_i, \tag{13}$$

or
$$s = -\frac{\partial \mu}{\partial T}, \qquad v = \frac{\partial \mu}{\partial p}, \qquad \mu_i = \frac{\partial \mu}{\partial c_i}, \tag{14}$$

so that for $T =$ const., $p =$ const., one has simply

$$d\mu = \sum_i \mu_i\,dc_i. \tag{15}$$

The most important theorem, which follows from these general equations, is Gibbs's phase rule. The system may exist in different phases if the n equations

$$\mu_i(T, p, c_1, \ldots, c_n) = C_i \quad (i = 1, \ldots, n) \tag{16}$$

have several solutions. Let m be the number of independent solutions; then there are m phases which can be ordered in such a way that each has contact with two others only. Hence there are $m-1$ interfaces and n equations of the form (16) for each, altogether $n(m-1)$ independent equations. On the other hand, there are $(n-1)$ independent concentrations $c_1, \ldots, c_{n-1}$ for each phase, i.e. $m(n-1)$ for the whole system, to which the two variables p, T have to be added; hence $m(n-1)+2$ independent variables. The number of arbitrary parameters, or the number of degrees of freedom of the system, is therefore

$$m(n-1)+2-n(m-1) = n-m+2.$$

So for a single pure substance, $n = 1$, the number of degrees of freedom is $3-m$; hence there are three cases $m = 1, 2, 3$ corresponding to one phase, two or three coexisting phases; more than three phases cannot be in equilibrium. All further progress in thermodynamics is based on special assumptions about the functions involved, either prompted by experiment, or chosen by an argument of simplicity, or—and this is the most important step—derived from statistical considerations.

9. (V. p. 44.) **Velocity of sound in gases**

The simple problem of calculating the adiabatic law for an ideal gas gives me the opportunity to show how the theory of Carathéodory determines uniquely the absolute temperature and entropy.

The ideal gas is defined by two properties: (1) Boyle's law, the isotherms are given by $pV = \text{const.}$; (2) the same quantity pV remains constant if the gas expands without doing work. In mathematical symbols,

$$pV = F(\vartheta), \qquad U = U(\vartheta).$$

Hence

$$dQ = dU + p\,dV = U'd\vartheta + F\frac{dV}{V}. \tag{1}$$

If θ is defined by

$$\log\theta = \int \frac{U'(\vartheta)\,d\vartheta}{F(\vartheta)}, \tag{2}$$

(1) can be written

$$dQ = F(\vartheta)\, d\log(\theta V);$$

hence one can put $\lambda = F(\vartheta)$, $\phi = \log(\theta V)$ and obtain from the equation (5.25) of the text

$$g(\vartheta) = \frac{\partial(\log\lambda)}{\partial\vartheta} = \frac{\partial \log F(\vartheta)}{\partial\vartheta}.$$

Then (5.27) gives, writing $C = 1/R$, the usual form of the equation of state

$$RT = F(\vartheta) = pV, \tag{3}$$

and

$$S = S_0 + R\log(\theta V).$$

If the special assumption is made, that U depends linearly on pV (which holds for dilute gases with the same approximation as Boyle's law), one has $U = c_v T$ and, from (2),

$$\log\theta = \int \frac{c_v\, dT}{RT} = \frac{c_v}{R}\log T.$$

The entropy becomes therefore

$$S = S_0 + \log(T^{c_v} V^R), \tag{4}$$

or, substituting p for T from (3),

$$S = S_1 + \log(p^{c_v} V^{c_p}), \tag{5}$$

where

$$c_p = c_v + R \tag{6}$$

is the specific heat for constant pressure. Hence the adiabatic law $S =$ const. is equivalent to

$$pV^\gamma = \text{const.}, \qquad \gamma = \frac{c_p}{c_v}, \tag{7}$$

which is identical with the equation $p = a\rho^\gamma$ in the text, as the density ρ is reciprocal to the volume V.

The velocity of sound was calculated in Appendix, **3**; according to (**3**.10) it is

$$c = \sqrt{\frac{dp}{d\rho}}.$$

F r the isothermal law, $p = a\rho$, this means

$$c = \sqrt{\frac{p}{\rho}},$$

while, for the adiabatic law, $p = a\rho^\gamma$, one finds

$$c = \sqrt{\frac{\gamma p}{\rho}},$$

which is considerably larger; e.g. for diatomic molecules (air) experiment, and kinetic theory as well, give $\gamma = \frac{7}{5} = 1{\cdot}4$.

10. (V. p. 45.) **Thermodynamics of irreversible processes**

Since I wrote this section of the text a new development of the descriptive or phenomenological theory has come to my knowledge which is remarkable enough to be mentioned.

It started in 1931 with a paper by Onsager in which the attempt was made to build up a thermodynamics of irreversible processes by taking from the kinetic theory one single result, called the theorem of microscopic reversibility, and to show that this suffices to obtain some important properties of the flow of heat, matter, and electricity. The starting-point is Einstein's theory of fluctuations (see Appendix, **20**), where the relation $S = k \log P$ between probability P and entropy S is reversed, using the known dependence of S on observable quantities to determine the probability P of small deviations from equilibrium. Then it is assumed that the law for the decay of an accidental accumulation of some quantity (mass, energy, temperature, etc.) is the same as that for the flow of the same quantity under artificially produced macroscopic conditions. This, together with the reversibility theorem mentioned, determines the main features of the flow. The theory has been essentially improved by Casimir and others, amongst whom the book of Prigogine, from de Donders's school of thermodynamics in Brussels, must be mentioned. Here is a list of the literature:

L. Onsager, *Phys. Rev.* **37**, p. 405 (1931); **38**, p. 2265 (1931).

H. B. G. Casimir, Philips Research Reports, **1**, 185–96 (April 1946); *Rev. Mod. Physics*, **17**, p. 343 (1945).

C. Eckhart, *Phys. Rev.* **58**, pp. 267, 269, 919, 924 (1940).

J. Meixner, *Ann. d. Phys.* (v), **39**, p. 333 (1941); **41**, p. 409 (1943); **43**, p. 244 (1943); *Z. phys. Chem.* B, **53**, p. 235 (1943).

S. R. de Groot, *L'Effet Soret*, thesis, Amsterdam (1945); *Journal de Physique*, no. 6, p. 191.

I. Prigogine, *Étude thermodynamique des phénomènes irréversibles* (Paris, Dunod; Liége, Desoer, 1947).

11. (VI. p. 47.) Elementary kinetic theory of gases

To derive equation (6.1) of the text, consider the molecules of a gas to be elastic balls which at impact on the wall of the vessel recoil without loss of energy and momentum. If the yz-plane coincides with the wall the x-component of the momentum $m\xi$ of a molecule is changed into $-m\xi$; hence the momentum $2m\xi$ is transferred to the wall. Let $n_{\mathbf{v}}$ be the number of molecules per unit of volume having the velocity vector $\mathbf{v}$. If one constructs a cylinder upon a piece of the wall of area unity and side $\mathbf{v}\,dt$, all molecules in it will strike the part of the wall within the cylinder in the time-element dt; the volume of the cylinder is $\xi\,dt$, hence the number of collisions per unit surface and unit time, $\xi n_{\mathbf{v}}$ and the total momentum transferred $2m\xi^2 n_{\mathbf{v}}$.

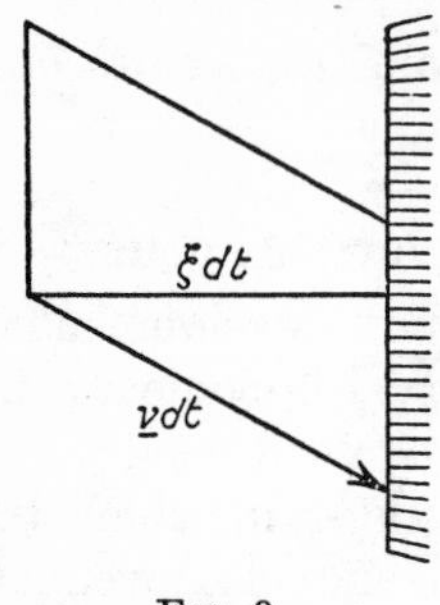

FIG. 9.

This has first to be summed over all angles of incidence (i.e. over a hemisphere); the result is obviously the same as one-half of the sum over the total sphere, namely

$$2m \sum \xi^2 n_{\mathbf{v}} = 2m\tfrac{1}{2}\overline{\xi^2}n_v,$$

where n_v is the number of molecules per unit of volume, with a velocity of magnitude v (but any direction). Now the 'principle of molecular chaos' is used according to which

$$\overline{\xi^2} = \overline{\eta^2} = \overline{\zeta^2} = \tfrac{1}{3}\overline{(\xi^2+\eta^2+\zeta^2)} = \tfrac{1}{3}\overline{v^2}.$$

Hence the last expression is equal to $\frac{m}{3}n_v\overline{v^2}$, and the pressure is finally obtained by summing over all velocities

$$p = \frac{m}{3}\sum v^2 n_v = \frac{m}{3}n\overline{v^2}. \tag{1}$$

The total (kinetic) energy in the volume V is

$$U = \frac{m}{2}n\overline{v^2}V;$$

hence one obtains the equation (6.1) of the text,

$$Vp = \tfrac{2}{3}U.$$

Now one can apply the considerations of Appendix, **9**, using the experimental fact expressed by Boyle's law (that all states of a gas at a fixed empirical temperature ϑ satisfy $pV = \text{const.}$). Then one obtains

$$pV = RT, \qquad U = \tfrac{3}{2}RT, \tag{2}$$

as stated in (6.2) of the text.

12. (VI. p. 50.) Statistical equilibrium

If H depends only on $\mathbf{p}$, not on $\mathbf{x}$, the equation $[H, f] = 0$ reduces to

$$\mathbf{p}.\frac{\partial f}{\partial \mathbf{x}} = 0, \tag{1}$$

and is equivalent to the set of ordinary differential equations

$$\frac{dx}{p_x} = \frac{dy}{p_y} = \frac{dz}{p_z}. \tag{2}$$

By integrating these ($\mathbf{p}$ is constant) one obtains the general solution of (1) as an arbitrary function of the integrals of (2), namely

$$f = \Phi(\mathbf{p}, \mathbf{m}), \tag{3}$$

where

$$\mathbf{m} = \mathbf{x} \wedge \mathbf{p}. \tag{4}$$

Now if the gas is isotropic, f can depend only on p^2 and m^2, and if it is to be homogeneous (i.e. all properties are independent of $\mathbf{x}$), m^2 cannot appear; hence

$$f = \Phi(p^2) = \Phi_1(H), \tag{5}$$

as stated in the text.

13. (VI. p. 51.) Maxwell's functional equation

To solve the equation (6.10) it suffices to take $\xi_3 = 0$; putting $\xi_1^2 = x$, $\xi_2^2 = y$, one has

$$f(x+y) = \phi(x)\phi(y). \tag{1}$$

Differentiating partially with respect to x,

$$f'(x+y) = \phi'(x)\phi(y), \tag{2}$$

and dividing by the original equation

$$\frac{f'(x+y)}{f(x+y)} = \frac{\phi'(x)}{\phi(x)}. \tag{3}$$

Now, the right-hand side is independent of y, and the left-hand side cannot therefore depend on y; hence, putting $x = 0$,

$$\frac{f'(y)}{f(y)} = -\beta, \tag{4}$$

where β is a constant. By integration,

$$f(y) = ae^{-\beta y} = e^{\alpha-\beta y}, \tag{5}$$

which is the formula (6.11') of the text.

14. (VI. p. 52.) **The method of the most probable distribution**

We have to determine the probability of a distribution of equal particles over N cells, where n_1 of them are in the first cell, n_2 of them in the second, etc. $(n_1+n_2+...+n_N = n)$. To do this we first take the particles in a fixed order; then the probability of distribution $(n_1, n_2,..., n_N)$ is, according to the multiplication law,

$$\underbrace{\omega_1\,\omega_1\,\omega_1...\omega_1}_{n_1}\;\underbrace{\omega_2\,\omega_2...\omega_2}_{n_2}...\;...\underbrace{\omega_N\,\omega_N...\omega_N}_{n_N} = \omega_1^{n_1}\,\omega_2^{n_2}\,...\omega_N^{n_N},$$

where $\omega_1, \omega_2,..., \omega_N$ are the relative volumes of the cells, normalized so that $\omega_1+\omega_2+...+\omega_N = 1$. To obtain the probability asked for, we have to destroy the fixed order of the particles. If one performs first all $n!$ permutations, one gets too many cases, as all those distributions, which differ only by permuting the particles in each cell, count only once. Therefore one has to divide $n!$ by the number of all these permutations inside a cell, that is by $n_1!\,n_2!...n_N!$ The total result is the expression (6.15)

$$P(n_1, n_2,..., n_N) = \frac{n!}{n_1!\,n_2!...n_N!}\,\omega_1^{n_1}\omega_2^{n_2}...\omega_N^{n_N}, \tag{1}$$

which is nothing but the general term in the polynomial expansion

$$\sum_{n_1 n_2 ... n_N} P(n_1, n_2,..., n_N) = \sum_{n_1...n_N} \frac{n!}{n_1!...n_N!}\,\omega_1^{n_1}...\omega_N^{n_N}$$
$$= (\omega_1+\omega_2+...+\omega_N)^n = 1.$$

We now deal with the approximation of $n!$ by Stirling's formula. The simplest way to obtain it is this: write

$$\log(n!) = \log(1.2.3...n) = \log 1+\log 2+\log 3+...+\log n$$

and replace the sum $\sum_{k=1}^{n} \log k$ by the integral

$$\int_0^n \log x\,dx = n(\log n - 1).$$

A more satisfactory derivation is the following: One can represent $n!$ by an integral and evaluate it with the help of the so-called method of steepest descent, which plays a great part in the modern treatment of statistical mechanics due to Darwin and Fowler (see p. 54). The approximate evaluation of $n!$ may serve as a simple example of this method.

If the identity

$$\frac{d}{dx}(e^{-x}x^n) = -e^{-x}x^n + ne^{-x}x^{n-1}$$

is integrated from 0 to ∞ and the abbreviation (Γ-function)

$$\Gamma(n+1) = \int_0^\infty e^{-x}x^n\,dx \quad (n > -1), \tag{2}$$

used, one obtains $\qquad \Gamma(n+1) = n\Gamma(n). \qquad (3)$

As $\Gamma(1) = 1$, one has

$$\Gamma(2) = 1.\Gamma(1) = 1, \qquad \Gamma(3) = 2\Gamma(2) = 1.2,$$
$$\Gamma(4) = 3\Gamma(3) = 1.2.3,$$

and in general $\qquad \Gamma(n+1) = n!. \qquad (4)$

The integral (2) can be written

$$\Gamma(n+1) = \int_0^\infty e^{f(n,x)}\,dx, \qquad f(n,x) = -x + n\log x. \tag{5}$$

The function $f(n,x)$ (hence also the integrand) has a maximum where

$$f'(x) = -1 + \frac{n}{x} = 0,$$

i.e. at $x = n$, and

$$f(n) = -n + n\log n,$$

$$f''(n) = -\frac{1}{n}.$$

The expansion of $f(x)$ in the neighbourhood of the maximum $x = n$ is therefore

$$f(x) = -n+n\log n-\frac{1}{2n}(x-n)^2+...,$$

and one has

$$\Gamma(n+1) = e^{-n+n\log n}\int\limits_0^\infty e^{-(x-n)^2/2n}(1+...)\,dx,$$

where the dots indicate terms of higher order which can be easily worked out. If these are neglected the integral becomes

$$\int\limits_0^\infty e^{-(x-n)^2/2n}\,dx = \int\limits_{-n}^\infty e^{-\xi^2/2n}\,d\xi \to \sqrt{(2\pi n)}$$

for large n. Hence

$$n! = \Gamma(n+1) = \sqrt{(2\pi n)}e^{-n}n^n+... \tag{6}$$

and
$$\log n! = n\log n-n+\tfrac{1}{2}\log(2\pi n)+..., \tag{7}$$

where the highest terms agree with the previous result.

Thus the logarithm of the probability P can be written

$$\log P = \sum_s \phi_s(n_s)+\text{const.}, \tag{8}$$

where
$$\phi_s(n_s) = n_s(\log\omega_s-\log n_s). \tag{9}$$

(8) and (9) are, for equal ω's, equivalent to formula (6.17) of the text.

One has to determine the maximum of $\log P$ with the conditions (6.13), (6.14), of the text, namely

$$\sum_{s=1}^N n_s = n, \qquad \sum_{s=1}^N n_s\epsilon_s = U. \tag{10}$$

Without using the special form of ϕ_s, one obtains

$$\frac{\partial\phi_s}{\partial n_s} = \lambda+\beta\epsilon_s \tag{11}$$

where λ, β are two Lagrangian factors. For the special function (9) one has

$$\frac{\partial\phi_s}{\partial n_s} = \log\omega_s-\log n_s-1, \tag{12}$$

and if this is substituted in (11) with $\lambda+1 = -\alpha$,

$$\log n_s = \log\omega_s+\alpha-\beta\epsilon_s,$$

$$n_s = \omega_s e^{\alpha-\beta\epsilon_s}; \tag{13}$$

that is, for equal ω's, the formula (6.18) of the text.

If one has two sets of systems A and B, as discussed in the text, there are three conditions

$$\sum_{r=1}^{N^{(A)}} n_r^{(A)} = n^{(A)}, \quad \sum_{r=1}^{N^{(B)}} n_r^{(B)} = n^{(B)}, \quad \sum_{r=1}^{N^{(A)}} n_r^{(A)}\epsilon_r^{(A)} + \sum_{r=1}^{N^{(B)}} n_r^{(B)}\epsilon_r^{(B)} = U,$$

and therefore instead of two multipliers three, $\lambda^{(A)}, \lambda^{(B)}, \beta$; and one obtains, with $\lambda^{(A)}+1 = -\alpha^{(A)}$, $\lambda^{(B)}+1 = -\alpha^{(B)}$, the formulae (6.19) of the text, which show that β is the equilibrium parameter, a function of the (empirical) temperature ϑ alone.

In order to see that β is reciprocal to the absolute temperature one must apply the second theorem of thermodynamics, which refers to quasi-static processes involving external work (for instance by changing the volume).

By an infinitely slow change of external parameters $a_1, a_2, \ldots$, the energies of the cells ϵ_r will be altered and at the same time the occupation numbers n_r; the total energy will be changed by

$$dU = \sum_r n_r \sum_\sigma \frac{\partial \epsilon_r}{\partial a_\sigma} da_\sigma + \sum_r \epsilon_r dn_r, \tag{14}$$

while the total number of particles is unchanged,

$$dn = \sum_r dn_r = 0. \tag{15}$$

The first term in (14) represents the total work done

$$dW = -n \sum_\sigma f_\sigma da_\sigma, \tag{16}$$

where

$$f_\sigma = -\frac{1}{n} \sum_r n_r \frac{\partial \epsilon_r}{\partial a_\sigma} \tag{17}$$

is the average force resisting a change of a_σ. Then the second term in (14)

$$dQ = \sum_r \epsilon_r dn_r \tag{18}$$

must represent the heat produced by the rearrangements of the systems over the cells.

The corresponding change of $\log P$ is obtained from (8) and (11),

$$d \log P = \sum_r \frac{\partial \phi_r}{\partial n_r} dn_r = \sum_r (\lambda + \beta \epsilon_r) dn_r,$$

which in virtue of (15) and (18) reduces to

$$d \log P = \beta\, dQ. \tag{19}$$

This shows that $\beta\, dQ$ is a total differential of a function depending on $\beta, a_1, a_2,...,$ and that $\beta(\vartheta)$ is the integrating factor.

Hence the second law of thermodynamics is automatically satisfied by the statistical assembly, and one has, with the notations of section V,

$$dQ = \lambda\, d\phi, \text{ with } \lambda = \frac{1}{\beta}, \quad \phi = \log P;$$

then (5.25) and (5.26) give, with $C = 1/k$, $\log\Phi = 0$, $\Phi = 1$, and (5.27)

$$T = \frac{1}{k\beta}, \quad S - S_0 = k\phi = k \log P. \tag{20}$$

k is called Boltzmann's constant.

Now the change of energy (14) becomes

$$dU = -n \sum_\sigma f_\sigma\, da_\sigma + T\, dS. \tag{21}$$

If one has a fluid with the only parameter $a_1 = V$, the corresponding force is the pressure

$$p = nf_1 = -\sum_r n_r \frac{\partial \epsilon_r}{\partial V}, \tag{22}$$

and one obtains the usual equation

$$dU = -p\, dV + T\, dS. \tag{23}$$

Returning to the general expression (21) one sees easily that one can express all quantities in terms of the so-called partition function (or 'sum-over-states')

$$Z = \sum_r \omega_r e^{-\beta\epsilon_r}. \tag{24}$$

For, from (10) and (13),

$$n = e^\alpha \sum_r \omega_r e^{-\beta\epsilon_r} = e^\alpha Z,$$

$$U = e^\alpha \sum_r \epsilon_r \omega_r e^{-\beta\epsilon_r} = -e^\alpha \frac{\partial Z}{\partial \beta},$$

hence $$\alpha = \log n - \log Z.$$

Now one has, after simple calculation, from (19), (20) with (8), (9), (17)

$$\left.\begin{aligned} u &= \frac{U}{n} = -\frac{\partial \log Z}{\partial \beta}, \\ s &= \frac{S}{n} = k\left(\log Z - \beta \frac{\partial \log Z}{\partial \beta}\right), \end{aligned}\right\} \tag{25}$$

and $$du = -\sum_{\sigma} f_{\sigma}\, da_{\sigma} + T\, ds. \tag{26}$$

The simplest thermodynamical function, from which all others can be derived by differentiation, is the free energy,

$$\left.\begin{aligned} f &= u - Ts = -kT\log Z, \\ df &= -\sum_{\sigma} f_{\sigma}\, da_{\sigma} - s\, dT; \end{aligned}\right\} \tag{27}$$

hence $$f_{\sigma} = -\frac{\partial f}{\partial a_{\sigma}} = -kT\frac{\partial \log Z}{\partial a_{\sigma}},$$

while $s = -\partial f/\partial T$ leads back to the second formula (25).

The application to ideal gases may be illustrated by the simplest model where each particle is regarded as a mass point with coordinates x, y, z, momenta p_x, p_y, p_z, and mass m. Then, according to Liouville's theorem, one has to take as cells ω_s elements of the phase space $dxdydzdp_x dp_y dp_z$ and replace the sums by integrals. The energy is $(p_x^2+p_y^2+p_z^2)/2m$. Then the partition function (24) becomes

$$Z = \int \overset{(6)}{\cdots} \int e^{-(\beta/2m)(p_x^2+p_y^2+p_z^2)}\, dxdydzdp_x dp_y dp_z.$$

The integration over the space coordinates gives V, the volume. If one puts $\sqrt{(\beta/2m)}p_x = \xi,\ldots$, one has

$$Z = V\left(\frac{2m}{\beta}\right)^{\frac{3}{2}} \iiint e^{-(\xi^2+\eta^2+\zeta^2)}\, d\xi d\eta d\zeta,$$

the integration extended for each variable from $-\infty$ to $+\infty$. The integral is a constant which is of no interest as all physical quantities depend on derivatives of Z. Hence, with $\beta = (kT)^{-1}$,

$$f = -kT\log Z = -kT\log V - \tfrac{3}{2}kT\log kT + \text{const.},$$

from which one obtains

$$p = -n\frac{\partial f}{\partial V} = \frac{nkT}{V}, \qquad s = -\frac{\partial f}{\partial T} = k\log V + \tfrac{3}{2}k(\log kT + 1),$$

$$u = f + Ts = \tfrac{3}{2}kT + \text{const.}$$

These are the well-known formulae for an ideal monatomic gas: Boyle's law, the entropy and energy per atom. The specific heat at constant volume is

$$c_v = \frac{dU}{dT} = \tfrac{3}{2}nk = \tfrac{3}{2}R,$$

if n refers to one mole.

15. (VI. p. 54.) The method of mean values

The method of Darwin and Fowler aims at computing the mean value of any quantity $f(n_r)$, depending on the occupation number n_r of a cell for all possible distributions $n_1, n_2,..., n_N$, satisfying the conditions

$$\sum_r n_r = n, \qquad \sum_r \epsilon_r n_r = U, \tag{1}$$

that is, the quantity

$$\overline{f(n_r)} = \sum_{n_1,n_2,...,n_N} P(n_1, n_2,..., n_N) f(n_r), \tag{2}$$

where P is the probability of the distribution $n_1, n_2,..., n_N$, defined by equation (6.15) or **14,** (1).

We consider the function $F(z)$ defined by (6.22),

$$F(z) = \omega_1 z^{\epsilon_1} + \omega_2 z^{\epsilon_2} + ... + \omega_N z^{\epsilon_N}, \tag{3}$$

and assume that a very small unit of energy is chosen so that all the ϵ_r are positive integers, which may be ordered in such a way that $\epsilon_1 \leqslant \epsilon_2 \leqslant \epsilon_3 \leqslant ... \leqslant \epsilon_N$; also, by choosing the zero of energy suitably we can arrange that $\epsilon_1 = 0$.

Then we expand $\{F(z)\}^n$ into powers of z according to the multinomial theorem and obtain a series of terms

$$\frac{n!}{n_1!\, n_2! ... n_N!} (\omega_1 z^{\epsilon_1})^{n_1} (\omega_2 z^{\epsilon_2})^{n_2} ... (\omega_N z^{\epsilon_N})^{n_N}$$
$$= P(n_1, n_2,..., n_N) z^{(\epsilon_1 n_1 + \epsilon_2 n_2 + ... + \epsilon_N n_N)};$$

by collecting all these terms with the same factor z^U we obtain all the $P(n_1, n_2,..., n_N)$ which belong to the same value of

$$U = \sum_r \epsilon_r n_r.$$

Now we substitute 1 for each $f(n_r)$ in (2) and obtain in this way the total probability of these distributions which have a given total energy U, in the form:

$$\sum_{(U)} P = \text{coefficient of } z^U \text{ in } \{F(z)\}^n.$$

This coefficient can be evaluated by Cauchy's theorem, if z is regarded as a complex variable; one has

$$\sum_{(U)} P = \frac{1}{2\pi i} \oint z^{-U-1} \{F(z)\}^n \, dz, \tag{4}$$

where the integral is taken round a closed contour surrounding the origin 0 in the z-plane. The integral can be evaluated approximately by the method of steepest descent which we have already explained, for real variables, in Appendix **14**, for the Γ-function.

The first step is to express the integrand in the form

$$z^{-(U+1)}\{F(z)\}^n = e^{G(z)}, \quad G(z) = n\log F(z) - (U+1)\log z.$$

Since

$$\frac{F'(z)}{F(z)} = \frac{\sum_r \epsilon_r z^{\epsilon_r}}{\sum_r z^{\epsilon_r}}$$

and

$$\frac{d}{dz}\left(\frac{F'(z)}{F(z)}\right) = \frac{1}{\left(\sum_r z^{\epsilon_r}\right)^2}\left\{\left(\sum_r z^{\epsilon_r}\right)\left(\sum_r \epsilon_r^2 z^{\epsilon_r}\right) - \left(\sum_r \epsilon_r z^{\epsilon_r}\right)^2\right\}$$

$$= \frac{1}{\left(\sum_r z^{\epsilon_r}\right)^2}\sum_r z^{\epsilon_r}\left\{\epsilon_r\sqrt{\left(\sum_s z^{\epsilon_s}\right)} - \frac{\sum_s \epsilon_s z^{\epsilon_s}}{\sqrt{\left(\sum_s z^{\epsilon_s}\right)}}\right\}^2,$$

both $\log F(z)$ and its derivative increase monotonically from a finite value to ∞ as z moves along the real axis between 0 and ∞. Also $-\log z$ and its negative derivative z^{-1} decrease monotonically along the same path. Hence $G(z)$ can have only one extremum, a minimum, on the real axis between 0 and ∞, and this minimum will be extremely steep if n and U are large.

Also let z_0 be the point of the real axis where the minimum happens to be; then at this point the first derivative of $G(z)$ vanishes and the second is positive and very large. Hence in the direction orthogonal to the axis the integrand must have a very sharp maximum. If we take as contour of integration a circle about 0 through z_0, only the immediate neighbourhood of this point will contribute appreciably to the integral.

The minimum z_0 is to be found as root of the equation

$$G'(z) = -\frac{U+1}{z} + n\frac{F'(z)}{F(z)} = 0, \tag{5}$$

and one has

$$G''(z) = \frac{U+1}{z^2} + n\left\{\frac{F''(z)}{F(z)} - \left(\frac{F'(z)}{F(z)}\right)^2\right\}.$$

This shows that for large U and n a proportional increase in U and n will not change the root z_0, while $G''(z_0)$, which is positive, can be made arbitrarily large.

Putting $z = z_0+iy$ one obtains for the integral (4)

$$\sum_{(U)} P = \frac{1}{2\pi i} e^{G(z_0)} \int_{-\infty}^{\infty} e^{-\frac{1}{2}G''(z_0)y^2} i\, dy,$$

where the terms of higher than second order are omitted and the limits of integration are taken to be $\pm\infty$ because of the sharp drop of the exponential function. This gives

$$\sum_{(U)} P = z_0^{-(U+1)}\{F(z_0)\}^n \frac{1}{\sqrt{\{2\pi G''(z_0)\}}}. \tag{6}$$

$U+1$ can be replaced by U, because of the smallness of the energy unit chosen; if one puts

$$z_0 = e^{-\beta} \tag{7}$$

one has, for $N \to \infty$,

$$F(z_0) = \sum_r \omega_r z_0^{\epsilon_r} = \sum_r \omega_r e^{-\beta\epsilon_r} = Z(\beta), \tag{8}$$

which shows that the function $F(z)$ is equivalent to the partition function introduced in (**14**.24), p. 158.

If one now takes the logarithm of (6) the leading terms are

$$\log \sum_{(U)} P = \beta U + n \log Z.$$

On the other hand, one has from (5) to the same approximation

$$U = nz_0 \frac{F'(z_0)}{F(z_0)} = -\frac{n}{Z}\frac{dZ}{d\beta} = -n\frac{d\log Z}{d\beta}, \tag{9}$$

in agreement with (**14**.25); hence

$$\log \sum_{(U)} P = n\left(\log Z - \beta\frac{d\log Z}{d\beta}\right). \tag{10}$$

Comparison with (**14**.25) shows that the entropy in this theory is to be defined by

$$S = ns = k \log \sum_{(U)} P, \tag{11}$$

while in the Appendix, **14**, the definition was $S = k\log P$, where P means the maximum value of the probability.

Thus it becomes clear that owing to the enormous sharpness of the maximum it does not matter whether one averages over all states or picks out only the state of maximum probability. In fact, the two methods, that of the most probable distribution and that of mean values, do not differ as much as it appears. Both use asymptotic approximations for the combinatorial quantities: either for each factorial in the probability before averaging, or for the resultant integral after averaging. The results are completely identical. Yet there are apostles and disciples for each of the two doctrines who regard their creed as the only orthodox one. In my opinion it is just a question of training and practice which formalism is more convenient. The method of Darwin and Fowler has perhaps the advantage of greater flexibility. The partition function is nothing but a 'generating function' for the probabilities, and allows the representation of these by complex integrals. In this way the powerful methods of the theory of analytic functions of complex integrals can be utilized for thermodynamics.

16. (VI. p. 56.) Boltzmann's collision integral

The collision integral (6.24) can be derived in the following way.

The gas is supposed to be so diluted that only binary encounters are to be taken into account. Then the relative motion of two colliding particles has an initial and a final straight line asymptote.

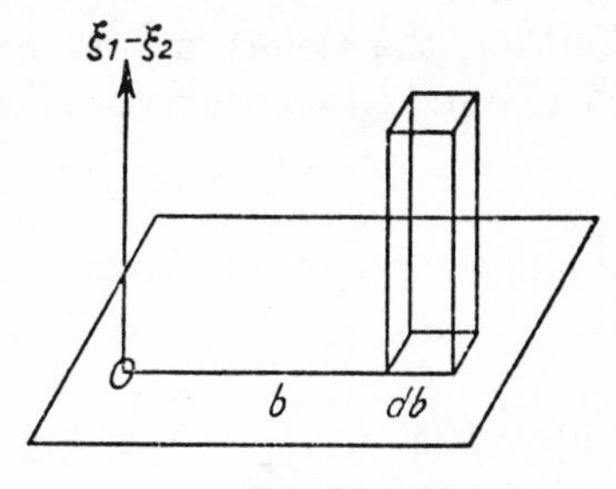

FIG. 10.

To specify an encounter we define the 'cross-section' as the plane through a point O with a normal parallel to the relative velocity $\boldsymbol{\xi}_1-\boldsymbol{\xi}_2$ of two particles before an encounter and introduce the position vector $\mathbf{b}$ in this plane. We erect a cylindrical volume element over the area $d\mathbf{b}$ with the height $|\boldsymbol{\xi}_1-\boldsymbol{\xi}_2|\,dt$; then all particles in this element having the relative velocity $\boldsymbol{\xi}_1-\boldsymbol{\xi}_2$ will pass through $d\mathbf{b}$ in time dt. The probability of a particle 2 passing a particle 1 at O within the cross-section element $d\mathbf{b}$ is obtained from the product $f(1)\,d\mathbf{x}_1\,d\boldsymbol{\xi}_1\,f(2)\,d\mathbf{x}_2\,d\boldsymbol{\xi}_2$ by replacing $d\mathbf{x}_2$ by the volume of the cylinder $|\boldsymbol{\xi}_1-\boldsymbol{\xi}_2|\,d\mathbf{b}dt$,

$$f(1)f(2)|\boldsymbol{\xi}_1-\boldsymbol{\xi}_2|\,d\mathbf{b}d\mathbf{x}_1\,d\boldsymbol{\xi}_1\,d\boldsymbol{\xi}_2\,dt.$$

Every encounter changes the velocities and removes therefore the particle 1 from the initial range. The total loss is obtained by integrating over all $d\mathbf{b}$ and $d\boldsymbol{\xi}_2$:

$$d\mathbf{x}_1\,d\boldsymbol{\xi}_1\,dt\iint f(1)f(2)|\boldsymbol{\xi}_1-\boldsymbol{\xi}_2|\,d\mathbf{b}d\boldsymbol{\xi}_2. \tag{1}$$

But there are other encounters such that the final state of the particle 1 is in the element $d\mathbf{x}_1\, d\boldsymbol{\xi}_1$; they are called inverse encounters.

If the final velocities of the direct encounters are $\boldsymbol{\xi}_1', \boldsymbol{\xi}_2'$ the laws of collision (conservation of momentum and energy) allow one to express $\boldsymbol{\xi}_1', \boldsymbol{\xi}_2'$ in terms of $\boldsymbol{\xi}_1, \boldsymbol{\xi}_2$ and two further parameters (the components of $\mathbf{b}$ in the cross-section plane). These relations are linear in $\boldsymbol{\xi}_1, \boldsymbol{\xi}_2$ and may be shortly written

$$(\boldsymbol{\xi}_1', \boldsymbol{\xi}_2') = \mathscr{L}(\boldsymbol{\xi}_1, \boldsymbol{\xi}_2), \tag{2}$$

where $\mathscr{L}$ represents a 6×6 matrix. It is obvious that the solutions of these equations for $\boldsymbol{\xi}_1$ and $\boldsymbol{\xi}_2$ in terms of $\boldsymbol{\xi}_1'$ and $\boldsymbol{\xi}_2'$ must have the same form; that means that $\mathscr{L}^{-1} = \mathscr{L}$, so that $\mathscr{L}^2 = 1$ and $|\mathscr{L}| = 1$ or

$$d\boldsymbol{\xi}_1'\, d\boldsymbol{\xi}_2' = d\boldsymbol{\xi}_1\, d\boldsymbol{\xi}_2. \tag{3}$$

Further, the elementary theory of collisions (conservation of energy and momentum) implies

$$|\boldsymbol{\xi}_1' - \boldsymbol{\xi}_2'| = |\boldsymbol{\xi}_1 - \boldsymbol{\xi}_2|. \tag{4}$$

Hence the number of inverse encounters is

$$d\mathbf{x}_1\, d\boldsymbol{\xi}_1\, dt \iint f'(1)f'(2)\,|\boldsymbol{\xi}_1 - \boldsymbol{\xi}_2|\, d\mathbf{b}\, d\boldsymbol{\xi}_2, \tag{5}$$

where $f'(1)$ means $f(t, \mathbf{x}_1, \boldsymbol{\xi}_1')$, $\boldsymbol{\xi}_1'$ being the linear function of $\boldsymbol{\xi}_1, \boldsymbol{\xi}_2$ given by (2).

Combining (1) and (5), one obtains for the total gain of particles (1) in $d\mathbf{x}_1\, d\boldsymbol{\xi}_1$, per time-element dt,

$$d\mathbf{x}_1\, d\boldsymbol{\xi}_1\, dt \iint \{f'(1)f'(2) - f(1)f(2)\}\,|\boldsymbol{\xi}_1 - \boldsymbol{\xi}_2|\, d\mathbf{b}\, d\boldsymbol{\xi}_2. \tag{6}$$

This has to be equated to the change of $f(1)$ calculated without assuming interactions, namely,

$$\frac{df(1)}{dt}\, d\mathbf{x}_1\, d\boldsymbol{\xi}_1\, dt = \left\{\frac{\partial f(1)}{\partial t} - [H, f(1)]\right\} d\mathbf{x}_1\, d\boldsymbol{\xi}_1\, dt. \tag{7}$$

The results are the combined formulae (6.23) and (6.24) of the text,

$$\frac{\partial f(1)}{\partial t} - [H, f(1)] = \iint \{f'(1)f'(2) - f(1)f(2)\}\,|\boldsymbol{\xi}_1 - \boldsymbol{\xi}_2|\, d\mathbf{b}\, d\boldsymbol{\xi}_2. \tag{8}$$

17. (VI. p. 57.) Irreversibility in gases

Assuming no external forces, the Hamiltonian of a particle is $H = \frac{1}{2m}p^2$, hence Boltzmann's equation (6.23), or (Appendix, **16**.8) reduces to

$$\frac{\partial f(1)}{\partial t}+\boldsymbol{\xi}_1\cdot\frac{\partial f(1)}{\partial \mathbf{x}_1} = \iint \{f'(1)f'(2)-f(1)f(2)\}|\boldsymbol{\xi}_1-\boldsymbol{\xi}_2|\, d\mathbf{b}d\boldsymbol{\xi}_2. \tag{1}$$

If now the entropy is defined by (6.25) or, using the velocity instead of the momentum, by

$$S = -k\iint f(1)\log f(1)\, d\mathbf{x}_1 d\boldsymbol{\xi}_1, \tag{2}$$

one obtains

$$\frac{dS}{dt} = -k\iint \{1+\log f(1)\}\frac{\partial f(1)}{dt}\,d\mathbf{x}_1\, d\boldsymbol{\xi}_1,$$

and substituting $\partial f(1)/\partial t$ from (1)

$$\begin{aligned}\frac{dS}{dt} &= k\iint \{1+\log f(1)\}\boldsymbol{\xi}_1\cdot\frac{\partial f(1)}{\partial \mathbf{x}_1}\,d\mathbf{x}_1\, d\boldsymbol{\xi}_1 - \\ &\quad -k\iiiint \{1+\log f(1)\}\{f'(1)f'(2)-f(1)f(2)\}\times \\ &\quad \times|\boldsymbol{\xi}_1-\boldsymbol{\xi}_2|\, d\mathbf{b}d\mathbf{x}_1\, d\boldsymbol{\xi}_1\, d\boldsymbol{\xi}_2.\end{aligned} \tag{3}$$

Here the first integral can be written

$$\iint \boldsymbol{\xi}_1\cdot\frac{\partial}{\partial \mathbf{x}_1}\{f(1)\log f(1)\}\, d\mathbf{x}_1 d\boldsymbol{\xi}_1$$

and transformed, by Gauss's theorem, into a surface integral over the walls of the container,

$$\int d\sigma \int \boldsymbol{\xi}_1.\boldsymbol{\nu} f(1)\log f(1)\, d\boldsymbol{\xi}_1,$$

where $\boldsymbol{\nu}$ is the unit vector parallel to the outer normal of the surface, $d\sigma$ the surface element.

The inner integral is n times the mean value over all velocities of $\boldsymbol{\xi}_1.\boldsymbol{\nu}\log f(1)$, where $n = \int f(1)\, d\boldsymbol{\xi}_1$ is the number density. But this average vanishes at the surface which is supposed to be perfectly elastic and at rest, external interference being excluded; for the numbers of incident and reflected particles with the same absolute value of the normal component of the velocity, $|\boldsymbol{\xi}.\boldsymbol{\nu}|$, will be equal.

Hence there remains only the second integral in (3). This can be written in four different forms, namely, apart from the one given in (3), where the factor $1+f(1)$ appears, three others where this factor is replaced by $1+f(2)$ or $1+f'(1)$ or $1+f'(2)$. For it is obvious that 1 and 2 can be interchanged as the integration is extended over both points in a symmetric way; and the dashed variables can be exchanged with the undashed ones as

$$d\boldsymbol{\xi}_1'\,d\boldsymbol{\xi}_2' = d\boldsymbol{\xi}_1\,d\boldsymbol{\xi}_2, \qquad |\boldsymbol{\xi}_1'-\boldsymbol{\xi}_2'| = |\boldsymbol{\xi}_1-\boldsymbol{\xi}_2|$$

(see Appendix, **16**.3, 4). Hence

$$\frac{dS}{dt} = -\frac{k}{4}\iiiint \{\log f(1)+\log f(2)-\log f'(1)-\log f'(2)\}\times$$
$$\times\{f'(1)f'(2)-f(1)f(2)\}|\boldsymbol{\xi}_1-\boldsymbol{\xi}_2|\,d\mathbf{b}d\mathbf{x}_1\,d\boldsymbol{\xi}_1\,d\boldsymbol{\xi}_2$$

or

$$\frac{dS}{dt} = \frac{k}{4}\iiiint \log\frac{f'(1)f'(2)}{f(1)f(2)}\,.\{f'(1)f'(2)-f(1)f(2)\}\times$$
$$\times|\boldsymbol{\xi}_1-\boldsymbol{\xi}_2|\,d\boldsymbol{\xi}_1\,d\boldsymbol{\xi}_2\,d\mathbf{b}d\mathbf{x}_1. \quad (4)$$

Now $\log\dfrac{f'(1)f'(2)}{f(1)f(2)}$ is positive or negative according as $f'(1)f'(2)$ is greater or smaller than $f(1)f(2)$; it has therefore always the same sign as $f'(1)f'(2)-f(1)f(2)$, and one obtains

$$\frac{dS}{dt} \geqslant 0; \quad (5)$$

the $=$ sign can hold only if

$$f'(1)f'(2) = f(1)f(2) \quad (6)$$

or

$$\log f'(1)+\log f'(2) = \log f(1)+\log f(2). \quad (7)$$

One can express this also by saying that

$$\log f(1)+\log f(2) \quad (8)$$

is a collision invariant.

The mechanics of the two-body problem teaches that there are only four quantities conserved at a collision: the three components of the momentum $m\boldsymbol{\xi}_1+m\boldsymbol{\xi}_2$ and the total energy $\frac{1}{2}m\xi_1^2+\frac{1}{2}m\xi_2^2$. Hence $\log f$ must be a linear combination of these:

$$\log f = \alpha-\tfrac{1}{2}\beta m\xi^2+\boldsymbol{\gamma}.\boldsymbol{\xi}, \quad (9)$$

or

$$f = e^{\alpha-\frac{1}{2}\beta m\xi^2+\boldsymbol{\gamma}.\boldsymbol{\xi}}.$$

This can also be written

$$f = e^{\alpha_1 - \frac{1}{2}\beta m(\boldsymbol{\xi}-\mathbf{u})^2}, \tag{10}$$

where $\mathbf{u} = \dfrac{1}{m\beta}\boldsymbol{\gamma}$ and $\alpha_1 = \alpha + \dfrac{\gamma^2}{2m\beta}$.

(10) shows that $\mathbf{u}$ is the mean velocity. For a gas at rest (in a fixed vessel) one has therefore $\mathbf{u} = 0$, hence $\boldsymbol{\gamma} = 0$ and

$$f = e^{\alpha-\beta\epsilon}, \qquad \epsilon = \tfrac{1}{2}m\xi^2. \tag{11}$$

This is the dynamical proof of Maxwell's distribution law.

18. (VI. p. 60.) Formalism of statistical mechanics

As said in the text, Gibbs's statistical mechanics is formally identical with Boltzmann's theory of gases if the actual gas is replaced by a virtual assembly of copies of the system under consideration. Hence all formulae referring to averages per particle (small letters) can be taken over if the word 'particle' is replaced by 'system under consideration'. One forms the partition function (**14**.24) or (**15**.8) $F(z) = Z(\beta)$, $z = e^{-\beta}$, and from that the free energy (**14**.27)

$$f = -kT\log Z, \tag{1}$$

from which all thermodynamical quantities can be obtained by differentiation:

$$s = -\frac{\partial f}{\partial T}, \qquad f_\sigma = -\frac{\partial f}{\partial a_\sigma}. \tag{2}$$

This formalism includes also the case of chemical mixtures where the number of particles of a certain type is variable. One has to know how the quantity Z depends on these numbers; then the chemical potentials, introduced in Appendix, **8**, are obtained by differentiating f with respect to the concentrations. We shall mention only the method of the 'great ensemble' which can be used in this case.

In the theory of non-ideal gases the Hamiltonian splits up into a sum

$$H = \frac{1}{2m}\sum_{k=1}^{N}\mathbf{p}_k^2 + U(\mathbf{x}_1, \mathbf{x}_2,\ldots, \mathbf{x}_N), \tag{3}$$

and the partition function into a product

$$Z = \int\overset{(3N)}{\cdots}\int \exp\Big\{-(\beta/2m)\sum_{k=1}^{N}\mathbf{p}_k^2\Big\}\, d\mathbf{p}_1\ldots d\mathbf{p}_N \times$$
$$\times \int\overset{(3N)}{\cdots}\int \exp\{-\beta U(\mathbf{x}_1,\ldots, \mathbf{x}_N)\}\, d\mathbf{x}_1\ldots d\mathbf{x}_N.$$

The first integral can easily be evaluated and gives

$$(2\pi m/\beta)^{3N/2} = (2\pi mkT)^{3N/2};$$

hence one has

$$Z = (2\pi mkT)^{3N/2}Q, \tag{4}$$

where

$$Q = \int \overset{(3N)}{\cdots} \int \exp\{-U(\mathbf{x}_1,\dots,\mathbf{x}_N)/kT\}\, d\mathbf{x}\dots d_1\mathbf{x}_N, \tag{5}$$

as in (6.35) of the text.

The method of Ursell for the evaluation of this integral applies to the case where the potential energy is supposed to consist of interaction in pairs between the centres of the particles,

$$U = \sum_{i>j} \Phi_{ij}, \qquad \Phi_{ij} = \Phi(r_{ij}). \tag{6}$$

Then one can write

$$e^{-\beta U} = \prod_{i>j} e^{-\beta\Phi_{ij}} = \prod_{i>j} (1-f_{ij}), \tag{7}$$

where

$$f_{ij} = 1-e^{-\beta\Phi_{ij}}. \tag{8}$$

The product (7) can be expanded into a series

$$e^{-\beta U} = 1-\sum_{i>j} f_{ij}+\sum_{\substack{i>j\\h>k}} f_{ij}\, f_{hk}+\dots, \tag{9}$$

and the problem of calculating Q is reduced to finding the 'cluster integrals'

$$\int\dots\int f_{ij}\, d\mathbf{x}_1\dots d\mathbf{x}_N, \qquad \int\dots\int f_{ij}\, f_{hk}\, d\mathbf{x}_1\dots d\mathbf{x}_N, \qquad \dots, \tag{10}$$

which are obviously proportional to V^{N-1}, V^{N-2},.... Hence one obtains for QV^{-N} an expansion in powers of V^{-1} which holds for small interactions ($\beta\Phi_{ij}$ small implies f_{ij} small):

$$Q = V^N\left(1-\frac{\alpha}{V}+\frac{\beta}{V^2}-\dots\right). \tag{11}$$

Then (1) and (4) give

$$f = -kT\left\{\frac{3N}{2}\log(2\pi mkT)+\log Q\right\}, \tag{12}$$

hence

$$p = -\frac{\partial f}{\partial V} = kT\frac{\partial \log Q}{\partial V} = \frac{NkT}{V}\left(1-\frac{A}{V}+\frac{B}{V^2}-\dots\right), \tag{13}$$

where $A = \alpha/N$, $B = (\alpha^2-2\beta)/N$,.... That is the formula (6.36) given in the text.

The actual evaluation of the cluster integrals is extremely difficult and cumbersome. The analytical properties of the power series (11) have been carefully investigated by J. Mayer, and by myself in collaboration with K. Fuchs. The theory has been generalized so as to include quantum effects by Uhlenbeck, Kahn, de Boer. Here is a list of publications:

H. D. Ursell, *Proc. Camb. Phil. Soc.* **23**, p. 685 (1927).
J. E. Mayer, *J. Chem. Phys.* **5**, p. 67 (1937).
J. E. Mayer and P. J. Ackermann, ibid. p. 74.
J. E. Mayer and S. F. Harrison, ibid. **6**, pp. 87, 101 (1938).
M. Born, *Physica*, **4**, p. 1034 (1937).
M. Born and K. Fuchs, *Proc. Roy. Soc.* A, **166**, p. 391 (1938).
K. Fuchs, ibid. A, **179**, p. 340 (1942).
B. Kahn and G. E. Uhlenbeck, *Physica*, **4**, p. 299 (1938).
B. Kahn, *The Theory of the Equation of State.* Utrecht Dissertation.
J. de Boer and A. Michels, *Physica*, **6**, p. 97 (1939).
S. F. Streeter and J. E. Mayer, *J. Chem. Phys.* **7**, p. 1025 (1939).
J. E. Mayer and E. W. Montroll, ibid. **9**, p. 626 (1941).
J. E. Mayer and M. Goeppert-Mayer, *Statistical Mechanics*, J. Wiley & Sons, New York (1940).
J. E. Mayer, *J. Chem. Phys.* **10**, p. 629 (1942).
W. G. MacMillan and J. E. Mayer, ibid. **13**, p. 276 (1945).
J. E. Mayer, ibid. **43**, p. 71 (1939); **15**, p. 187 (1947).
H. S. Green, *Proc. Roy. Soc.* A, **189**, p. 103 (1947).
J. de Boer and A. Michels, *Physica*, **7**, p. 369 (1940).
J. de Boer, *Contributions to the Theory of Compressed Gases.* Amsterdam Dissertation (1940).
J. Yvon, *Actualités scientifiques et industrielles*, **203**, p. 1 (1935); p. 542 (1937); *Cahiers de physique*, **28**, p. 1 (1945).

19. (VI. p. 62.) Quasi-periodicity

The state of a mechanical system can be represented by a point in the $6N$-dimensional phase space p, q, and its motion by a single orbit on a 'surface' of constant energy in this space. Following this orbit one must come very near to the initial point; the time needed will be considerable, in the range of observability. This is the quasi-period considered by Zermelo. Yet there are much smaller quasi-periods if one takes into account that all particles are equal and indistinguishable; the gas is already in almost the same state as the initial one if any particle has come near the initial position of any other. Then the orbit defined above is not closed at all, yet the system has performed another kind of quasi-period. These periods are presumably small; I cannot give a mathematical proof, but it seems evident from the overwhelming probability of distributions near the most probable one. Einstein has this quasi-period in mind. It is certainly extremely short in the scale of observable time-intervals, and one can therefore say that the representing 'point' sweeps over the whole energy surface if this point is defined without regard to the individuality of the particles (i.e. if an enormous number of single points corresponding to permutation of all particles are regarded as one point).

20. (VI. p. 63.) Fluctuations and Brownian motion

The statistical conception of matter in bulk implies that spontaneous deviations from equilibrium are possible. There are several different types of problems, some of them concerned with the deviations from the average or fluctuations found by repeated observations, others with actual motion of suspended visible particles—the Brownian motion.

The simplest case of fluctuations is that of density, i.e. of the number of particles in a small part ωV of the whole volume V. One has in this case two cells of relative size ω and $1-\omega$, and the probability of a distribution $n_1, n_2 = n-n_1$, is according to (6.15) or (**14**.1)

$$W(n_1) = \frac{n!}{n_1!\,(n-n_1)!}\,\omega^{n_1}(1-\omega)^{n-n_1}. \tag{1}$$

The expectation value of n_1 found by repeated experiments is

$$\overline{n_1} = \sum_{n_1=0}^{n} n_1 W(n_1) = \sum_{n_1=0}^{n} \frac{n_1\,n!}{n_1!\,(n-n_1)!}\,\omega^{n_1}(1-\omega)^{n-n_1},$$

or

$$\overline{n_1} = n\omega \sum_{n_1=1}^{n} \frac{(n-1)!}{(n_1-1)!\,\{(n-1)-(n_1-1)\}!}\,\omega^{n_1-1}(1-\omega)^{(n-1)-(n_1-1)}.$$

According to the binomial theorem this reduces to

$$\overline{n_1} = n\omega, \tag{2}$$

as might be expected.

In order to calculate $\overline{n_1^2}$ we note that $\overline{n_1(n_1-1)}$ can be found in exactly the same way as $\overline{n_1}$, namely,

$$\begin{aligned}\overline{n_1(n_1-1)} &= \sum_{n_1=0}^{n} n_1(n_1-1)\,W(n_1)\\ &= n(n-1)\omega^2 \sum_{n_1=2}^{n} \frac{(n-2)!}{(n_1-2)!\,\{(n-2)-(n_1-2)\}!}\times\\ &\qquad\times\omega^{n_1-2}(1-\omega)^{(n-2)-(n_1-2)},\end{aligned}$$

whence $$\overline{n_1(n_1-1)} = n(n-1)\omega^2. \tag{3}$$

Therefore

$$\overline{n_1^2} = \overline{n_1(n_1-1)}+\overline{n_1} = n(n-1)\omega^2+n\omega, \tag{4}$$

so that the mean square deviation is

$$\overline{(\Delta n_1)^2} = \overline{(n_1-\bar{n}_1)^2} = \overline{n_1^2}-(\bar{n}_1)^2 = n\omega-n\omega^2 = n\omega(1-\omega). \tag{5}$$

If ω is a small fraction, one obtains the well-known fluctuation formula for independent events

$$\overline{(\Delta n_1)^2} = \overline{n_1}. \tag{6}$$

This is directly applicable to the density fluctuation of an ideal gas and can be used to explain the scattering of light by a gas, as observed for instance in the blue of the sky (Lord Rayleigh; *Atomic Physics*, Appendix IV, p. 280).

There are also fluctuations of other properties of a gas. As the state of a fluid is determined by two independent macroscopic variables (p, V for instance), it suffices to calculate the fluctuation of one further quantity. The most convenient one is the energy.

The following consideration holds, however, not only for ideal gases, but for any set of independent equal systems of given total (or mean) energy; it supposes only that the distribution is canonical.

Then all averages can be obtained with the help of the partition function (**14**.24) or (**15**.8),

$$Z(\beta) = \sum_r \omega_r e^{-\beta\epsilon_r}, \qquad \beta = \frac{1}{kT}. \tag{7}$$

In particular the mean energy is (**14**.25)

$$u = \bar{\epsilon} = \frac{\sum_r \omega_r \epsilon_r e^{-\beta\epsilon_r}}{\sum_r \omega_r e^{-\beta\epsilon_r}} = -\frac{Z'}{Z} = -\frac{d\log Z}{d\beta}, \tag{8}$$

and the mean of its square

$$\overline{\epsilon^2} = \frac{\sum_r \omega_r \epsilon_r^2 e^{-\beta\epsilon_r}}{\sum \omega_r e^{-\beta\epsilon_r}} = \frac{Z''}{Z}. \tag{9}$$

Hence the mean fluctuation of energy

$$\overline{(\Delta\epsilon)^2} = \overline{(\epsilon-\bar{\epsilon})^2} = \overline{\epsilon^2}-(\bar{\epsilon})^2 = \frac{Z''}{Z}-\left(\frac{Z'}{Z}\right)^2$$

$$= \frac{ZZ''-Z'^2}{Z^2} = \frac{d}{d\beta}\left(\frac{Z'}{Z}\right),$$

or with (8)

$$\overline{(\Delta\epsilon)^2} = -\frac{du}{d\beta}. \tag{10}$$

If the mean energy is known as a function of temperature, hence of β, one obtains its fluctuation by differentiation. For example, for an ideal gas one has $u = c_v T = (c_v/k)\beta^{-1}$, hence $\overline{(\Delta\epsilon)^2} = c_v kT^2 = (k/c_v)u^2$. Another application, to the fluctuation of radiation, is made in section VIII, p. 79.

If one wishes to determine the fluctuations of a part of a body which cannot be decomposed into independent systems, these simple methods are not applicable.

Einstein has invented a most ingenious method which can be applied in such cases. It consists in reversing Boltzmann's equation

$$S = k\log P, \tag{11}$$

taking S as a known function of observable parameters, and determining the probability P from it,

$$P = e^{S/k}. \tag{12}$$

Assume the whole system is divided into N small, but still macroscopic parts and Δu_i is the fluctuation of energy in one of them; then one has for the entropy in this part

$$S_i = S_i^0+\left(\frac{\partial S}{\partial U}\right)_0 \Delta u_i+\frac{1}{2}\left(\frac{\partial^2 S}{\partial U^2}\right)_0 (\Delta u_i)^2+\dots.$$

If the whole system is adiabatically isolated one has

$$\sum_i \Delta u_i = 0.$$

By adding up all fluctuations one gets for the entropy

$$S = S_0-k\gamma \sum_i \xi_i^2+\dots, \tag{13}$$

where the abbreviations

$$k\gamma = -\frac{1}{2}\left(\frac{\partial^2 S}{\partial U^2}\right)_0, \qquad \xi_i = \Delta u_i \tag{14}$$

are used. According to the second law of thermodynamics one has for constant volume

$$dS = \frac{dU}{T}, \qquad \frac{\partial S}{\partial U} = \frac{1}{T},$$

hence

$$\gamma = -\frac{1}{2k}\left(\frac{\partial^2 S}{\partial U^2}\right)_0 = -\frac{1}{2k}\frac{\partial}{\partial U}\left(\frac{1}{T}\right) = -\frac{1}{2k}\frac{\frac{\partial}{\partial T}\left(\frac{1}{T}\right)}{\frac{\partial U}{\partial T}} = \frac{1}{2kT^2 c_v}, \tag{15}$$

where $c_v = dU/dT$ is the specific heat for constant volume.

Substituting (13) in (12) one obtains approximately

$$P = P_0 e^{-\gamma \sum_i \xi_i^2};$$

hence the mean square fluctuation of energy in one (macroscopic) cell is

$$\overline{(\Delta u_i)^2} = \overline{\xi_i^2} = \frac{\int_{-\infty}^{\infty} \xi_i^2 e^{-\gamma \xi_i^2}\, d\xi_i}{\int_{-\infty}^{\infty} e^{-\gamma \xi_i^2}\, d\xi_i} = -\frac{d}{d\gamma}\log \int_{-\infty}^{\infty} e^{-\gamma \xi_i^2}\, d\xi_i = \frac{1}{2\gamma},$$

or

$$\overline{(\Delta u_i)^2} = kT^2 c_v. \tag{16}$$

This result is formally identical with that for an ideal gas obtained above, yet holds also if c_v is any function of T.

In a similar way other fluctuations can be expressed in terms of macroscopic quantities.

We now turn to the theory of Brownian motion which is also due to Einstein. His original papers on this subject are collected in a small volume *Investigations on the Theory of the Brownian Movement*, by R. Fürth, translated by A. D. Cowper (Methuen & Co. Ltd., London, 1926) and make delightful reading. Here I give the main ideas of this theory in a slight modification formulated independently by Planck and Fokker.

Let $f(x, t)\, dx$ be the probability that the centre of a colloidal (visible) particle has an x-coordinate between x and $x+dt$ at time t. The particle may be subject to a constant force F and to the collisions of the surrounding molecules. The latter will produce a friction-like effect; if the particle is big compared with the molecules, its acceleration may be neglected and the velocity component in the x-direction assumed to be proportional to the force

$$\xi = BF, \tag{17}$$

where B is called the 'mobility'. Apart from this quasi-continuous action, the collisions will produce tiny irregular displacements which can be described by a statistical law, namely, by defining a function $\phi(x)$ which represents the probability for a particle to be displaced in the positive x-direction by x during a small but finite interval of time τ.

Then one obtains a kind of collision equation (which is simpler than Boltzmann's in the kinetic theory of gases, as no attempt is made to analyse the mechanism of collision in detail): The convective increase of $f(x,t)$ in the time-interval τ, $\tau\frac{df}{dt} = \tau\left(\frac{\partial f}{\partial t}+\frac{\partial f}{\partial x}\xi\right)$ is not zero but equal to the difference of the effect of the collisions which carry a particle from x_1 to x and those which remove the particle at x to any other place x_1:

$$\tau\left(\frac{\partial f}{\partial t}+\frac{\partial f}{\partial x}\xi\right) = \int\limits_{-\infty}^{\infty} \{f(x_1)\phi(x-x_1)-f(x)\phi(x_1-x)\}\, dx_1$$

$$= \int\limits_{-\infty}^{\infty} \{f(x-x')-f(x)\}\phi(x')\, dx'. \tag{18}$$

$\phi(x)$ may be normalized to unity and the mean of the displacement and of its square introduced by

$$\int\limits_{-\infty}^{\infty} \phi(x)\, dx = 1, \qquad \int\limits_{-\infty}^{\infty} x\phi(x)\, dx = \overline{\Delta x}, \qquad \int\limits_{-\infty}^{\infty} x^2\phi(x)\, dx = \overline{(\Delta x)^2}. \tag{19}$$

Further it may be supposed that the range of $\phi(x)$ is small; then one can expand $f(x-x')$ on the right-hand side of (18) and obtain a differential equation for $f(x,t)$ which, with (17) and (19), can be written

$$\frac{\partial f}{\partial t}+\left(BF-\frac{\overline{\Delta x}}{\tau}\right)\frac{\partial f}{\partial x}-\frac{1}{2}\frac{\overline{(\Delta x)^2}}{\tau}\frac{\partial^2 f}{\partial x^2} = 0. \tag{20}$$

Let us assume that the irregular action of the collisions is symmetric in x, $\phi(x) = \phi(-x)$; then $\overline{\Delta x} = 0$.

Consider first statistical equilibrium; then

$$BF\frac{\partial f}{\partial x}-\frac{1}{2\tau}\overline{(\Delta x)^2}\frac{\partial^2 f}{\partial x^2}=0. \tag{21}$$

Now the coordinate x of the colloidal particle can be included in the total set of coordinates of the whole system, if a term $-Fx$ is added to the Hamiltonian, so that the canonical law of distribution contains the factor $e^{\beta Fx}, \beta = 1/kT$. Hence the solution of (21) must have the form

$$f = f_0 e^{\beta Fx}, \tag{22}$$

so that

$$\frac{\partial^2 f}{\partial x^2} = \beta F\frac{\partial f}{\partial x}.$$

If this is substituted in (21), one finds

$$D = \frac{\overline{(\Delta x)^2}}{2\tau} = \frac{B}{\beta} = kTB. \tag{23}$$

We consider now the motion of the particles without an external field ($F = 0$), under the action of the collisions only. Then (20) reads

$$\frac{\partial f}{\partial t} = D\frac{\partial^2 f}{\partial x^2}. \tag{24}$$

This is the well-known equation of diffusion. Einstein's main result consists in the double formula (23) which connects the mean square displacement with the coefficient of diffusion D and with temperature and mobility.

If the particle is known to be at a given position, say $x = 0$, at $t = 0$, the probability of finding it at x after the time t is the following solution of (24):

$$f(x,t) = \frac{1}{\sqrt{(4\pi Dt)}}e^{-x^2/4Dt}; \tag{25}$$

the mean square of the coordinate, or the 'spread' of probability after the time t is found by a simple calculation:

$$\overline{\{\Delta x(t)\}^2} = \int_{-\infty}^{\infty} x^2 f(x,t)\,dx = 2Dt, \tag{26}$$

which for $t = \tau$ is equal to the mean square displacement $\overline{(\Delta x)^2}$ given by (23).

These formulae can be used in different ways to determine

Boltzmann's constant k, or Avogadro's number $N = R/k$ (where R is the gas constant per mole), i.e. the number of molecules per mole. A static method consists in observing the sedimentation under gravity of a colloid solution; then $F = -mg$, where m is the mass of the colloid particle, and the number of particles decreases with height according to the law (22), which now reads

$$n = n_0 e^{-(mg/kT)x}.$$

In order to apply this formula one has to determine the mass. For spherical particles $m = (4\pi/3)r^3\rho$, where ρ is the density and r the radius. The mobility of a sphere in a liquid of viscosity η has been calculated by Stokes from the hydrodynamical equations, with the result

$$B = \frac{1}{6\pi\eta r}; \tag{27}$$

hence it falls under gravity, $F = -mg = -(4\pi/3)r^3\rho g$, with the velocity (17)

$$\xi = -BF = \frac{2}{9}\frac{g\rho}{\eta}r^2.$$

As ξ can be measured, r can be found, if ρ and η are known, and finally m.

Another method is a dynamical one. One observes the displacements $\Delta x_1, \Delta x_2,...,$ of a single colloid particle in equal intervals τ of time and forms the mean square $\overline{(\Delta x)^2}$. Then using the same method as just described for determining the radius r, one finds B from (27) and then k from (23).

In this way the first reliable determinations of N have been made. Among those who have developed the theory M. v. Smoluchowski has played a distinguished part, while the first systematic measurements are due to J. Perrin.

A new and interesting approach to the theory of Brownian motion may be mentioned: J. G. Kirkwood, *J. Chem. Phys.* **14**, p. 180 (1946); **15**, p. 72 (1947).

21. (VI. p. 67.) Reduction of the multiple distribution function

The total Hamiltonian H_N of N particles can be split into two parts, the first being the Hamiltonian H_{N-1} of $N-1$ particles, the second the interaction of these with the last particle:

$$H_N = H_{N-1} + \frac{1}{2m}\mathbf{p}^{(N)2} + \Phi^{(N)} + \sum_{i=1}^{N}\Phi^{(iN)}, \tag{1}$$

where $\Phi^{(i)}$ is the external potential on the particle i and $\Phi^{(ij)}$ the mutual potential between two particles i and j.

Now we apply the operator χ_N to the equation for the total system

$$\frac{\partial f_N}{\partial t} = [H_N, f_N]. \tag{2}$$

From (6.40) we have, for $q = N-1$,

$$\chi_N f_N = f_{N-1}.$$

Hence

$$\chi_N \frac{\partial f_N}{\partial t} = \frac{\partial}{\partial t}(\chi_N f_N) = \frac{\partial f_{N-1}}{\partial t},$$

and

$$\chi_N[H_N, f_N] = \chi_N[H_{N-1}, f_N] + \chi_N[(1/2m)\mathbf{p}^{(N)2} + \Phi^{(N)}, f_N] + \\ + \chi_N\Big[\sum_{i=1}^{N} \Phi^{(iN)}, f_N\Big].$$

Here the first term on the right-hand side becomes

$$\chi_N[H_{N-1}, f_N] = [H_{N-1}, \chi_N f_N] = [H_{N-1}, f_{N-1}],$$

since H_{N-1} does not depend on the particle N to which the operator χ_N refers. Further,

$$\chi_N\Big[\frac{1}{2m}\mathbf{p}^{(N)2} + \Phi^{(N)}, f_N\Big] = \chi_N\Big(\frac{1}{m}\frac{\partial \Phi^{(N)}}{\partial \mathbf{x}^{(N)}} \cdot \frac{\partial f_N}{\partial \boldsymbol{\xi}^{(N)}} - \boldsymbol{\xi}^{(N)} \frac{\partial f_N}{\partial \mathbf{x}^{(N)}}\Big) = 0;$$

for if the integration χ_N is performed, the result refers to values of f_N at infinity of the $\mathbf{x}^{(N)}$ and $\boldsymbol{\xi}^{(N)}$ respectively, and these vanish as there is no probability for particles to be at an infinite distance or to have infinite velocities.

If all this is substituted in (2) one obtains

$$\frac{\partial f_{N-1}}{\partial t} = [H_{N-1}, f_{N-1}] + \sum_{i=1}^{N-1} \chi_N[\Phi^{(iN)}, f_N]. \tag{3}$$

Repeating the same process with $\chi_{N-1}, \chi_{N-2}, \ldots$ one obtains the chain of equations (6.44), (6.45) of the text.

22. (VI. p. 68.) Construction of the multiple distribution function

The fundamental multiplication theorem for non-independent events can be obtained in the following way.

Any event of a given set may have a certain property A or

not, $\bar{A}$. If B is another property we indicate by AB those events which have both the properties A and B.

Then all events can be split into four groups AB, $A\bar{B}$, $\bar{A}B$, $\bar{A}\bar{B}$, with the probabilities p_{AB}, $p_{A\bar{B}}$, $p_{\bar{A}B}$, $p_{\bar{A}\bar{B}}$.

The probability of A is

$$p_A = p_{AB}+p_{A\bar{B}}. \tag{1}$$

On the other hand, if A is known to occur, the cases $\bar{A}B$, $\bar{A}\bar{B}$ are excluded, hence the probability of B is

$$p_B(A) = \frac{p_{AB}}{p_{AB}+p_{A\bar{B}}} = \frac{p_{AB}}{p_A},$$

or

$$p_A\, p_B(A) = p_{AB}, \tag{2}$$

which is the multiplication rule; it reduces to the ordinary one for independent events if $p_B(A)$ does not depend on A and is equal to p_B.

This rule can be applied to a mechanical system of N particles in the following way.

Let A signify that q particles are in given elements of phase space; the probability of A can be written

$$p_A = f_q\, d\mathbf{x}^{(1)} d\boldsymbol{\xi}^{(1)} \dots d\mathbf{x}^{(q)} d\boldsymbol{\xi}^{(q)}. \tag{3}$$

Let B mean that the element $q+1$ is occupied. Then AB expresses that all $q+1$ elements are occupied, or

$$p_{AB} = f_{q+1}\, d\mathbf{x}^{(1)} d\boldsymbol{\xi}^{(1)} \dots d\mathbf{x}^{(q)} d\boldsymbol{\xi}^{(q)} d\mathbf{x}^{(q+1)} d\boldsymbol{\xi}^{(q+1)}. \tag{4}$$

Hence $p_B(A)$, the probability for the element $q+1$ being occupied, if q particles are in given elements, is

$$p_B(A) = \frac{p_{AB}}{p_A} = \frac{f_{q+1}}{f_q}\, d\mathbf{x}^{(q+1)} d\boldsymbol{\xi}^{(q+1)}. \tag{5}$$

If this is summed over all possible positions and velocities of the last particle $(q+1)$, the result is equal to the number of particles excluding the q fixed ones, $N-q$; hence, with the normalization described in the text, (6.42) and (6.43),

$$(N-q) f_q = \iint f_{q+1}\, d\mathbf{x}^{(q+1)} d\boldsymbol{\xi}^{(q+1)} = \chi_{q+1} f_{q+1}, \tag{6}$$

which is the formula (6.40) of the text.

In order to construct the equation (6.44) for the rate of change of f_q, one has to introduce a generalized distribution function which depends not only on the position $\mathbf{x}$ and the velocity $\boldsymbol{\xi}$

but also on the acceleration $\boldsymbol{\eta}$ of the particles; the probability for a set of q particles to be in the element

$$d\mathbf{x}^{(1)}d\boldsymbol{\xi}^{(1)}d\boldsymbol{\eta}^{(1)}\dots d\mathbf{x}^{(q)}d\boldsymbol{\xi}^{(q)}d\boldsymbol{\eta}^{(q)}$$

shall be denoted by

$$g_q(t, \mathbf{x}^{(1)}, \boldsymbol{\xi}^{(1)}, \boldsymbol{\eta}^{(1)}, \dots, \mathbf{x}^{(q)}, \boldsymbol{\xi}^{(q)}, \boldsymbol{\eta}^{(q)})\, d\mathbf{x}^{(1)}d\boldsymbol{\xi}^{(1)}d\boldsymbol{\eta}^{(1)}\dots d\mathbf{x}^{(q)}d\boldsymbol{\xi}^{(q)}d\boldsymbol{\eta}^{(q)}.$$

One has obviously

$$\int \overset{(q)}{\cdots} \int g_q\, d\boldsymbol{\eta}^{(1)}\dots d\boldsymbol{\eta}^{(q)} = f_q. \tag{7}$$

Now the motion of the molecules follows causal laws; hence the probability f_q of a configuration in $\mathbf{x}, \boldsymbol{\xi}$-space at a time t must be the same as that at the time $t+\delta t$ of that configuration which is obtained from the first by substituting $\mathbf{x}^{(i)}+\boldsymbol{\xi}^{(i)}\delta t$ and $\boldsymbol{\xi}^{(i)}+\boldsymbol{\eta}^{(i)}\delta t$ for $\mathbf{x}^{(i)}$ and $\boldsymbol{\xi}^{(i)}$.

Hence (7) leads to

$$\int \overset{(q)}{\cdots} \int g_q(t+\delta t, \mathbf{x}+\boldsymbol{\xi}\,\delta t, \boldsymbol{\xi}+\boldsymbol{\eta}\,\delta t, \eta)\, d\boldsymbol{\eta}^{(1)}\dots d\boldsymbol{\eta}^{(q)}$$
$$= \int \overset{(q)}{\cdots} \int g_q(t, \mathbf{x}, \boldsymbol{\xi}, \boldsymbol{\eta})\, d\boldsymbol{\eta}^{(1)}\dots d\boldsymbol{\eta}^{(q)},$$

or

$$\int \overset{(q)}{\cdots} \int \left\{\frac{\partial g_q}{\partial t} + \sum_{i=1}^{q} \left(\frac{\partial g_q}{\partial \mathbf{x}^{(i)}}\cdot\boldsymbol{\xi}^{(i)} + \frac{\partial g_q}{\partial \boldsymbol{\xi}^{(i)}}\cdot\boldsymbol{\eta}^{(i)}\right) d\boldsymbol{\eta}^{(1)}\dots\, d\boldsymbol{\eta}^{(q)} = 0. \tag{8}$$

The integration in the first two terms can be performed with the help of (7); that of the last leads to the integral

$$\int \overset{(q)}{\cdots} \int g_q \boldsymbol{\eta}^{(i)} d\boldsymbol{\eta}^{(1)}\dots d\boldsymbol{\eta}^{(q)} = f_q \overline{\boldsymbol{\eta}^{(i)}}, \tag{9}$$

where the symbol $\overline{\boldsymbol{\eta}^{(i)}}$ is evidently the mean acceleration.

Hence one obtains from (8)

$$\frac{\partial f_q}{\partial t} + \sum_{i=1}^{q} \left\{\frac{\partial f_q}{\partial \mathbf{x}^{(i)}}\cdot\boldsymbol{\xi}^{(i)} + \frac{\partial}{\partial \boldsymbol{\xi}^{(i)}}\cdot(f_q \overline{\boldsymbol{\eta}^{(i)}})\right\} = 0. \tag{10}$$

The final step consists in using the laws of mechanics for determining $\overline{\boldsymbol{\eta}^{(i)}}$. The equations of motion are (force $\mathbf{P}^{(r)}$)

$$\boldsymbol{\eta}^{(r)} = -\frac{1}{m}\left(\sum_{s=1}^{N} \frac{\partial \Phi^{(rs)}}{\partial \mathbf{x}^{(r)}} - \mathbf{P}^{(r)}\right). \tag{11}$$

Now the function f_q refers to the case where the positions and velocities of q particles are given, the others unknown. Hence one has to split the sum (11) into two parts, the first referring to the given particles, the second to the rest. For this rest the probability of finding a particle in a given element $q+1$ is known, namely $(f_{q+1}/f_q)\,d\mathbf{x}^{(q+1)}d\boldsymbol{\xi}^{(q+1)}$; hence the average of this sum can be determined by integrating over $d\mathbf{x}^{(q+1)}d\boldsymbol{\xi}^{(q+1)}$, i.e. by applying the operator χ_{q+1}. In this way the mean acceleration is found to be

$$\overline{\eta^{(i)}} = \frac{1}{m}\mathbf{P}^{(i)} - \frac{1}{m}\sum_{j=1}^{q}\frac{\partial\Phi^{(ij)}}{\partial\mathbf{x}^{(i)}} - \frac{1}{mf_q}\chi_{q+1}\left(\frac{\partial\Phi^{(i,q+1)}}{\partial\mathbf{x}^{(i)}}f_{q+1}\right). \quad (12)$$

Substituting this in (10), one obtains

$$\frac{\partial f_q}{\partial t} = \sum_{i=1}^{q}\left\{-\frac{\partial f_q}{\partial\mathbf{x}^{(i)}}\cdot\boldsymbol{\xi}^{(i)} + \frac{1}{m}\left(\sum_{j=1}^{q}\frac{\partial\Phi^{(ij)}}{\partial\mathbf{x}^{(i)}} - \mathbf{P}^{(i)}\right)\right\} +$$
$$+\frac{1}{m}\sum_{i=1}^{q}\chi_{q+1}\left(\frac{\partial\Phi^{(i,q+1)}}{\partial\mathbf{x}^{(i)}}\cdot\frac{\partial f_{q+1}}{\partial\boldsymbol{\xi}^{(i)}}\right), \quad (13)$$

which is easily confirmed to be identical with the formulae (6.44), (6.45) of the text.

23. (VI. p. 69.) Derivation of the collision integral from the general theory of fluids

From the standpoint of statistical theory a fluid differs from a solid by the absence of a long-range order, so that for two events A and B happening a long distance apart one has, with the notations of Appendix, **22**, $p_{AB} = p_A \cdot p_B$; for instance, for large $|\mathbf{x}^{(2)}-\mathbf{x}^{(1)}|$ one has $f_2(\mathbf{x}^{(1)},\mathbf{x}^{(2)}) = f_1(\mathbf{x}^{(1)})f_1(\mathbf{x}^{(2)})$, while in solids this is not the case.

The distinction between liquid and gas is not so sharp and may even be said to disappear above the critical state. However, if one is not specially concerned with these intermediate conditions there is a wide region where liquid and gas can be distinguished by the extreme difference of density. From the atomistic standpoint this has to be formulated thus:

The potential energy $\Phi(\mathbf{x}^{(i)},\mathbf{x}^{(j)})$ between two molecules at $\mathbf{x}^{(i)}$ and $\mathbf{x}^{(j)}$ decreases rapidly with the distance between their mass centres, and (except in the case of ions, where Coulomb forces act) a distance r_0, small by macroscopic standards, may be specified, beyond which the interaction may without error be assumed to vanish completely. In a liquid proper, there are many molecules within this distance r_0 of a given molecule; in a gas there are usually none, and the probability that there is more than one is very small, except near condensation. The neglect of this small probability is equivalent to the assumption of 'binary encounters' in gas-theory. Green has shown that when this assumption is made, on taking $q = 1$ in the equations (6.44) and (6.45) of the text,

$$\frac{\partial f_1}{\partial t} - [H_1, f_1] = S_1, \tag{1}$$

$$S_1 = \chi_2[\Phi^{(1,2)}, f_2], \tag{2}$$

one obtains Boltzmann's collision equations (6.46), (6.47).

To prove this we first work out the expression S_1 using the definition (6.5) of the Poisson bracket and of the operator χ, (6.39):

$$S_1 = \frac{1}{m} \int\int \frac{\partial \Phi^{(1,2)}}{\partial \mathbf{x}^{(1)}} \cdot \frac{\partial f_2}{\partial \boldsymbol{\xi}^{(2)}} \, d\mathbf{x}^{(2)} d\boldsymbol{\xi}^{(2)} \tag{3}$$

(see also **22**.13). With the assumption of binary encounters f_2 can be expressed in terms of f_1 by using the mechanical laws of collision.

Consider the motion of two molecules which at time t have positions $\mathbf{x}^{(1)}, \mathbf{x}^{(2)}$, such that $|\mathbf{x}^{(2)} - \mathbf{x}^{(1)}| < r_0$, and velocities $\boldsymbol{\xi}^{(1)}, \boldsymbol{\xi}^{(2)}$, while at time t_0 ($< t$), when the molecules were last at a distance r_0 from another, their positions and velocities were $\mathbf{x}_0^{(1)}, \mathbf{x}_0^{(2)}$ and $\boldsymbol{\xi}_0^{(1)}, \boldsymbol{\xi}_0^{(2)}$. The configurational probability

$$f_2(t, \mathbf{x}^{(1)}, \mathbf{x}^{(2)}, \boldsymbol{\xi}^{(1)}, \boldsymbol{\xi}^{(2)}) \, d\mathbf{x}^{(1)} d\mathbf{x}^{(2)} d\boldsymbol{\xi}^{(1)} d\boldsymbol{\xi}^{(2)}$$

must remain unchanged during the interval (t_0, t) as the motion follows a causal law; also, by Liouville's theorem, the volume in phase space $d\mathbf{x}^{(1)} d\mathbf{x}^{(2)} d\boldsymbol{\xi}^{(1)} d\boldsymbol{\xi}^{(2)}$ is unaltered. Since, as explained above, molecular events in fluids which occur beyond the range of interaction must be considered independent, one has

$$f_2(t, \mathbf{x}^{(1)}, \mathbf{x}^{(2)}, \boldsymbol{\xi}^{(1)}, \boldsymbol{\xi}^{(2)}) = f_1(t_0, \mathbf{x}_0^{(1)}, \boldsymbol{\xi}_0^{(1)}) f_1(t_0, \mathbf{x}_0^{(2)}, \boldsymbol{\xi}_0^{(2)}). \tag{4}$$

Next one introduces an approximate assumption which is always made in gas-theory, that $t_0, \mathbf{x}_0^{(1)}, \mathbf{x}_0^{(2)}$ may be replaced by $t, \mathbf{x}^{(1)}$ and $\mathbf{x}^{(2)}$ on the right-hand side of (4) (but of course not $\boldsymbol{\xi}_0^{(1)}, \boldsymbol{\xi}_0^{(2)}$, by $\boldsymbol{\xi}^{(1)}, \boldsymbol{\xi}^{(2)}$). As r_0 is very small the resulting error is of microscopic order; nevertheless it is not without importance, for it allows small deviations from Maxwell's velocity distribution law (and other 'fluctuations'), which would otherwise be unexplainable, as this law is a rigorous consequence of Boltzmann's collision equation in equilibrium conditions.

It remains to calculate $\boldsymbol{\xi}_0^{(1)}$ and $\boldsymbol{\xi}_0^{(2)}$ in terms of $\boldsymbol{\xi}^{(1)}, \boldsymbol{\xi}^{(2)}$ and

$\mathbf{r} = \mathbf{x}^{(2)} - \mathbf{x}^{(1)}$, which can be done by using the canonical equations of motion or their independent integrals (conservation of energy, momentum, and angular momentum). The resulting formulae are the same as used in Boltzmann's theory (see Appendix, **16**). The reduction of S_2 can be performed without making use of explicit expressions. One has only to remark that

$$f_2(t, \mathbf{x}^{(1)}, \mathbf{x}^{(2)}, \boldsymbol{\xi}^{(1)}, \boldsymbol{\xi}^{(2)})$$

now satisfies the equation

$$[H_2, f_2] = 0, \tag{5}$$

where
$$H_2 = \frac{m}{2}(\boldsymbol{\xi}^{(1)2} + \boldsymbol{\xi}^{(2)2}) + \Phi(\mathbf{r}) \tag{6}$$

is the Hamiltonian of the two particles which are considered to move independently of all the others. Now (5) becomes

$$m(\boldsymbol{\xi}^{(2)} - \boldsymbol{\xi}^{(1)}) \cdot \frac{\partial f_2}{\partial \mathbf{r}} = \frac{\partial \Phi}{\partial \mathbf{r}} \cdot \left(\frac{\partial f_2}{\partial \boldsymbol{\xi}^{(2)}} - \frac{\partial f_2}{\partial \boldsymbol{\xi}^{(1)}} \right). \tag{7}$$

We integrate this over $d\mathbf{x}^{(2)} d\boldsymbol{\xi}^{(2)}$; then the term with $\partial f_2/\partial \boldsymbol{\xi}^{(2)}$ on the right-hand side vanishes, because there are no particles with infinite velocities. The other term, with $\partial f_2/\partial \boldsymbol{\xi}^{(1)}$, becomes identical with mS_1, according to (3), since

$$\frac{\partial \Phi}{\partial \mathbf{r}} = -\frac{\partial \Phi}{\partial \mathbf{x}^{(1)}}.$$

Hence, with (4),

$$S_1 = \iint (\boldsymbol{\xi}^{(2)} - \boldsymbol{\xi}^{(1)}) \cdot \frac{\partial}{\partial \mathbf{r}} \{ f_1(\boldsymbol{\xi}_0^{(1)}) f_1(\boldsymbol{\xi}_0^{(2)}) \} \, d\mathbf{r} \, d\boldsymbol{\xi}^{(2)}, \tag{8}$$

where the domain of integration over $\mathbf{r}$ may be limited by the sphere of radius r_0 surrounding $\mathbf{x}^{(1)}$.

This integration can be performed by imagining the sphere to be partitioned by elementary tubes parallel to the relative velocity $\boldsymbol{\xi}^{(2)} - \boldsymbol{\xi}^{(1)}$; one may then integrate, first over a typical tube specified by the cross-section radius $\mathbf{b}$, perpendicular from the centre of the sphere to the tube (see Appendix, **16**), and then over all values of $\mathbf{b}$. At the beginning of the tube, where

$$(\boldsymbol{\xi}^{(2)} - \boldsymbol{\xi}^{(1)}) \cdot \mathbf{r} < 0,$$

the interaction between the molecules is negligible, and the functions giving $\boldsymbol{\xi}_0^{(1)}$ and $\boldsymbol{\xi}_0^{(2)}$ in terms of $\boldsymbol{\xi}^{(1)}, \boldsymbol{\xi}^{(2)}$, and $\mathbf{r}$ reduce to

$\boldsymbol{\xi}^{(1)}$ and $\boldsymbol{\xi}^{(2)}$. At the end of the tube the values $\boldsymbol{\xi}^{(1)'}$ and $\boldsymbol{\xi}^{(2)'}$ of these functions have to be calculated from the collision integrals, just as in Boltzmann's theory. Thus one obtains

$$S_1 = \iint |\boldsymbol{\xi}^{(2)}-\boldsymbol{\xi}^{(1)}|\{f_1(\boldsymbol{\xi}^{(1)'})f_1(\boldsymbol{\xi}^{(2)'})-f_1(\boldsymbol{\xi}^{(1)})f_1(\boldsymbol{\xi}^{(2)})\}\, d\mathbf{b}d\boldsymbol{\xi}^{(2)}, \quad (9)$$

which is identical with (6.47) of the text and the collision integral in (**16**.8).

This derivation is not more complicated than Boltzmann's original one and is preferable because it reveals clearly the assumptions made.

24. (VII. p. 72.) Irreversibility in fluids

A rigorous proof of the irreversibility in dense matter from the classical standpoint seems to be very difficult, or at least extremely tedious. Green has, however, suggested a derivation which, though not quite rigorous, is plausible enough and certainly based on reasonable approximations.

It has to be shown that the entropy S defined by (7.1) never decreases in time, so that

$$\frac{dS}{dt} = -\frac{k}{N!}\int \overset{(2N)}{\cdots} \int (1+\log f_N)\frac{\partial f_N}{\partial t}\, d\mathbf{x}^{(1)}d\boldsymbol{\xi}^{(1)}...d\mathbf{x}^{(N)}d\boldsymbol{\xi}^{(N)} \geqslant 0, \quad (1)$$

if f_N satisfies the equation

$$\frac{\partial f_N}{\partial t} = [H_N, f_N]+S_N(f_{N+1}), \quad (2)$$

which expresses that one particle of unknown position and velocity is added to a system of N particles.

If Φ is the total potential energy between the N particles and $\Phi^{(i,N+1)}$ that between the ith of these and the additional particle, one has

$$\frac{\partial f_N}{\partial t} = -\sum_{i=1}^{N} \frac{\partial f_N}{\partial \mathbf{x}^{(i)}}\cdot \boldsymbol{\xi}^{(i)} + \frac{1}{m}\sum_{i=1}^{N} \frac{\partial f_N}{\partial \boldsymbol{\xi}^{(i)}}\cdot\frac{\partial \Phi}{\partial \mathbf{x}^{(i)}} +$$

$$+\frac{1}{m}\iint \sum_{i=1}^{N} \frac{\partial f_{N+1}}{\partial \boldsymbol{\xi}^{(i)}}\cdot \frac{\partial \Phi^{(i,N+1)}}{\partial \mathbf{x}^{(i)}}\, d\mathbf{x}^{(N+1)}d\boldsymbol{\xi}^{(N+1)}. \quad (3)$$

If this is substituted in (1) the integrals of the first two terms vanish on transformation to surface integrals. In the last sum all terms contribute the same, as f_N and f_{N+1} can be assumed to be symmetric in regard to all particles. Hence

$$\frac{dS}{dt} = -\frac{kN}{mN!}\int^{(2N+2)}_{\cdots}\int (1+\log f_N)\times$$
$$\times \frac{\partial f_N}{\partial \boldsymbol{\xi}^{(1)}}\cdot\frac{\partial \Phi^{(1,N+1)}}{\partial \mathbf{x}^{(1)}}\,d\mathbf{x}^{(1)}d\boldsymbol{\xi}^{(1)}\ldots d\mathbf{x}^{(N+1)}d\boldsymbol{\xi}^{(N+1)}. \quad (4)$$

Now the reasoning follows very closely that of Appendix, **23**, where (**23**.3) was transformed into the integrable expression (**23**.8) with the help of the identity (**23**.7).

For this purpose one introduces instead of the velocities of the two particles (1) and $(N+1)$ appearing explicitly in (4) new variables, namely their total momentum $\mathbf{m}$, two components of the relative angular momentum $\mathbf{a}$, and the relative energy w,

$$\mathbf{m} = m(\boldsymbol{\xi}^{(1)}+\boldsymbol{\xi}^{(N+1)}), \quad \mathbf{a} = \tfrac{1}{2}m(\mathbf{x}^{(N+1)}-\mathbf{x}^{(1)})\wedge(\boldsymbol{\xi}^{(N+1)}-\boldsymbol{\xi}^{(1)}),$$
$$w = \tfrac{1}{4}m|\boldsymbol{\xi}^{(N+1)}-\boldsymbol{\xi}^{(1)}|^2+\Phi(|\mathbf{x}^{(N+1)}-\mathbf{x}^{(1)}|), \quad (5)$$

and regards f_{N+1} as a function of these, so that

$$f_{N+1} = \bar{f}_{N+1}(t, \mathbf{x}^{(1)},\ldots, \mathbf{x}^{(N+1)}, \boldsymbol{\xi}^{(2)},\ldots, \boldsymbol{\xi}^{(N)}, \mathbf{m}, \mathbf{a}, w).$$

Then by direct differentiation it can be verified that

$$\frac{1}{m}\left(\frac{\partial f_{N+1}}{\partial \boldsymbol{\xi}^{(1)}}-\frac{\partial f_{N+1}}{\partial \boldsymbol{\xi}^{(N+1)}}\right)\cdot\frac{\partial \Phi^{(1,N+1)}}{\partial \mathbf{x}^{(1)}} = (\boldsymbol{\xi}^{(N+1)}-\boldsymbol{\xi}^{(1)})\cdot\left(\frac{\partial f_{N+1}}{\partial \mathbf{x}^{(N+1)}}-\frac{\partial \bar{f}_{N+1}}{\partial \mathbf{x}^{(N+1)}}\right),$$

an equation similar to (**23**.7).

If $\dfrac{\partial f_{N+1}}{\partial \boldsymbol{\xi}^{(1)}}\cdot\dfrac{\partial \Phi^{(1,N+1)}}{\partial \mathbf{x}^{(1)}}$ is taken from it and substituted in (4), the only term which does not vanish is found to be

$$\frac{dS}{dt} = \frac{k}{(N-1)!}\int^{(2N+2)}_{\cdots}\int (1+\log f_N)\times$$
$$\times(\boldsymbol{\xi}^{(N+1)}-\boldsymbol{\xi}^{(1)})\cdot\frac{\partial \bar{f}_{N+1}}{\partial \mathbf{x}^{(N+1)}}\,d\mathbf{x}^{(1)}d\boldsymbol{\xi}^{(1)}\ldots d\mathbf{x}^{(N+1)}d\boldsymbol{\xi}^{(N+1)}. \quad (6)$$

$\mathbf{m}, \mathbf{a}, w$ are parameters specifying the trajectories which would be followed by the particles numbered (1) and $(N+1)$ if no other particles were present. Now one can apply the same reasoning as in Appendix, **23**, partitioning the $\mathbf{x}^{(N+1)}$-domain by tubes formed by the trajectories of $(N+1)$ relative to (1), where $\mathbf{m}, \mathbf{a}, w$ are constant, and one can perform the integration with respect to $\mathbf{x}^{(N+1)}$ first along such a tube, then over all values of the cross-section $\mathbf{b}$. At each end of the trajectory where the interaction $\Phi^{(1,N+1)}$ can be neglected, the function f_{N+1} would factorize into $f_1^{(N+1)} f_N$, provided no other particle were near to the particle $(N+1)$.

This is, of course, not the case; but it seems to be reasonable to assume that the factorization is at least approximately correct as the action of the rest will nearly cancel. This is the simplification made by Green. It is clear that it could be corrected by a more detailed consideration; but let us be content with it.

Since the sphere around $\mathbf{x}^{(1)}$ in which $\Phi^{(1,N+1)}$ is effectively different from zero is of microscopic dimensions, the values of $\mathbf{x}^{(N+1)}$ and $\mathbf{x}^{(1)}$ need not be distinguished, nor the instants when these points are reached. The initial velocities $\boldsymbol{\xi}^{(1)\prime}, \boldsymbol{\xi}^{(N+1)\prime}$ must, however, be determined from the actual final velocities from the 'conservation' law, i.e. the definitions (5) for constant $\mathbf{m}, \mathbf{a}, w$:

$$m(\boldsymbol{\xi}^{(1)\prime}+\boldsymbol{\xi}^{(N+1)\prime}) = m(\boldsymbol{\xi}^{(1)}+\boldsymbol{\xi}^{(N+1)}),$$

$$m(\mathbf{x}^{(1)}\wedge\boldsymbol{\xi}^{(1)\prime}+\mathbf{x}^{(N+1)}\wedge\boldsymbol{\xi}^{(N+1)\prime}) = m(\mathbf{x}^{(1)}\wedge\boldsymbol{\xi}^{(1)}+\mathbf{x}^{(N+1)}\wedge\boldsymbol{\xi}^{(N+1)}),$$

$$\tfrac{1}{2}m(\boldsymbol{\xi}^{(1)\prime 2}+\boldsymbol{\xi}^{(N+1)\prime 2}) = \tfrac{1}{2}m(\boldsymbol{\xi}^{(1)2}+\boldsymbol{\xi}^{(N+1)2}).$$

If the integration in (5) is performed as described, one obtains

$$\frac{dS}{dt}=\frac{kN}{N!}\int \overset{(2N+2)}{\cdots} \int (1+\log f_N)(f_N f_1^{(N+1)}-f'_N f_1^{(N+1)\prime})\times$$
$$\times |\boldsymbol{\xi}^{(N+1)}-\boldsymbol{\xi}^{(1)}|\, d\mathbf{b}d\mathbf{x}d\mathbf{x}^{(2)}...d\mathbf{x}^{(N)}d\boldsymbol{\xi}^{(1)}...d\boldsymbol{\xi}^{(N+1)}, \quad (7)$$

where instead of $\mathbf{x}^{(1)}$ the centre $\mathbf{x} = \frac{1}{2}(\mathbf{x}^{(1)}+\mathbf{x}^{(N+1)})$ is introduced. Here $f_1^{(N+1)}$ means $f_1(\mathbf{x}^{(N+1)}, \boldsymbol{\xi}^{(N+1)})$ which can be replaced, according to formula (6.40) of the text, by

$$\frac{1}{N-1}\iint f_2(\mathbf{x}^{(N+1)}, \mathbf{x}^{(N+2)}, \boldsymbol{\xi}^{(N+1)}, \boldsymbol{\xi}^{(N+2)})\, d\mathbf{x}^{(N+2)}d\boldsymbol{\xi}^{(N+2)}.$$

If this is introduced into (7) one has an integral over $2N+4$ variables, where the integrand contains the factor $f_N f_2 - f'_N f'_2$. By repeating the procedure one can transform (7) into the expression

$$\frac{dS}{dt}=\frac{k}{\{(N-1)!\}^2}\int \overset{(4N)}{\cdots} \int (1+\log f_N)(f_N F_N-f'_N F'_N)\times$$
$$\times |\boldsymbol{\xi}^{(N+1)}-\boldsymbol{\xi}^{(1)}|\, d\mathbf{b}d\mathbf{x}d\mathbf{x}^{(2)}...d\mathbf{x}^{(N)}d\mathbf{x}^{(N+2)}...d\mathbf{x}^{(2N)}d\boldsymbol{\xi}^{(1)}d\boldsymbol{\xi}^{(2)}...d\boldsymbol{\xi}^{(2N)},$$

where F_N is the function obtained by replacing the variables $\mathbf{x}^{(i)}$ and $\boldsymbol{\xi}^{(i)}$ in f_N by $\mathbf{x}^{(i+N)}$ and $\boldsymbol{\xi}^{(i+N)}$ respectively.

Now one can apply the same transformations as for gases, as explained in Appendix, **17**, which lead from (**17**.3) to (**17**.4), exchanging the dashed and undashed variables, and exchanging the two groups $(1, 2, \ldots, N)$ and $(1+N, 2+N, \ldots, 2N)$. As it is obvious that the integral is invariant for these changes, one obtains

$$\frac{dS}{dt} = \frac{k}{\{2(N-1)!\}^2} \int \overset{(4N)}{\cdots} \int \log\left\{\frac{f_N F_N}{f'_N F'_N}\right\}(f_N F_N - f'_N F'_N) \times$$
$$\times |\boldsymbol{\xi}^{(N+1)} - \boldsymbol{\xi}^{(1)}|\, d\mathbf{b} d\mathbf{x} d\mathbf{x}^{(2)} \ldots d\mathbf{x}^{(N)} d\mathbf{x}^{(N+2)} \ldots d\mathbf{x}^{(2N)} d\boldsymbol{\xi}^{(1)} \ldots d\boldsymbol{\xi}^{(2N)}, \quad (8)$$

which makes it clear that dS/dt is positive or zero, and that the latter happens only if

$$f_N F_N = f'_N F'_N. \quad (9)$$

The solution of this equation leads again essentially to the canonical distribution. I shall, however, not reproduce the derivation but refer the reader to the original papers:

M. Born and H. S. Green, *Nature*, **159,** pp. 251, 738 (1947).
—— —— *Proc. Roy. Soc.* A, **188,** p. 10 (1946); **190,** p. 455 (1947); **191,** p. 168 (1947); **192,** p. 166 (1948).
H. S. Green, ibid. **189,** p. 103 (1947); **194,** p. 244 (1948).

The reader may compare this involved and, in spite of the complication, not quite rigorous derivation from classical theory with the simple and straightforward proof from quantum theory given in section IX.

I wish to add an argument, also due to Green, which shows that once the increase of entropy is secured the distribution approaches the canonical one. The latter is given by

$$f_N^0 = e^{\alpha-\beta E}, \qquad \alpha = \frac{A}{kT}, \qquad \beta = \frac{1}{kT}. \quad (10)$$

A is the free energy and E the energy, given by

$$E = \tfrac{1}{2}m \sum_{i=1}^{N} (\boldsymbol{\xi}^{(i)} - \mathbf{u}^{(i)})^2 + \tfrac{1}{2} \sum_{i=1}^{N} \Phi^{(i)}, \quad (11)$$

$\mathbf{u}^{(i)}$ being the macroscopic velocity at the point $\mathbf{x}^{(i)}$.

Let the actual distribution be

$$f_N = f_N^0 + f'_N; \quad (12)$$

one has

$$\iint f_N\, d\mathbf{x}d\boldsymbol{\xi} = N!, \qquad \iint f_N\, E\, d\mathbf{x}d\boldsymbol{\xi} = N!\, U,$$

where U is the internal energy, and the same holds, of course, for f_N^0, so that

$$\iint f'_N\, d\mathbf{x}d\boldsymbol{\xi} = 0, \qquad \iint f'_N\, E\, d\mathbf{x}d\boldsymbol{\xi} = 0. \tag{13}$$

Then

$$f_N \log f_N = (f_N^0+f'_N)\log\left\{f_N^0\left(1+\frac{f'_N}{f_N^0}\right)\right\}$$

$$= f_N^0 \log f_N^0 + f'_N(\log f_N^0+1) + \frac{f_N'^2}{2f_N^0} + \dots. \tag{14}$$

Hence

$$S = -\frac{k}{N!}\iint \left\{f_N^0 \log f_N^0 + f'_N(\alpha-\beta E+1) + \frac{f_N'^2}{2f_N^0} + \dots\right\} d\mathbf{x}d\boldsymbol{\xi}.$$

Here the terms linear in f'_N vanish in virtue of (13), and one obtains

$$S = S^0 - \frac{k}{2N!}\iint \frac{f_N'^2}{f_N^0}\, d\mathbf{x}d\boldsymbol{\xi} + \dots. \tag{15}$$

This shows that an increase in the value of S requires a decrease in the average value of $|f'_N|$ and therefore an approach to the canonical distribution.

25. (VIII. p. 75.) Atomic physics

It seems impossible to supplement this and the following sections, which deal with atomic physics in general, by appendixes in the same way as before. The reader must consult the literature; he will find a condensed account of these things in my own book *Atomic Physics* (Blackie & Son, Glasgow; 4th edition 1948), which is constructed in a similar way to the present lectures; the text uses very little mathematics, while a series of appendixes contain short and rigorous proofs of the theorems used. For instance, Einstein's law of the equivalence of mass and energy is dealt with in Chapter III, § 2, p. 52, and a short derivation of the formula $\epsilon = mc^2$ given in *A. Ph.* Appendix VII, p. 288. Whenever in the following sections I wish to direct the reader to a section or appendix of my other book, an abbreviation like (*A. Ph.* Ch. III. 2, p. 52; A. VII, p. 288) is used.

26. (VIII. p. 77.) **The law of equipartition**

If the Hamiltonian has the form (8.5), or

$$H = \epsilon + H', \qquad \epsilon = \frac{a}{2}\xi^2, \tag{1}$$

where H' does not depend on ξ, one has for the average of ϵ in a canonical assembly

$$\bar{\epsilon} = \frac{\int \epsilon e^{-\beta H} dpdq}{\int e^{-\beta H} dpdq} = \frac{\int \epsilon e^{-\beta\epsilon} d\xi}{\int e^{-\beta\epsilon} d\xi}, \qquad \beta = \frac{1}{kT},$$

as all other integrations in numerator and denominator cancel. Now this can be written

$$\bar{\epsilon} = -\frac{d}{d\beta}\log Z, \qquad Z = \int_{-\infty}^{\infty} e^{-\beta\epsilon}\, d\xi. \tag{2}$$

If the integration variable $\eta = \sqrt{(\beta a/2)}\xi$ is introduced one gets

$$Z = \beta^{-\frac{1}{2}} A,$$

where A is a constant. Hence $\log Z = \text{const.} - \frac{1}{2}\log\beta$ and

$$\bar{\epsilon} = \frac{1}{2\beta} = \tfrac{1}{2}kT, \tag{3}$$

in agreement with (8.6).

27. (VIII. p. 91.) **Operator calculus in quantum mechanics**

The failure of matrix mechanics to deal with aperiodic motions, continuous spectra, was less a matter of conception than of practical methods. An indication of using integral operators instead of matrices is contained in a paper by M. Born, W. Heisenberg, and P. Jordan, *Z. f. Phys.* **35**, 557 (1926), which follows immediately after Heisenberg's first publication. The idea that physical quantities correspond to linear operators in general acting on functions was suggested by M. Born and N. Wiener, *Journ. Math. and Phys.* **5**, 84 (1926) and *Z. f. Phys.* **36**, 174 (1926), where in particular operators of the form

$$q\ldots = \lim_{T\to\infty} \frac{1}{2T} \int_{-T}^{T} q(t,s)\ldots\, ds$$

were used. Here the kernel $q(t,s)$ is a 'continuous matrix', also introduced by Dirac. This paper contains also the representation of special quantities by differential operators (with respect to time) which satisfy identically the commutation law between energy and time $Et-tE = i\hbar$.

Schrödinger's discovery, which was made quite independently, consists in using a representation where the coordinates are multiplication operators and the momenta differential operators, so that the commutation laws

$$q_\alpha p_\beta - p_\beta q_\alpha = i\hbar\delta_{\alpha\beta}$$

are identically satisfied. This opened the way to finding the relation between matrix mechanics and wave mechanics and to the later development of the general transformation theory of quantum mechanics which is brilliantly represented in Dirac's famous book.

The early development of quantum mechanics as represented in text-books has become rather legendary. To mention a few instances: the matrices and the commutation law $[q,p] = 1$ which are traditionally called Heisenberg's, are not explicitly contained in his first publication: W. Heisenberg, *Z. f. Phys.* **33**, 879 (1925); his formulae correspond only to the diagonal terms of the commutator. The complete formulae in matrix notation are in the paper by M. Born and P. Jordan, *Z. f. Phys.* **34**, 858 (1925). Further, the perturbation theory of quantum mechanics, traditionally called Schrödinger's, is contained already in the next publication of Heisenberg, Jordan, and myself (quoted at the beginning), not only for matrices, but also for vectors on which these matrices operate, and not only for simple eigenvalues, but also degenerate systems. The only difference of Schrödinger's derivation is that he starts from a representation with continuous wave functions which he abandons at once in favour of a discontinuous one (by a Fourier transformation).

28. (IX. p. 94.) **General formulation of the uncertainty principle**

The derivation of the most general form of the uncertainty principle can be found in my book (*A. Ph.* A. XXII, p. 326). As it is fundamental for the reasoning in these lectures, I shall give it here in a little more abstract form.

We assume that for a complex operator $C = A+iB$ and its conjugate $C^* = A-iB$ the mean value of the product CC^* is real and not negative:

$$\overline{CC^*} \geqslant 0, \tag{1}$$

where the bar indicates any form of linear averaging, as described in the text. Then writing λB instead of B, where λ is a real parameter, one has

$$\overline{(A+i\lambda B)(A-i\lambda B)} = \overline{A^2}+\overline{B^2}\lambda^2-\hbar\overline{[A,B]}\lambda \geqslant 0, \tag{2}$$

where the abbreviation (9.4)

$$[A,B] = \frac{i}{\hbar}(AB-BA) \tag{3}$$

is used. As the left-hand side of (2) is real and also the first two terms on the right, it follows that $\overline{[A,B]}$ is real. The minimum of the quadratic expression in λ, given by (2), occurs when

$$\lambda = \frac{\hbar}{2}\frac{\overline{[A,B]}}{\overline{B^2}},$$

and it is equal to $$\overline{A^2}-\frac{\hbar^2}{4}\frac{\overline{[A,B]}^2}{\overline{B^2}} \geqslant 0.$$

Hence $$\overline{A^2}.\overline{B^2} \geqslant \frac{\hbar^2}{4}\overline{[A,B]}^2. \tag{4}$$

Now replace A by $A-\bar{A}$ and B by $B-\bar{B}$. As $\bar{A}$, $\bar{B}$ are numbers and commute with A and B, the commutator $[A,B]$ remains unchanged. Putting, as in (9.2),

$$\delta A = \{\overline{(A-\bar{A})^2}\}^{\frac{1}{2}}, \qquad \delta B = \{\overline{(B-\bar{B})^2}\}^{\frac{1}{2}},$$

one obtains from (4) the formula (9.3) of the text,

$$\delta A\,.\,\delta B \geqslant \frac{\hbar}{2}|\overline{[A,B]}|, \tag{5}$$

and as $[q,p] = 1$, especially (9.5),

$$\delta p\,.\,\delta q \geqslant \frac{\hbar}{2}. \tag{6}$$

This derivation reveals the simple algebraic root of the uncertainty relation. But it is not superfluous at all to study the meaning of this relation for special cases; simple examples can be found in *A. Ph.* A. XII, p. 296, A. XXXII, p. 357, and in many other books, for instance, Heisenberg, *The Physical Principles of the Quantum Theory*.

29. (IX. p. 97.) Dirac's derivation of the Poisson brackets in quantum mechanics

It is fashionable to-day to represent quantum mechanics in an axiomatic way without explaining why just these axioms have been chosen, justifying them only by the success. I think that no real understanding of the theory can be obtained in this way. One must follow to some degree the historical development and learn how things have actually happened. Now the decisive fact was the conviction held by theoretical physicists that many features of Hamiltonian mechanics must be right, in spite of the fundamentally different aspect of quantum theory. This conviction was based on the surprising successes of Bohr's principle of correspondence. In fact, the solution of the problem consisted in preserving the formalism of Hamiltonian mechanics as a whole with the only modification that the physical quantities are to be represented by non-commuting quantities.

If this is accepted, there is a most elegant consideration of Dirac which leads in the shortest way to the rule for translating formulae of classical mechanics into quantum mechanics. It starts from the fact that classical mechanics can be condensed into the equation

$$\frac{\partial f}{\partial t} - [H, f] = 0, \tag{1}$$

which any function $f(t, q, p)$ representing a quantity carried by the motion must satisfy. Here the Poisson bracket is used

$$[\xi, \eta] = \sum_r \left(\frac{\partial \xi}{\partial q_r} \frac{\partial \eta}{\partial p_r} - \frac{\partial \xi}{\partial p_r} \frac{\partial \eta}{\partial q_r} \right). \tag{2}$$

If (1) is to be generalized for non-commuting quantities, it is necessary to consider how the Poisson bracket should be translated into the new language.

Dirac uses the fact that these brackets have a series of formal properties, namely

$$[\xi, \eta] = -[\eta, \xi], \qquad [\xi, c] = 0, \tag{3}$$

where c is a constant; further

$$\begin{aligned}[\xi_1+\xi_2, \eta] &= [\xi_1, \eta]+[\xi_2, \eta], \\ [\xi, \eta_1+\eta_2] &= [\xi, \eta_1]+[\xi, \eta_2],\end{aligned} \tag{4}$$

and finally

$$\begin{aligned}[\xi_1 \xi_2, \eta] &= [\xi_1, \eta]\xi_2+\xi_1[\xi_2, \eta], \\ [\xi, \eta_1 \eta_2] &= [\xi_1, \eta_1]\eta_2+\eta_1[\xi_1, \eta_2].\end{aligned} \tag{5}$$

Here the factors are written in a definite order, though in classical mechanics this does not matter. We have to do so if we want to use these expressions for non-commuting quantities, and the rule followed is simply to leave the order of factors unchanged.

The question is, What do the brackets mean in this case? To see this, we form the bracket $[\xi_1 \xi_2, \eta_1 \eta_2]$ in two ways, using the two formulae (5) first in one order, then in the opposite one. Then

$$\begin{aligned}[\xi_1 \xi_2, \eta_1 \eta_2] &= [\xi_1, \eta_1 \eta_2]\xi_2+\xi_1[\xi_2, \eta_1 \eta_2] \\ &= \{[\xi_1, \eta_1]\eta_2+\eta_1[\xi_1, \eta_2]\}\xi_2+\xi_1\{[\xi_2, \eta_1]\eta_2+\eta_1[\xi_2, \eta_2]\} \\ &= [\xi_1, \eta_1]\eta_2 \xi_2+\eta_1[\xi_1, \eta_2]\xi_2+\xi_1[\xi_2, \eta_1]\eta_2+\xi_1 \eta_1[\xi_2, \eta_2]\end{aligned}$$

and in the same way

$$\begin{aligned}[\xi_1 \xi_2, \eta_1 \eta_2] &= [\xi_1 \xi_2, \eta_1]\eta_2+\eta_1[\xi_1 \xi_2, \eta_2] \\ &= [\xi_1, \eta_1]\xi_2 \eta_2+\xi_1[\xi_2, \eta_1]\eta_2+\eta_1[\xi_1, \eta_2]\xi_2+\eta_1 \xi_1[\xi_2, \eta_2].\end{aligned}$$

Equating these two expressions one obtains

$$[\xi_1, \eta_1](\xi_2 \eta_2-\eta_2 \xi_2) = (\xi_1 \eta_1-\eta_1 \xi_1)[\xi_2, \eta_2]. \tag{6}$$

As $[\xi_1, \eta_1]$ must be independent of ξ_2, η_2 and vice versa, it follows that

$$\begin{aligned}\xi_1 \eta_1-\eta_1 \xi_1 &= \lambda[\xi_1, \eta_1], \\ \xi_2 \eta_2-\eta_2 \xi_2 &= \lambda[\xi_2, \eta_2],\end{aligned} \tag{7}$$

where λ is independent of all four quantities and commutes with $\xi_1 \eta_1-\eta_1 \xi_1$ and $\xi_2 \eta_2-\eta_2 \xi_2$. Hence λ is a number. That it must be purely imaginary, $\lambda = i\hbar$, cannot be derived in such a formal way; but it follows from considerations like those used in the previous appendix, where it is shown that a reasonable definition of averages implies (**28**.3) that

$$[\xi, \eta] = -\frac{i}{\hbar}(\xi\eta-\eta\xi) \tag{8}$$

is real. Thus it is established that the Poisson brackets in quantum theory correspond to properly normalized commutators.

If one inserts in the classical expression (2) for ξ and η a coordinate or a momentum, one finds

$$[q_r, q_s] = 0, \qquad [p_r, p_s] = 0, \qquad [q_r, p_s] = \delta_{rs}, \tag{9}$$

where $\delta_{rr} = 1$, $\delta_{rs} = 0$ for $r \neq s$.

The same relations (9) must be postulated to hold in quantum mechanics. In this way the fundamental commutation laws are obtained.

30. (IX. p. 100.) Perturbation theory for the density matrix

We consider the problem of solving the equation

$$\frac{\partial \rho}{\partial t} = [H, \rho], \qquad H = H_0 + V, \tag{1}$$

where the perturbation function V is small.

The method is essentially the same as that used for the corresponding problem in matrix or wave mechanics.

Assume that λ represents the eigenvalues of a complete set of integrals Λ of H_0, so that $[H_0, \Lambda] = 0$ and H_0 becomes diagonal in the λ-representation; put

$$H_0(\lambda, \lambda) = E, H_0(\lambda', \lambda') = E', \text{while } H_0(\lambda, \lambda') = 0 \text{ for } \lambda \neq \lambda'. \tag{2}$$

Introduce instead of ρ and V the functions σ and U given by

$$\begin{aligned} \rho(\lambda, \lambda') &= \sigma(\lambda, \lambda') e^{(i/\hbar)(E-E')t}, \\ V(\lambda, \lambda') &= U(\lambda, \lambda') e^{(i/\hbar)(E-E')t}. \end{aligned} \tag{3}$$

Then one has

$$\frac{\hbar}{i} \frac{\partial \rho(\lambda, \lambda')}{\partial t} = \left\{ \frac{\hbar}{i} \frac{\partial \sigma(\lambda, \lambda')}{\partial t} + (E - E')\sigma(\lambda, \lambda') \right\} e^{(i/\hbar)(E-E')t},$$

$$(H_0 \rho - \rho H_0)(\lambda, \lambda') = (E - E')\sigma(\lambda, \lambda') e^{(i/\hbar)(E-E')t}.$$

Hence the equation (1) reduces to

$$\begin{aligned} \frac{\hbar}{i} \frac{\partial \sigma(\lambda, \lambda')}{\partial t} &= (U\sigma - \sigma U)(\lambda, \lambda') \\ &= \sum_{\lambda''} \{U(\lambda, \lambda'')\sigma(\lambda'', \lambda') - \sigma(\lambda, \lambda'')U(\lambda'', \lambda')\}. \end{aligned} \tag{4}$$

Now assume that σ is expanded in a series

$$\sigma = \sigma_0 + \sigma_1 + \sigma_2 + \dots, \tag{5}$$

where σ_0 is diagonal and independent of the time and $\sigma_1, \sigma_2,...$ of order $1, 2,...$ in the perturbation. Then one obtains

$$\frac{\partial \sigma_1(\lambda, \lambda')}{\partial t} = \frac{i}{\hbar} U(\lambda, \lambda')\{\sigma_0(\lambda') - \sigma_0(\lambda)\},$$

hence
$$\sigma_1(\lambda, \lambda') = u(\lambda, \lambda')\{\sigma_0(\lambda') - \sigma_0(\lambda)\}, \tag{6}$$

where

$$u(\lambda, \lambda') = \frac{i}{\hbar} \int_0^t U(\lambda, \lambda')\, dt = \frac{i}{\hbar} \int_0^t V(\lambda, \lambda') e^{-(i/\hbar)(E-E')t}\, dt. \tag{7}$$

It follows for the diagonal elements from (6) that

$$\sigma_1(\lambda, \lambda) = 0. \tag{8}$$

The next approximation σ_2 has to satisfy the equation

$$\begin{aligned}
\frac{\partial \sigma_2(\lambda, \lambda')}{\partial t} &= \frac{i}{\hbar} \sum_{\lambda''} \{U(\lambda, \lambda'')\sigma_1(\lambda'', \lambda') - \sigma_1(\lambda, \lambda'')U(\lambda'', \lambda')\} \\
&= \frac{i}{\hbar} \sum_{\lambda''} [U(\lambda, \lambda'')u(\lambda'', \lambda')\{\sigma_0(\lambda'') - \sigma_0(\lambda')\} - \\
&\qquad - u(\lambda, \lambda'')U(\lambda'', \lambda')\{\sigma_0(\lambda) - \sigma_0(\lambda'')\}] \\
&= \sum_{\lambda''} \Big[\frac{\partial u(\lambda, \lambda'')}{\partial t} u(\lambda'', \lambda')\{\sigma_0(\lambda'') - \sigma_0(\lambda')\} - \\
&\qquad - u(\lambda, \lambda'')\frac{\partial u(\lambda'', \lambda')}{\partial t}\{\sigma_0(\lambda) - \sigma_0(\lambda'')\}\Big].
\end{aligned}$$

We need only the diagonal elements; for these one has

$$\begin{aligned}
\frac{\partial \sigma_2(\lambda, \lambda)}{\partial t} &= \sum_{\lambda''} \left\{\frac{\partial u(\lambda, \lambda'')}{\partial t} u(\lambda'', \lambda) + u(\lambda, \lambda'')\frac{\partial u(\lambda'', \lambda)}{\partial t}\right\}\{\sigma_0(\lambda'') - \sigma_0(\lambda)\} \\
&= \frac{\partial}{\partial t} \sum_{\lambda'} u(\lambda, \lambda')u(\lambda', \lambda)\{\sigma_0(\lambda') - \sigma_0(\lambda)\},
\end{aligned}$$

which gives by integration

$$\sigma_2(\lambda, \lambda) = \sum_{\lambda'} |u(\lambda, \lambda')|^2\{\sigma_0(\lambda') - \sigma_0(\lambda)\}, \tag{9}$$

since, according to (7), $u(\lambda, \lambda')$ is hermitian, $u(\lambda, \lambda') = u^*(\lambda', \lambda)$, and vanishes for $t = 0$.

It is seen from (3) that the diagonal elements of ρ and σ are identical; they represent the probability $P(t, \lambda)$ of finding the system at time t in the state λ. Now (5), (8), and (9) give, in agreement with (9.25) of the text,

$$P(t,\lambda) = P(\lambda)+\sum_{\lambda'} J(\lambda,\lambda')\{P(\lambda')-P(\lambda)\}+..., \tag{10}$$

where

$$J(\lambda,\lambda') = |u(\lambda,\lambda')|^2 = \frac{1}{\hbar^2}\left|\int_0^t V(\lambda,\lambda')e^{-(i/\hbar)(E-E')t}\,dt\right|^2. \tag{11}$$

When $V(\lambda,\lambda')$ is independent of the time one can perform the integration, with the result

$$J(\lambda,\lambda') = \frac{1}{\hbar^2}|V(\lambda,\lambda')|^2\left|\frac{1-e^{-(i/\hbar)(E-E')t}}{(i/\hbar)(E-E')}\right|^2. \tag{12}$$

Now the function $\frac{1}{2\pi}\left|\frac{1-e^{i\gamma t}}{i\gamma}\right| = \frac{\sin\frac{1}{2}\gamma t}{\pi\gamma}$ behaves for large t like a Dirac δ-function, i.e. one has

$$\frac{1}{2\pi}\int_{\Delta\gamma}\left|\frac{1-e^{i\gamma t}}{i\gamma}\right|^2 f(\gamma)\,d\gamma \to f(0)t,$$

if the interval of integration $\Delta\gamma$ includes $\gamma = 0$ and if $t\Delta\gamma \gg 1$.

Suppose that the energy values are distributed so closely that they are forming a practically continuous spectrum. Then one can split the index λ into (λ, E) and replace the simple summation in (10) by a summation over λ and an integration over E; the latter can be performed on the coefficients $J(\lambda, E;\lambda', E')$ with the result that the formula (10) is unchanged, if the coefficients are given by

$$J(\lambda,\lambda') = \frac{2\pi t}{\hbar}|V(\lambda,\lambda')|^2\delta(E-E'), \tag{13}$$

which combines the equations (9.27) and (9.28) of the text.

As mentioned in the text, Green has found a formula which allows one to calculate the higher approximations in a very simple way. This formula is so elegant and useful that I shall give it here, though without proof (which can be found in the Appendix I, p. 178, of the paper by M. Born and H. S. Green, *Proc. Roy. Soc.* A, **192**, 166, 1948). Starting from the equation (7) or

$$\dot{u} = \frac{i}{\hbar}U, \tag{14}$$

where U is known for a given perturbation V by (3), one forms the successive commutators

$$\dot{u}_{22} = \dot{u}u - u\dot{u}, \qquad \dot{u}_{23} = \dot{u}_{22}u - u\dot{u}_{22}, \ldots, \tag{15}$$

and from them the expansion

$$\dot{u}_2 = \frac{1\dot{u}_{22}}{2!} + \frac{2\dot{u}_{23}}{3!} + \frac{3\dot{u}_{24}}{4!} + \ldots. \tag{16}$$

If the initial condition $u_2 = 0$ for $t = 0$ is added, u_2 can be determined by integrating this series term by term.

Then one forms

$$\dot{u}_{34} = \dot{u}_2 u_2 - u_2 \dot{u}_2, \qquad \dot{u}_{36} = \dot{u}_{34} u_2 - u_2 \dot{u}_{34}, \qquad \ldots, \tag{17}$$

and the expansion

$$\dot{u}_3 = \frac{1\dot{u}_{34}}{2!} + \frac{2\dot{u}_{36}}{3!} + \frac{3\dot{u}_{38}}{4!} + \ldots, \tag{18}$$

from which one can determine u_3 so that $u_3 = 0$ for $t = 0$.

The second suffix l in u_{kl} has been chosen to indicate the power of V which is involved in the expression; one has $u_k = O(V^{2^{k-1}})$ and this decreases rapidly with k when V or t are small. This rule makes it possible to construct $u_4, u_5, \ldots,$ in a similar manner. Then one has the solution of (4)

$$\sigma = e^{u}e^{u_2}e^{u_3}\ldots\rho_0\ldots e^{-u_3}e^{-u_2}e^{-u} \tag{19}$$

from which ρ is obtained by (3).

The explicit expressions for the expansion (5) of σ are

$$\begin{aligned} \sigma_1 &= u\rho_0 - \rho_0 u, \\ \sigma_2 &= \tfrac{1}{2}(u^2\rho_0 - 2u\rho_0 u + \rho_0 u^2) + \tfrac{1}{2}(u_{22}\rho_0 - \rho_0 u_{22}), \\ \sigma_3 &= \tfrac{1}{6}(u^3\rho_0 - 3u^2\rho_0 u + 3u\rho_0 u^2 - \rho_0 u^3) + \\ &\quad + \tfrac{1}{2}\{u(u_{22}\rho_0 - \rho_0 u_{22}) - (u_{22}\rho_0 - \rho_0 u_{22})u\} + \tfrac{1}{3}(u_{23}\rho_0 - \rho_0 u_{23}), \ldots . \end{aligned} \tag{20}$$

These formulae will be useful for many purposes in quantum theory. Concerning thermodynamics, the third-order terms will have a direct application to the theory of fluctuations and Brownian motion. The customary theory derives these phenomena from considerations about the probability of distributions in an assembly which differs from the most probable one. The theory described here deals with one single system with the methods of quantum mechanics (which allows anyhow only statistical predictions); deviations from the average will then depend on higher approximations. It can be hoped that this idea leads to a new approach to the theory of fluctuations in quantum mechanics.

31. (IX. p. 112.) The functional equation of quantum statistics

The equation (9.37),

$$P(E^{(1)}+E^{(2)}) = P_1(\lambda^{(1)})P_2(\lambda^{(2)}),$$

where $\lambda^{(1)}$ depends on $E^{(1)}$, but not on $E^{(2)}$, and $\lambda^{(2)}$ vice versa, is obviously of the form

$$f(x+y) = \phi(x)\phi(y)$$

treated in Appendix, **13,** and has as solution general exponential functions; hence the distribution for all three systems is canonical.

32. (IX. p. 113.) Degeneration of gases

The theory of gas degeneration is treated in my book *Atomic Physics*, but in a way which appears not to conform with the general principles of quantum statistics as explained in these lectures. According to these one always has in statistical equilibrium canonical distribution, $P = e^{\alpha-\beta E}$, while the presentation in *A. Ph.* gives the impression that, by means of a modified method of statistical enumeration, a different result is obtained. This impression is only due to the terms used, which were those of the earlier authors (Bose, Einstein, Fermi, Sommerfeld), while in fact there is perfect agreement between the general theory and the application to gases. A simple and clear exposition of this subject is found in the little book by E. Schrödinger, *Statistical Thermodynamics* (Cambridge University Press, 1946). I shall give here a short outline of the theory.

In classical theory an ideal gas is regarded as a system of independent particles. In quantum theory this is not permitted, because the particles are indistinguishable. If $\psi_1(\mathbf{x}^{(1)})$ and $\psi_2(\mathbf{x}^{(2)})$, or shortly $\psi_1(1)$ and $\psi_2(2)$, are the wave functions of two identical particles with the energies E_1 and E_2, the Schrödinger equation for the system of both particles, without interaction, has obviously the solution $\psi_1(1)\psi_2(2)$ with the energy E_1+E_2; but as the particles are identical there is another solution belonging to the same energy, namely $\psi_1(2)\psi_2(1)$. Hence any linear combination of these is also a solution. Two of these, namely the symmetric one and the anti-symmetric one,

$$\begin{aligned} \psi_s(1,2) &= \psi_1(1)\psi_2(2)+\psi_1(2)\psi_2(1), \\ \psi_a(1,2) &= \psi_1(1)\psi_2(2)-\psi_1(2)\psi_2(1) \end{aligned} \tag{1}$$

have a special property: the squares of their moduli, $|\psi_s|^2$ and $|\psi_a|^2$, are unchanged if the particles are interchanged. One can further show that they do not 'combine', i.e. the mixed interaction integrals (matrix elements) vanish,

$$\int \psi_s(1,2)A\psi_a(1,2)\,d\mathbf{x}^{(1)}d\mathbf{x}^{(2)} = 0, \tag{2}$$

for any operator A symmetric in the particles. Hence they represent two entirely independent states of the system; each state being characterized by two energy-levels of the single particle occupied, without saying by which particle.

The same holds for any number of particles. If $E_1, E_2,..., E_n$ are the energies of the states of the isolated particles, the total system (without interaction) has not only the eigenfunction $\psi_1(1)\psi_2(2)...\psi_n(n)$ belonging to the energy $E_1+E_2+...+E_n$ but all functions $P\psi_1(1)\psi_2(2)...\psi_n(n)$, where P means any permutation of the particles, hence also all linear combinations of these. There are in particular two combinations, the symmetric one and the antisymmetric one,

$$\left.\begin{aligned} \psi_s(1,2,...,n) &= \sum_P P\psi_1(1)\psi_2(2)...\psi_n(n), \\ \psi_a(1,2,...,n) &= \sum_P \pm P\psi_1(1)\psi_2(2)...\psi_n(n) \\ (+ \text{ for even}, &- \text{ for odd permutations}), \end{aligned}\right\} \tag{3}$$

which have the same simple properties as described in the case of two particles: ψ_s remains unaltered when two particles are exchanged, while ψ_a (which can be written as a determinant) changes its sign; hence $|\psi_s|^2$ and $|\psi_a|^2$ remain unchanged. Further, the two states do not combine, a fact expressed by formula (2).

The functions ψ_s and ψ_a describe the state of the n-particle system in such a way that the particles have lost their individuality; the only thing which counts is the number of particles having a definite energy-level.

Experiment has shown that this description is adequate for all particles in nature; every type of particle belongs either to one or the other of these two classes.

The eigenfunctions of electrons belong, in view of spectroscopic and other evidence, to the antisymmetric type; hence they vanish if two of the single eigenfunctions $\psi_\alpha(\beta)$ are identical, i.e. if two particles are in the same quantum state. This is the mathematical formulation of Pauli's exclusion principle. Nucleons (neutrons or protons) and neutrinos are of the same type; one speaks of a Fermi–Dirac (F.D.) gas. Photons and mesons, however, and many nuclei (containing an even number of nucleons) are of the other type, having symmetric eigenfunctions; they form a Bose–Einstein (B.E.) gas.

In both cases the total energy may be written

$$E = n_1 \epsilon_1 + n_2 \epsilon_2 + \ldots = \sum_s n_s \epsilon_s, \tag{4}$$

where $\epsilon_1, \epsilon_2, \ldots$ are the possible energy-levels of the single particles and $n_1, n_2, \ldots$ integers which indicate how often this level appears in the original sum $E_1+E_2+\ldots+E_n$ (where each E_k was attributed to one definite particle).

The sum of these occupation numbers $n_1, n_2, \ldots$

$$n_1+n_2+\ldots = \sum_s n_s = n \tag{5}$$

may be given or it may not. The latter holds if particles are absorbed or emitted, as in the case of photons. For a B.E. gas, including the case of photons, there is no restriction of the n_s, while for a F.D. gas each energy-value ϵ_s can only appear once, if it appears at all. Hence one has the two cases

$$\begin{aligned} &(\text{B.E.}) \quad n_s = 0, 1, 2, 3, \ldots \\ &(\text{F.D.}) \quad n_s = 0, 1. \end{aligned} \tag{6}$$

Now we apply the general laws of statistical equilibrium, which have to be supplemented by the fundamental rule of quantum mechanics that each non-degenerate (simple) quantum state has the same weight. (This is implied by the equation (9.14) of the text which shows that the diagonal element of the density matrix determines the number of particles in the corresponding state.) As we have seen in Appendix, **14,** it suffices to calculate the partition function Z (**14**.24), p. 158, with all $\omega_s = 1$,

$$Z = \sum_{n_1, n_2, \ldots} e^{-\beta E(n_1, n_2 \ldots)}, \tag{7}$$

where the sum is to be extended over all quantum numbers n_s, which describe a definite state of the system. These are just the numbers introduced in (4), with or without the restriction (5) according to the type of particle. Introducing the abbreviation

$$z_s = e^{-\beta\epsilon_s} \tag{8}$$

one has

$$Z = \sum_{n_1, n_2, \ldots} z_1^{n_1} z_2^{n_2} \ldots = \sum_{n_1} z_1^{n_1} \sum_{n_2} z_2^{n_2} \ldots = \prod_s \sum_{n_s} z_s^{n_s}. \tag{9}$$

The sum is easily evaluated for the two cases (6),

$$\text{(B.E.)} \quad \sum_s z_s^{n_s} = 1+z_s+z_s^2+z_s^3+\ldots = \frac{1}{1-z_s},$$

$$\text{(F.D.)} \quad \sum_s z_s^{n_s} = 1+z_s.$$

One can conveniently combine the results into one expression

$$Z = \prod_s (1 \mp z_s)^{\mp 1}, \qquad \begin{matrix}\text{(B.E.)} \\ \text{(F.D.)}\end{matrix} \tag{10}$$

where the upper sign refers throughout to the B.E. case.

This formula contains the theory of radiation, where the condition (5) does not apply. But it is more convenient to deal with the instance where (5) holds and to relax this condition in the final result.

A glance at the original form (9) of Z shows that the condition (5) indicates the selection from (10) of those terms which are homogeneous of order n in all the z_s.

This can be done by the method of complex integration. We form the generating function

$$f(\zeta) = \prod_s (1 \mp \zeta z_s)^{\mp 1} \tag{11}$$

and expand it in powers of ζ. The coefficient of ζ^n is obviously equal to the product (9) with the restriction (5). Hence we obtain instead of (10)

$$Z = \frac{1}{2\pi i} \oint \zeta^{-n-1} f(\zeta)\, d\zeta, \tag{12}$$

where the path of integration surrounds the origin in such a way that no other singularity is included except $\zeta = 0$.

For large n this integral can be evaluated by the method of steepest descent. It is easy to see that the integrand has one and only one minimum on the real positive axis.

As in previous cases (see Appendix, **14**, **15**) the crudest approximation suffices. One writes the integrand in the form $e^{g(\zeta)}$, where

$$g(\zeta) = -(n+1)\log\zeta + \log f(\zeta),$$

and determines the minimum of the function $g(\zeta)$ from

$$g'(\zeta) = -\frac{n+1}{\zeta} + \frac{d}{d\zeta}\log f(\zeta) = 0; \tag{13}$$

then one has to calculate $g(\zeta)$ and

$$g''(\zeta) = \frac{n+1}{\zeta^2} + \frac{d^2}{d\zeta^2}\log f(\zeta),$$

for the value of ζ which is the root of (13). To a first approximation one finds

$$Z = \zeta^{-n-1} f(\zeta)\frac{1}{\sqrt{\{2\pi g''(\zeta)\}}},$$

$$\log Z = -(n+1)\log\zeta + \log f(\zeta) - \tfrac{1}{2}\log\{2\pi g''(\zeta)\}.$$

Neglecting 1 compared with n and the last term (which can be seen to be of a smaller order), one obtains

$$\log Z = -n\log\zeta + \log f(\zeta); \tag{14}$$

here ζ is the root of (13), where also $n+1$ can be replaced by n. Now one gets from (11)

$$\log f(\zeta) = \sum_s \mp\log(1\mp\zeta z_s),$$

$$\frac{d\log f(\zeta)}{d\zeta} = \sum_s \frac{z_s}{1\mp\zeta z_s}. \tag{15}$$

Hence, from (8) and (13),

$$\sum_s \frac{1}{e^{\alpha+\beta\epsilon_s}\mp 1} = n \qquad \begin{cases} \alpha = -\log\zeta, \\ \beta = 1/kT. \end{cases} \tag{16}$$

From this equation α (or ζ) can be determined as function of the particle number and of temperature. One easily sees now that the case where the number of particles n is not given is obtained by just omitting the equation (16) and putting $\alpha = 0$ or $\zeta = 1$. Yet the equation (16) is not entirely meaningless now, it gives the changing number of particles actually present.

The mean number of particles of the kind s is obviously

$$\overline{n}_s = \frac{\sum\limits_{n_1, n_2 \dots} n_s e^{-\beta E}}{\sum\limits_{n_1, n_2 \dots} e^{-\beta E}} = -\frac{1}{Z}\frac{\partial Z}{\partial \beta \epsilon_s} = -\frac{1}{\beta}\frac{\partial \log Z}{\partial \epsilon_s};$$

hence, from (14) and (15),

$$n_s = \frac{1}{e^{\alpha+\beta\epsilon_s} \mp 1}, \qquad (17)$$

which confirms (16) with (5). This formula, for the B.E. case (minus sign), has been mentioned in VIII (8.20), where it was obtained by a completely different consideration of Einstein's.

In the same way, the average energy of the system is found to be

$$U = -\frac{d \log Z}{d\beta} = \sum_s \frac{\epsilon_s}{e^{\alpha+\beta\epsilon_s} \mp 1} = \sum_s \overline{n}_s \epsilon_s = \bar{E}, \qquad (18)$$

in agreement with (4).

These are the fundamental formulae of quantum gases, derived from the general kinetic theory. They are to be found in *A. Ph.* Ch. VII, p. 197; in particular the fundamental formula (17) in § 5, p. 224, for B.E., and in § 6, p. 228, for F.D. All further developments may be read there (or in any other of the many books dealing with the subject). I wish to conclude this presentation by giving the explicit formulae for monatomic gases, where the energy is $\epsilon = p^2/2m$ and the summation over cells is to be replaced by an integration over the momentum space. The weight of a cell is found, by a simple quantum-mechanical consideration, for a single particle without spin (*A. Ph.* Ch. VII, § 4, p. 215) to be

$$\omega = \frac{1}{h^3} dxdydzdp_x dp_y dp_z.$$

Hence, introducing the integration variable

$$x = p\sqrt{\frac{\beta}{2m}} = \frac{p}{\sqrt{(2mkT)}},$$

one obtains from (17) and (18)

$$n = \frac{4\pi V}{h^3}(2mkT)^{3/2} \int\limits_0^\infty \frac{x^2\,dx}{e^{\alpha+x^2} \mp 1}, \qquad (19)$$

$$U = \frac{4\pi V}{h^3}(2mkT)^{5/2} \int\limits_0^\infty \frac{x^4\,dx}{e^{\alpha+x^2} \mp 1}, \qquad (20)$$

which are the quantum generalizations of the formulae given in Appendix **14** and reduce to them for $\alpha \to \infty$. A detailed discussion would be outside the plan of this book. It need only be said that the F.D. statistics of electrons have been fully confirmed by the study of the properties of metals (*A. Ph.* Ch. VII. 7, p. 229; 8, p. 232; 9, p. 235; 10, p. 236; A. XXX, p. 352).

33. (IX. p. 116.) Quantum equations of motion

At the end of Chapter VI, which deals with the kinetic theory of (dense) matter from the classical standpoint, the statistical derivation of the phenomenological hydro-thermal equations was mentioned and reference made to this later Appendix, which belongs to quantum theory. This was done to save space; for the classical derivation is essentially the same as that based on quantum theory, and one easily obtains it from the latter by a few simple rules.

The first of these rules is, of course, the correspondence of the normalized commutator $[\alpha, \beta] = \frac{1}{i\hbar}(\alpha\beta - \beta\alpha)$ with the Poisson bracket

$$[\alpha, \beta] = \sum_{i=1}^{q} \left(\frac{\partial \alpha}{\partial \mathbf{x}^{(i)}} \frac{\partial \beta}{\partial \mathbf{p}^{(i)}} - \frac{\partial \alpha}{\partial \mathbf{p}^{(i)}} \frac{\partial \beta}{\partial \mathbf{x}^{(i)}} \right), \tag{1}$$

if $\mathbf{x}^{(i)}$ and $\mathbf{p}^{(i)}$ are the position and momentum vectors on which α and β depend.

The second rule concerns the operator χ, which in the text is described in words; expressed in mathematical symbols it is

$$\chi_q \cdots = \iint d\mathbf{x}^{(q)} d\mathbf{x}^{(q)\prime} \delta(\mathbf{x}^{(q)} - \mathbf{x}^{(q)\prime}) \ldots. \tag{2}$$

It has to be interpreted classically to mean

$$\chi_q \cdots = \iint d\mathbf{x}^{(q)} d\boldsymbol{\xi}^{(q)} \ldots. \tag{3}$$

Thus the classical operation $\int d\boldsymbol{\xi}^{(q)}$ corresponds to

$$\int d\mathbf{x}^{(q)\prime} \delta(\mathbf{x}^{(q)} - \mathbf{x}^{(q)\prime}),$$

i.e. to substituting $\mathbf{x}^{(q)}$ for $\mathbf{x}^{(q)\prime}$ as stated in the text.

In using the correspondence principle to proceed from classical to quantum mechanics a product $\alpha\beta$ may not be left unchanged unless α and β commute; in general one must replace $\alpha\beta$ by $\{\alpha\beta\} = \frac{1}{2}(\alpha\beta + \beta\alpha)$.

By applying these rules one can easily go over from quantum

to classical formulae (and in many cases also vice versa). Therefore we give here only the quantum treatment.

To derive the equation (9.48) from (9.46) with the help of (9.47), one proceeds by steps of which only the first need be given, as the following ones are precisely similar. One has:

$$H_N = H_{N-1}+\frac{1}{2m}\mathbf{p}^{(N)2}+\sum_{i=1}^{N}\Phi^{(iN)}. \qquad (4)$$

Hence, applying the operation χ_N to (9.46), one obtains, using $\chi_N \rho_N = \rho_{N-1}$,

$$\frac{\partial \rho_{N-1}}{\partial t} = [H_{N-1}, \rho_{N-1}]+\chi_N\left[\frac{1}{2m}\mathbf{p}^{(N)2}, \rho_N\right]+\sum_{i=1}^{N}\chi_N[\Phi^{(iN)}, \rho_N]. \qquad (5)$$

The middle term on the right-hand side is

$$\frac{1}{2mi\hbar}\chi_N\{\mathbf{p}^{(N)}.(\mathbf{p}^{(N)}\rho_N+\rho_N\mathbf{p}^{(N)})-(\mathbf{p}^{(N)}\rho_N+\rho_N\mathbf{p}^{(N)}).\mathbf{p}^{(N)}\}$$
$$= -\frac{1}{m}\int \frac{\partial}{\partial \mathbf{x}^{(N)}}\cdot\{\mathbf{p}^{(N)}\rho_N\}_{\mathbf{x}^{(N)\prime}=\mathbf{x}^{(N)}}\, d\mathbf{x}^{(N)},$$

and vanishes on transformation to a surface integral, because there is no flow across the boundary at a large distance. Hence (5) reduces to the equation (9.48) with $q = N-1$, which completes the first step. The following steps are of the same pattern.

In order to make the transition from the 'microscopic' equations of motion (9.48) of the molecular clusters to the macroscopic equations of hydrodynamics, one needs first to define the density and macroscopic velocity in terms of the molecular quantities. The generalized 'density' n_q, which reduces to the ordinary number density n_1 for $q = 1$, is obtained as a function of the positions $\mathbf{x}^{(1)},..., \mathbf{x}^{(q)}$ by writing $\mathbf{x}^{(i)\prime} = \mathbf{x}^{(i)}$ $(i = 1, 2,..., q)$ in the density matrix $\rho_q(\mathbf{x}, \mathbf{x}')$. The macroscopic velocity $\mathbf{u}_q^{(i)}$ for a molecule (i) in the cluster of q molecules whose positions are given is the average value of the quantity represented by the operator $\frac{1}{m}\mathbf{p}^{(i)}$:

$$\mathbf{u}_q^{(i)} = \frac{1}{mn_q}\{\rho_q\mathbf{p}^{(i)}\}_{\mathbf{x}'=\mathbf{x}}, \qquad (6)$$

where the bracket $\{...\}$ indicates the symmetrized product, as introduced above, and the subscript $\mathbf{x}' = \mathbf{x}$ the diagonal elements of the matrix.

By expressing (9.48) in the coordinate representation and writing $\mathbf{x}^{(i)\prime} = \mathbf{x}^{(i)}$, one obtains the equation of continuity

$$\frac{\partial n_q}{\partial t} = -\sum_{i=1}^{q} \frac{\partial}{\partial \mathbf{x}^{(i)}} \cdot (n_q \mathbf{u}_q^{(i)}), \tag{7}$$

since

$$\frac{1}{2m}[\mathbf{p}^{(i)2}, \rho_q]_{\mathbf{x}'=\mathbf{x}} = \frac{1}{2mi\hbar}\{\mathbf{p}^{(i)} . (\mathbf{p}^{(i)}\rho_q + \rho_q \mathbf{p}^{(i)}) -$$

$$-(\mathbf{p}^{(i)}\rho_q + \rho_q \mathbf{p}^{(i)}) . \mathbf{p}^{(i)}\}_{\mathbf{x}'=\mathbf{x}}$$

$$= -\frac{1}{m}\frac{\partial}{\partial \mathbf{x}^{(i)}} \cdot \{\rho_q \mathbf{p}^{(i)}\}_{\mathbf{x}'=\mathbf{x}},$$

and

$$[\Phi^{(ij)}, \rho_q]_{\mathbf{x}'=\mathbf{x}}$$

$$= [\{\Phi(|\mathbf{x}^{(i)} - \mathbf{x}^{(j)}|) - \Phi(|\mathbf{x}^{(i)\prime} - \mathbf{x}^{(j)\prime}|)\}\rho(\mathbf{x}, \mathbf{x}')]_{\mathbf{x}'=\mathbf{x}} = 0.$$

Next, multiply (9.48) by the operator $\mathbf{p}^{(i)}$ before and after, taking half the sum, and then write $\mathbf{x}^{(j)\prime} = \mathbf{x}^{(j)}$ ($j = 1, 2, \ldots, q$).

The left-hand side evidently reduces to $m\frac{\partial}{\partial t}(n_q \mathbf{u}_q^{(i)})$. One has further

$$\frac{1}{2m}[\mathbf{p}^{(j)2}, \{\rho_q \mathbf{p}^{(i)}\}]_{\mathbf{x}'=\mathbf{x}} = -\frac{1}{m}\frac{\partial}{\partial \mathbf{x}^{(j)}} \cdot \{\mathbf{p}^{(j)}(\mathbf{p}^{(i)}\rho_q)\}_{\mathbf{x}'=\mathbf{x}}$$

and

$$\{\mathbf{p}^{(i)}, [\Phi^{(ij)}, \rho_q]\}_{\mathbf{x}'=\mathbf{x}} = -n_q \frac{\partial \Phi^{(ij)}}{\partial \mathbf{x}^{(i)}},$$

$$\{\mathbf{p}^{(i)}, \chi_{q+1}[\Phi^{(iq+1)}, \rho_{q+1}]\}_{\mathbf{x}'=\mathbf{x}} = -\int n_{q+1} \frac{\partial \Phi^{(iq+1)}}{\partial \mathbf{x}^{(i)}} d\mathbf{x}^{(q+1)}.$$

Hence, if a tensor $\mathsf{l}^{(ji)}$ is defined by

$$\sum_{j=1}^{q} \frac{\partial}{\partial \mathbf{x}^{(j)}} \cdot \mathsf{l}^{(ji)} = n_q \sum_{j=1}^{q} \frac{\partial \Phi^{(ij)}}{\partial \mathbf{x}^{(i)}} + \int n_{q+1} \frac{\partial \Phi^{(iq+1)}}{\partial \mathbf{x}^{(i)}} d\mathbf{x}^{(q+1)},$$

one has

$$m\frac{\partial}{\partial t}(n_q \mathbf{u}_q^{(i)}) + \sum_{j=1}^{q} \frac{\partial}{\partial \mathbf{x}^{(j)}} \cdot \left[\frac{1}{m}\{\mathbf{p}^{(j)}(\mathbf{p}^{(i)}\rho_q)\}_{\mathbf{x}'=\mathbf{x}} + \mathsf{l}^{(ji)}\right] = 0. \tag{8}$$

By using (7) one obtains

$$\frac{\partial}{\partial t}(n_q \mathbf{u}_q^{(i)}) = n_q \frac{\partial \mathbf{u}_q^{(i)}}{\partial t} - \sum_{j=1}^{q} \frac{\partial}{\partial \mathbf{x}^{(j)}} \cdot (n_q \mathbf{u}_q^{(j)}) \mathbf{u}_q^{(i)}$$

or, if d/dt is the convective derivative $\frac{\partial}{\partial t}+\sum_{j=1}^{q}\mathbf{u}_q^{(j)}\cdot\frac{\partial}{\partial\mathbf{x}^{(j)}}$,

$$\frac{\partial}{\partial t}(n_q\,\mathbf{u}_q^{(i)}) = n_q\frac{d\mathbf{u}_q^{(i)}}{dt}-\sum_{j=1}^{q}\frac{\partial}{\partial\mathbf{x}^{(j)}}\cdot(n_q\,\mathbf{u}_q^{(j)}\mathbf{u}_q^{(i)}). \tag{9}$$

Hence (8) may be written in the form

$$mn_q\frac{d\mathbf{u}_q^{(i)}}{dt}+\sum_{j=1}^{q}\frac{\partial}{\partial\mathbf{x}^{(j)}}\cdot\mathsf{p}^{(ji)} = 0, \tag{10}$$

where

$$\mathsf{p}^{(ji)} = \mathsf{k}^{(ji)}+\mathsf{l}^{(ji)},$$

$$\mathsf{k}^{(ji)} = \frac{1}{m}\{\mathbf{p}^{(j)}(\mathbf{p}^{(i)}\rho_q)\}_{\mathbf{x}'=\mathbf{x}}-mn_q\,\mathbf{u}_q^{(j)}\mathbf{u}_q^{(i)} \tag{11}$$

$$= m\{\mathbf{v}^{(j)}(\mathbf{v}^{(i)}\rho_q)\}_{\mathbf{x}'=\mathbf{x}};$$

here

$$\mathbf{v}^{(i)} = \frac{1}{m}\,\mathbf{p}^{(i)}-\mathbf{u}_q^{(i)}\prod_{j=1}^{q}\delta(\mathbf{x}^{(j)}-\mathbf{x}^{(j)\prime}) \tag{12}$$

is the relative molecular velocity referred to the visible motion.

The equation (10) is the generalized equation of motion of the cluster of q molecules, which reduces to the ordinary equation of hydrodynamics when $q = 1$.

$\mathsf{p}^{(ji)}$, the generalized pressure tensor, is seen to consist of two parts $\mathsf{k}^{(ji)}$ and $\mathsf{l}^{(ji)}$ associated with the kinetic energy of motion and the potential energy between the molecules respectively.

The diagonal element of the tensor $\mathsf{k}^{(ji)}$ is a multiple of the kinetic temperature $T_q^{(i)}$ defined by

$$\tfrac{3}{2}kn_q\,T_q^{(i)} = \tfrac{1}{2}m\{\mathbf{v}^{(i)}(\mathbf{v}^{(i)}\rho_q)\}_{\mathbf{x}'=\mathbf{x}}. \tag{13}$$

The equation of energy transfer can be obtained in the same way as the equation of motion by calculating the rate of change with time of $T_q^{(i)}$.

34. (IX. p. 118.) Supraconductivity

There exists a satisfactory phenomenological theory of supraconductivity, mainly due to F. London; it is excellently presented in a book by M. von Laue, where the literature can be found. (*Theorie der Supraleitung*: Springer, Berlin u. Göttingen, 1947).

Many attempts to formulate an electronic theory have been made, without much success. Recently W. Heisenberg has published some papers (*Z. f. Naturforschung*, 2 a, p. 185, 1947) which claim to explain the essential features of the phenomenon. According to this theory every metal ought to be supraconductive for sufficiently low temperatures. Actually the alkali metals which have one 'free' electron are not supraconductive even at the lowest temperatures at present obtainable, and it is not very likely that a further decrease of temperature will change this. There are also theoretical objections against Heisenberg's method.

A different theory has been developed by my collaborator Mr. Kai Chia Cheng and myself, which connects supraconductivity with certain properties of the crystal lattice and predicts correlations between structure and supraconductive state, which are confirmed by the facts (e.g. the behaviour of the alkali metals). The complete theory will be worked out in due course.

35. (X. p. 124.) **Economy of thinking**

The ideal of simplicity has found a materialistic expression in Ernst Mach's principle of economy in thought (*Prinzip der Denk-Ökonomie*). He maintains that the purpose of theory in science is to economize our mental efforts. This formulation, often repeated by other authors, seems to me very objectionable. If we want to economize thinking the best way would be to stop thinking at all. A minimum principle like this has, as is well known to mathematicians, a meaning only if a constraining condition is added. We must first agree that we are confronted with the task not only of bringing some order into a vast expanse of accumulated experience but also of perpetually extending this experience by research; then we shall readily consent that we would be lost without the utmost efficiency and clarity in thinking. To replace these words by the expression 'economy of thinking' may have an appeal to engineers and others interested in practical applications, but hardly to those who enjoy thinking for no other purpose than to clarify a problem.

36. (X. p. 127.) **Concluding remarks**

I feel that any critical reference to philosophical literature ought to be based on quotations. Yet, as I have said before, my reading of philosophical books is sporadic and unsystematic, and what I say here is a mere general impression. A book which

I have recently read with some care is E. Cassirer's *Determinismus und Indeterminismus in der modernen Physik* (Göteborg, Elanders, 1937), which gives an excellent account of the situation, not only in physics itself but also with regard to possible applications of the new physical ideas to other fields. There one finds references to and quotations from all great thinkers who have written about the problem. The last section contains Cassirer's opinion on the ethical consequences of physical indeterminism which is essentially the same as that expressed by myself. I quote his words (translated from p. 259): 'From the significance of freedom, as a mere possibility limited by natural laws, there is no way to that "reality" of volition and freedom of decision with which ethics is concerned. To mistake the choice (*Auswahl*) which an electron, according to Bohr's theory has between different quantum orbits, with a choice (*Wahl*) in the ethical sense of this concept, would mean to become the victim of a purely linguistic equivocality. To speak of an ethical choice there must not only be different possibilities but a conscious distinction between them and a conscious decision about them. To attribute such acts to an electron would be a gross relapse into a form of anthropomorphism. . . .' Concerning the inverse problem whether the 'freedom' of the electron helps us to understand the freedom of volition he says this (p. 261): 'It is of no avail whether causality in nature is regarded in the form of rigorous "dynamical" laws or of merely statistical laws. . . . In neither way does there remain open an access to that sphere of "freedom" which is claimed by ethics'.

My short survey of these difficult problems cannot be compared with Cassirer's deep and thorough study. Yet it is a satisfaction to me that he also sees the philosophical importance of quantum theory not so much in the question of indeterminism but in the possibility of several complementary perspectives or aspects in the description of the same phenomena as soon as different standpoints of meaning are taken. There is no unique image of our whole world of experience.

This last Appendix, added after delivering the lectures, gives me the opportunity to express my thanks to those among my audience who came to me to discuss problems and to raise objections. One of these was directed against my expression 'observational invariants'; it was said that the conception of invariant presupposes the existence of a group of transformations which is lacking in this case. I do not think that this is right. The problem is, of course, a psychological one; what I call 'observational invariants' corresponds roughly to the *Gestalten* of the psychologists. The essence of *Gestalten* theory is that the primary perceptions consist not in uncoordinated sense impressions but in total shapes or configurations which preserve their identity independently of their own movements and the changing standpoint of the observer. Now compare this with a mathematical example, say the definition of the group of rotations as those linear transformations of the coordinates x, y, z for which $x^2+y^2+z^2$ is invariant. The latter condition can be interpreted geometrically as postulating the invariance of the shape of spheres. Hence the group is defined by assuming the existence of a definite invariant configuration or *Gestalt*, not the other way round. The situation in psychology seems to me quite analogous, though much less precise. Yet I think that this analogy is of some help in understanding what we mean by real things in the flow of perceptions.

Another objection was raised against my use of the expression 'metaphysical' because of its association with speculative systems of philosophy. I need hardly say that I do not like this kind of metaphysics, which pretends that there is a definite goal to be reached and often claims to have reached it. I am convinced that we are on a never-ending way; on a good and enjoyable way, but far from any goal. Metaphysical systematization means formalization and petrification. Yet there are metaphysical problems, which cannot be disposed of by declaring them meaningless, or by calling them with other names, like epistemology. For, as I have repeatedly said, they are 'beyond physics' indeed and demand an act of faith. We have to accept this fact to be honest. There are two objectionable types of believers: those who believe the incredible and those who believe that 'belief' must be discarded and replaced by 'the scientific method'. Between these two extremes on the right and the left there is enough scope for believing the reasonable and reasoning on sound beliefs. Faith, imagination, and intuition are decisive factors in the progress of science as in any other human activity.

ADDENDUM 1950

In Chapter V (p. 39) I have complained that there are no books in which Carathéodory's thermodynamics is explained, and I have amended this in Appendix **6**, by mentioning one book where it is done, but not quite in the correct way. There is, however, another book, namely, S. Chandrasekhar, *An Introduction to the Study of Stellar Structure* (University of Chicago Press, 1939), which also uses Carathéodory's form of thermodynamics in a satisfactory way. It is, in fact, an English version of my own old paper of *Phys. Zeitschr.*, quoted in Appendix **6**.

In the section on Statistical Mechanics (p. 58), I have discussed on page 62 the apparent paradox connected with the long and short period of mechanical systems of many particles, and in Appendix **19** (p. 169) I have tried to solve this paradox. I think the idea of this consideration is perfectly right, but my attention has been drawn to publications of M. von Smoluchowski, where he gives an explicit formula for the time of recurrence in some simple systems. As in the theory of Brownian motion it is assumed that the value of a parameter (density, or a coordinate of a suspended particle) can be observed in regular intervals of time. Thus the average time T between two equal readings of this parameter can be determined and a relatively simple formula is obtained. The length of this time of recurrence varies rapidly with the size of the system considered. If the latter is, for instance, a sphere of radius a in air of normal density, and the question is asked, after what time one can expect a one per cent. fluctuation of the density of oxygen, one finds the following values:

$a =$	1	3×10^{-5}	$2{\cdot}5\times 10^{-5}$	1×10^{-5} cm.
$T =$	$10^{(10^{14})}$	10^{6}	7	10^{-11} sec.

The enormous differences in T demonstrate the fact that the mixing of two gases can be regarded as perfectly irreversible for visible parts of space, while for microscopic regions it is definitely reversible.

The original paper by M. von Smoluchowski is published in

Sitzungsber. Akad. der Wissenschaften, Wien, IIa, **124**, p. 339 (1915). It is also reported in the book by R. Fürth, *Schwankungserscheinungen in der Physik* (Friedr. Vieweg und Sohn, Braunschweig, 1920), and in an article by S. Chandrasekhar, *Reviews of Modern Physics*, **15**, p. 1 (1934).

I take this opportunity to correct an impression which the reader may get from the book, that the theory of fluctuations is solely the work of Einstein. In fact, Smoluchowski's work was independent and much more detailed.

APPENDIX TWO (1964)

Addendum

PHYSICAL research of the last sixteen years has made some passages of this book obsolete. In the following I have listed these passages with my comments.

NOTE 1 (see p. 11). Astronomy remained observational until the first "Sputnik." Today Newton's equations for planetary motion can be checked by experiment with the help of artificial celestial bodies.

NOTE 2 (see p. 15). Recent pendulum experiments by Dicke (1961) have confirmed the older results with a ten times higher accuracy.

NOTE 3 (see p. 29). The relativistic theory of planetary motion has been much perfected. L. Infeld and J. Plebanski have represented it in a systematic and elegant way in their book *Motion and Relativity* (Pergamon Press, London, 1960). There are also new empirical confirmations of the general theory of relativity; they can be found, for instance, in my book *Einstein's Theory of Relativity* (revised edition, Dover Publications, New York, 1962). Production and measurement of gravitational waves which would constitute a direct proof of contiguity of the gravitational field (see pp. 16 and 30) have not yet been achieved, but preparations are well advanced.

NOTE 4 (see p. 39). There is now a textbook by P. T. Landsberg, *Thermodynamics* (Interscience Publishers, New York–London, 1961) which uses the method of Carathéodory.

NOTE 5 (see p. 64). The general kinetic theory of matter has made considerable progress, which cannot be summarized in a few lines or pages.

NOTE 6 (see p. 83). Einstein's "induced emission" of light was regarded as an idea important only for a theoretical understanding of the radiation formula. Now it has been confirmed by direct experiment and may even become important for practical purposes. The discovery of the maser and laser has opened a new chapter in optics. Einstein would have enjoyed it—though he would have protested against any military projects which might intend to develop and use them as "death rays."

NOTE 7 (see p. 117). The theories of supra-conductivity of metals and supra-fluidity of helium have been intensely developed, the latter mainly by the Russian physicist Landau. The considerations of the text (see pp. 117, 118) and in Appendix, 34 (see p. 206) are hardly valid any more.

* * *

In addition to these remarks about special problems I wish to say that my lectures have bypassed large sections of theoretical physics: field quantization, nuclear physics and elementary particles. One could certainly gain new insight by illustrating the problem of cause and chance with the help of these subjects. I have omitted them just because I have not participated in their development and did not feel familiar with them. I must leave it to somebody of the younger generation to extend the survey given in this book to these branches of modern physics.

But there is one point, mentioned on p. 33, on which I have spent much thought and which ought to be treated more thoroughly in this new edition. I allude to the sentence: "The problem is to transform the subjective sense impressions . . . into objective measurable statements." I have come to the conclusion that there are two kinds of objectivity: The first is based on the natural agreement between people on everyday matters and things (naive realism); this is never complete and leads in doubtful cases to a majority decision or a struggle, or is even enforced by power. This is the ordinary kind of objectivity. The second kind is based on logical thinking by a single individual; it does not persuade but compel, as far as thinking can compel. This is the objectivity aimed at by the natural sciences. A systematic investigation explains why the latter method leads to abstract concepts, remote from the immediate sense impressions. It is a powerful but dangerous tool for mastering the world, as it entices into fields not suited for its application and leads thus to pseudo-scientific endeavours.

These considerations seemed to me a useful addition to this book, and as the publisher has agreed, they follow here as Appendix Three.

APPENDIX THREE (1964)

Symbol and Reality

Contents

*APPENDIX THREE (1964)**

Symbol and Reality

1. Why is science abstract and mathematical?

If somebody who is no physicist, chemist or astronomer, glances through this book, or any other book on these sciences, he will be struck by the amount of mathematical and other symbols and the scarcity of descriptions of natural phenomena. Even the instruments of observation are indicated only symbolically by diagrams. And yet the book claims to deal with natural science. Where in this accumulation of formulae is living nature? How are the physical and chemical symbols connected with the experienced reality of sense perceptions?

Even the scientist himself will occasionally ponder the reasons why he approaches nature in this abstract and formalistic way with the help of symbols. The opinion is often expressed that the symbols are just a matter of convenience, a kind of shorthand needed to handle and to master the abundance of the material. Yet I think the problem is deeper. I have alluded to it already on p. 33 when I discussed how science transforms the sensual experiences of the individual into objective knowledge. Since I wrote those lines I have considered this question in more detail and have convinced myself that the symbols are an essential part of the method for penetrating into the physical reality behind the phenomena. I shall try to explain this idea in the following.

2. Naive realism.

Reality to a simple, unlearned person is what he feels and perceives. The real existence of the things surrounding him seems to be just as assured as the sensations of pain, joy or hope which he feels. He is perhaps shown an optical illusion which reveals to him that a perception may lead to doubtful or even downright erroneous judgments about actual facts. But this always remains on the surface of consciousness, a curious, amusing exception.

* This is an English translation of a lecture presented in German to the annual meeting of Nobel Laureates at Lindau, Bodensee, on June 24, 1964. Both versions will appear in the bilingual periodical *Universitas*, Stuttgart, during the year 1964.

This attitude is called naive realism. The great majority of people preserve this state of mind throughout their life, even though they may learn to distinguish between subjective experience, like pleasure, pain, expectation, disappointment, and objective experiences which have to do with things of the external world.

But there are people to whom something happens which stirs them deeply and makes them sceptical. In my case it occurred in the following way.

I had an elder cousin who was a University student while I was still at school. Apart from lectures on chemistry he attended also a course on philosophy which impressed him. Once he asked me suddenly: "What exactly do you mean when you call this leaf green or the sky blue?" I regarded this question as rather superfluous and answered: "I just mean green and blue because I see these colours like that, exactly as you see them." But this did not satisfy him. "How do you know that I see green exactly as you see it?" My answer, "because all people see it in the same way, of course," still did not satisfy him: "There exist colour-blind people who see the colours differently; some of them, for instance, cannot distinguish red and green." Thus he drove me into a corner and made it plain to me that there is no way to ascertain what another person perceives and that even the statement "he perceives the same as I" has no clear meaning.

So it dawned upon me that fundamentally everything is subjective—everything without exception. This was a shock.

The problem was not to distinguish the subjective from the objective, but to understand how to free oneself from the subjective and to arrive at objective statements. I want to say right from the beginning that I have found no satisfactory answer to this in any philosophical treatise. But through my occupation with physics and its neighbour sciences I have arrived, near the end of my life, at a solution which appears to me to some extent acceptable.

3. Kant.

At that distant time, as a young fellow, I followed my cousin and mentor, who advised me to read Kant. Later on I learned that the problem—how objective knowledge arises from the sense perceptions of the individual and what this knowledge means—

is a much older one; that, e.g., Plato's doctrine of ideas is an early formulation, followed by divers speculations of ancient and mediaeval philosophers up to Kant's immediate precursors, the British empiricists Locke, Berkeley and Hume. However, I do not intend to speak about the history of philosophy; I only want to say a few words about Kant because he has influenced the thought of men up to our time, and because I intend to use some of his terminology.

I quote a passage from Kant's *Critique of Pure Reason* ("Transcendental Aesthetics"): "Objects are given us by way of sense impressions, they produce our perceptions. They are then taken up by reason which produces concepts." Thus Kant suggests that the objects of perception are transformed by reason into concepts. He takes it as self-evident that the objects of perception are the same for all individuals and that the concepts formed by reason are moulded alike by all individuals. According to Kant all knowledge refers to the phenomena but is not determined solely by experience (a posteriori) but also by the structure of our mind (a priori). The a priori forms of our perception are space and time; the a priori forms of reason are called categories; Kant gives a catalogue of these which contains, e.g., causality.

The question whether behind the world of phenomena there is another world of objects in their own right (noumena) is, as far as I can see, left unanswered by Kant. He speaks about the "thing in itself" but declares it as unknowable. I quote a passage from Bertrand Russell's book *Wisdom of the West* (Macdonald, London, 1957); on p. 241 he says:

> On the Kantian theory it is impossible to experience a thing in itself, since all experience occurs with the concurrence of space, time and the categories. We may at best infer that there are such things from the postulated external source of impressions. Strictly speaking, even that is not permissible, since we have no independent way of finding out that there are such sources, and even if we had, we could still not say that they were causing our sense impressions. For if we speak of causality we are already inside the network of a priori concepts operating within the understanding.

The vague concept of the "thing in itself" is generally considered a weak point of Kant's teaching. One has to assume something like that in order to understand how the sense perceptions and their conceptual elaborations of the single individuals can lead to objective statements valid for all individuals. But this precondition of all objective knowledge is declared by Kant to be itself unknowable.

I shall try to show how one can escape this dilemma by using scientific methods of thinking.

But first I wish to give a short survey of the attitude to this problem taken by philosophical systems after Kant.

4. Later philosophical systems.

I cannot dwell on the prehistory of the problem of how subjective experiences are transformed into objective knowledge, but only remark that it was already vaguely discussed by Plato in his well-known simile of the cave, and more thoroughly by later philosophers, in particular by the sceptic thinker David Hume. The philosophers after Kant have taken very different attitudes towards it.

There are some philosophical systems which admit as real only the world of the single individual, the ipse. In my youth a German book by Stirner, *The Only One and his Property* (*Der Einzige und sein Eigentum*) was widely read; as the title reveals, it takes this "solipsistic" standpoint. The fact that I remember the title shows that I was impressed by it.

Much more widely accepted is the opinion, apparently shared by Kant, that it is self-evident and needs no demonstration that the sense perceptions of different individuals are identical and that the question is only to investigate this common world of phenomena. This view is taken by the so-called idealistic systems which culminated in Hegel and by several others, among them the "phenomenology" of Husserl, whose lectures I attended sixty years ago in Göttingen. He taught that one could obtain knowledge by a process of the mind called "intuition of essence" (*Wesensschau*). But that did not satisfy me.

The school of logical positivism which has its roots in the work of the physicist and philosopher Ernst Mach and is today widely accepted teaches a doctrine less obscure but still more radical. Only the immediate sense impressions are regarded as real; everything else, the whole conceptual world of everyday life and of science is considered to have no other purpose than to constitute logical connections between the sense impressions. The American philosopher Henry Margenau has introduced the term "constructs" for all that. In the most radical interpretation this theory means a denial of the existence of an external world, or at least the negation of its knowability. In practical life a follower of this doctrine would hardly behave as if there were no external world. All these theories are relying on the assumption that the world of sensual perception is "the same" for all individuals. What this means is left open.

The "materialism" of the communistic bloc of Eastern nations calls all these theories "idealistic" and opposes them violently. It maintains, of course without a proof, just as an axiom, the existence of a reality independent of the subject. Marx and Engels seem to have regarded this like the naive realist: Matter is primary; consciousness of mind is one of its manifestations. This "mechanical materialism" however was not easily reconciled with the results of progressing physics. For here the primitive ideas about matter were dissolved and replaced by the concept of "field" and eventually by still more abstract ideas. Therefore Lenin invented "dialectical materialism," where the old term "matter" is preserved but understood in such a general way that nothing of its meaning is preserved (just as happened with his use of other words, such as "democracy"). The fundamental axiom is "the existence of a real, objectively knowable external world." Since Lenin's philosophy is in the East a kind of official religion, a problem which has occupied and worried the minds of so many thinkers has become an article of faith guarded by the power of the State.

Now, what is the opinion of the physicists, or more generally, of the scientists about the problem of reality?

I should think that most of them are naive realists who do not rack their brains about philosophical subtleties. They are content to observe a phenomenon, to measure it and describe it in their characteristic idiom. As long as they have to do with instruments and experimental arrangements they use ordinary language embellished by suitable technical terms, as is usual in every craft.

But as soon as they begin to theorize, i.e., to interpret their observations, they use another way of communication. Already in Newton's mechanics, the first physical theory in the modern sense of the term, there appear concepts which do not correspond to ordinary things, such as force, mass, energy. With the progress of research this tendency became more and more pronounced. In Maxwell's theory of electromagnetism the concept of the field was developed, which is quite outside the world of perceptible things. Quantitative laws expressed by mathematical formulae, like Maxwell's equations, became more and more prevalent. This happened in the theory of relativity, in atomic physics, in modern chemistry. Eventually we had in quantum mechanics a case where the mathematical formalism was developed rather completely and successfully before an interpretation in words of the ordinary language was found, and even today this is not finally fixed.

What is going on here? In physics the mathematical formulae are not an end in themselves, as in pure mathematics, but symbols for some kind of reality which lies beyond the level of everyday experiences. I maintain that this fact is closely connected with the question: how is it possible to obtain objective knowlege from subjective experiences?

5. METHODS OF THINKING IN PHYSICS.

I propose to approach this problem with the methods of thinking used by the physicist. Only a minor part of these methods is derived from philosophical systems. They have just been developed because the traditional thinking of philosophers has failed when applied to modern physics. Their strength lies in the fact that they have been successful. I mean not only that they have contributed to the understanding of natural phenomena but that they have led to the discovery of new, often overwhelmingly impressive phenomena, and to human domination over nature.

The consideration which I suggest does not however come under the title of "empiricism" which the metaphysicists look at with contempt. The rules of thought used by the physicist are not derived from experience, but are pure ideas, inventions of great thinkers. However, they are tested on an extremely large field of experience. Hence I do not intend to deal with philosophy of science, but to look at philosophy from the scientific standpoint. I am sure that the metaphysicists will object to it. But I cannot help it.

To begin with I shall enumerate some of these methods of thinking and discuss their origin and their successes.

A. Decidability.

I suggest the expression "decidability" for a fundamental rule of scientific thinking (although I did not find the word in the dictionary): Use a concept only if it is decidable whether it can be applied in a special case, or not.

When apparently unsurmountable difficulties were met in the fields of electrodynamics and the optics of moving bodies, Einstein discovered that these difficulties could be reduced to the assumption that the concept of simultaneity of events at different places has an absolute significance. This he showed is not the case, due to the fact that the velocity of light used for signalling is finite; with the help of physical means one can only establish relative simultaneity with respect to a definite coordinate (inertial) system. This idea led to the special theory of relativity and to a new doctrine of space and time. Kant's ideas of space and time as a priori forms of intuition were thus finally refuted.

Actually doubts about this had arisen much earlier. A short itme after Kant, non-Euclidean geometries had been discovered (by Gauss, Bolyai, Lobatchefski) as logical possibilities. Gauss made an attempt to decide experimentally whether Euclidean geometry was correct by measuring the angles of the triangle formed by three German hilltops (Brocken, Inselsberg, Hohe Hagen). He did not find a deviation of the sum of angles from the Euclidean value of 180 degrees. His successor Riemann took up the idea that geometry is a part of the empirical reality and developed a momentous generalisation in which the idea of a curved space was introduced and worked out with mathematical rigour.

In Einstein's theory of gravitation, usually called general relativity, the principle of decidability was used again. He started from the experimentally well-established fact that in a gravitational field the acceleration of all bodies is equal, independent of the mass. An observer in a closed box cannot therefore decide whether the acceleration of a body relative to the box is due to a gravitational field or to an acceleration of the box in the opposite direction. From this simple argument the enormous structure of the general theory of relativity was developed. The main mathematical tool was Riemann's geometry mentioned above, applied to the four-dimensional space, which is a combination of ordinary space and time.

I mention all this to illustrate the power and fertility of the principle of decidability. Another success of this principle is quantum mechanics. After a splendid beginning, Bohr's theory of the orbital motion of electrons in the atom had got into difficulties. Heisenberg observed that the theory worked with quantities which were fundamentally unobservable (electronic orbits of definite dimensions and periods) and he sketched a new theory which used only concepts whose validity was empirically decidable. The new mechanics, in the development of which I participated, did away with another of Kant's a priori categories: causality. In classical physics causality was always interpreted as determinism (and Kant doubtlessly also interpreted it as such). The new quantum mechanics was not deterministic but statistical (a point to which I shall return). Its success in all parts of physics is beyond dispute.

I consider it reasonable to apply the principle of decidability to the philosophical problem of the origin of an objective world picture, also.

B. Comparability. Symbols.

The point from which we started was the sceptical question: How is it possible to infer from the subjective world of experiences the existence of an objective external world? Actually, this inference is innate and so natural that to doubt it seems rather absurd. But the doubt exists, and all attempts at a solution, whether of the type of Kant's "thing in itself" or of Lenin's dogma are unsatisfactory because they violate the principle of decidability.

Now the impossibility of deciding whether the green I see is the same as the green you see is due to the attempt to agree about one *single* sense impression. No doubt that is impossible.

But already for *two* impressions of the same sense organ, e.g., two colours, there exist decidable, communicable, objectively testable statements: they refer to the comparison of the two impressions, particularly to equality or inequality. (Instead of equal or unequal it would be better to say indistinguishable or distinguishable; but such psychological finesse does not matter in this logical consideration.) There is no doubt that two individuals can agree about such comparisons. Though I cannot describe to another person what I perceive if I call a thing green, we can both find out and agree that two leaves which seem to me to be of the same hue appear to him also to be of the same hue. Apart from "equality" there exist other pair relations which are communicable and objective; foremost, those of the type more–less, e.g., brighter–darker, stronger–fainter, hotter–colder, harder–softer, etc. But we need not discuss these possibilities. The existence of communicable properties of pairs suffices.

In physics this principle of objectivation is known and practised systematically. Colours, sounds, even shapes are not considered singly, but in pairs. Every beginner learns the so-called zero-method in optics, for instance, where an instrument is so set that a perceptual difference of two visual fields (in brightness, hue, saturation) vanishes. The reading of a scale means the observation of a geometrical "equality," the coincidence of the pointer and a line of the scale. A major part of experimental physics consists in this kind of scale reading.

The fact that objective statements are possible through the comparison of pairs has an immense importance because it is the root of speaking and writing, and of the most powerful instrument of thinking, mathematics. I propose to use the term "symbols" for all these means of communication between individuals.

Symbols are easily reproducible, visual or audible signs or signals whose accurate shape is of no importance, but for which a crude reproduction suffices. If I write (or pronounce) *A* and somebody else also writes (or pronounces) *A*, each of us perceives his own *A* and that of the other as equal, optically and acoustically. What matters are rough equality or some similarity—the mathematician would say the topological aspect—not particulars such as the pitch of speaking, a flourish and ornament of writing or printing.

Symbols are the carriers of communication between individuals and thus decisive for the possibility of objective knowledge.

C. Correspondence. Coordination.

In his *Maximen und Reflektionen* (Maxims and Reflections), Goethe says the following: "There is some unknown regularity in the object which corresponds to the unknown regularity in the subject."

I quote this not only because of its relation to our discussion of subjectivity and objectivity but because of the word "correspond." Goethe, with his gift of divination, has used a concept which may be called *Urbegriff* (primary concept) of all learning, knowing, understanding. I say "primary," translating the German syllable *Ur* which Goethe himself uses in many similar cases: "primary plant" (*Urpflanze*) in his doctrine of metamorphoses; "primary phenomenon" (*Urphänomen*) in his theory of colours. Instead of "correspond" one now often uses the word "coordinate" which means to make things correspond.

"The child learns to speak" means: the child learns to coordinate words and sentences to things, persons, actions, perceptions. Writing is the coordination of visual symbols to such phenomena or to the corresponding words. Counting is the coordination of the numerals, "one, two, three, . . . ," learned by heart, to a sequence of similar things. Modern mathematics has extended this principle to infinite sets of things, in the so-called "theory of sets" (*Mengenlehre*) initiated by Georg Cantor, who has shown, for instance, that one cannot establish such a mutual one-to-one correspondence between the points of a (finite) line and the set of all integers (1, 2, . . . without an end); which means that infinite sets of different "numbers" exist.

In geometry points in space are connected with groups of numbers called "coordinates." Thus, to each geometrical fact there corresponds an analytical one, i.e., a theorem in the domain of numbers. The essential feature of mathematics is not numbers but the idea of coordination.† There are extended and fundamental mathematical doctrines, like group theory, where numbers play only an insignificant part. In physics the first not purely mechanical but properly physical discovery is a perfect example of coordination, namely, the discovery by Pythagoras that the

† It seems not to be superfluous to remark here that the current ideas about the essence of mathematics are somewhat wrong. For instance, it is repeated again and again that the whole of mathematics is a tautology. i.e., self-evident if properly considered. This opinion is expressed by the distinguished biologist and Nobel Laureate, F. B. Medawar, in his book *The Uniqueness of the Individual,* p. 15 (Methuen & Co., London). The truth is that mathematics begins only with the establishment and proof of theorems for infinite sets. Thus $1+2+3+4 = 10$ is not a mathematical theorem, but a trivial, verifiable fact. But $1+2+3+ \dots +n = \frac{1}{2}n\,(n+1)$ for all values $n = 1, 2, \dots$ (without end) is a mathematical theorem, simple to prove but only with the help of a principle beyond ordinary logic (the so-called principle of complete induction).

natural intervals in music, octave, fifth, fourth, etc., correspond to the divisions of a vibrating string according to simple ratios 2:1, 3:2, 4:3, etc. There is actually a double correspondence between perceptions of ear (musical intervals), eye or muscles (length of the string) and numbers.

The measurement of the intensity of heat (temperature) with a thermometer is the coordination of the perception of heat with a geometrical quantity (the length of a mercury column, the position of a galvanometer needle) and thus again with a number (scale value).

Chemistry coordinates the substances with combinations of symbols which are abbreviations of the names of a number of elementary substances (atoms). The historical root of this procedure is the fact that by coordinating atomic weights to the symbols of elements one can read off molecular weights from the combination of atomic symbols representing them; and by coordinating valences to the symbols of atoms one can predict possibilities of reactions. Later this elementary method of describing chemical bonds was absorbed by the general atomic theory.

D. Structures.

In every field of experience this correspondence of sense impressions with symbols has been established. It suffices for the needs of ordinary life: the words and sentences of a language, whether spoken or written, corresponding to perceptions, emotions, etc., are learned and used without being further analyzed (naive realism). Thus the mental image of the world is formed by the ordinary human being and refined in literature.

Science goes one step further. I do not know whether what I am going to say holds for all the sciences and the humanities. I wish to speak only about the exact sciences which I know. There *mathematical* symbols are used, and they have a particularity: they reveal structures.

Mathematics is just the detection and investigation of structures of thinking which lie hidden in the mathematical symbols. The simplest mathematical entity, the chain of integers 1, 2, 3, . . . , consists of symbols which are combined according to certain rules, the arithmetical axioms. The most important of these is an internal coordination: each integer is followed by another. These rules determine a vast number of structures, e.g., the prime numbers with their remarkable properties and complicated distribution, the reciprocity theorems of quadratic residues, etc. Geometry has to do with spatial structures which appear analytically as invariants at transformations. Group theory deals with structures which appear when certain sets of operations are repeated, such as the permutations of sets of letters or symmetry operations like rotations of mirror imaging, and others.

These are structures of pure thinking. The transition to reality is made by theoretical physics, which correlates symbols to observed phenomena. Where this can be done hidden structures are coordinated to phenomena; these very structures are regarded by the physicist as the objective reality lying behind the subjective phenomena.

It is impossible to describe this procedure in its enormous diversity. Only one historical point of view must be stressed: since Newton the structures contained in differential equations have been used and have become familiar. The reason is that they permit a direct connection with experiences about ordinary things in daily life. Galileo's mechanics started from such experiences. Then Newton generalized the mechanical concepts in such a way that they could be applied to celestial bodies. The first optical theories used mechanical models. Space was supposed to be filled with a substance called ether which functioned as a carrier of vibrations according to the laws of mechanics. Even Maxwell discovered and discussed his field equations at first with the help of a concealed mechanism In the early days of atomic theory mechanical models were used; in the kinetic theory of gases the atoms were considered to be small elastic balls which recoiled from each other and from the walls of the container.

Very slowly and against violent opposition the opinion spread that models were not only unnecessary, but even an obstruction to progress.

The first important example was Heinrich Hertz' treatment of Maxwell's theory of the electromagnetic field. Hertz cannot be called a theoretician exclusively, for to him we owe the experimental verification of the theory through his discovery of electromagnetic waves. But he regarded the electromagnetic field as an entity in its own right which ought to be described without mechanical models.

Since then the development has irresistibly proceeded in this direction. A natural phenomenon need not be reduced to models accessible to imagination and explicable in mechanical terms, but has its own mathematical structure directly derived from experience.

This change of outlook was decisive when Planck discovered in 1900, in an investigation of heat radiation, a new constant of nature, the quantum of action. This did not fit at all into the system of Newtonian mechanics and the physical theories built on its pattern. It is true, the models of electronic motions in atoms suggested by Niels Bohr were a micro-imitation of planetary motion. However, not all orbits were "allowed," but only certain "stationary" states characterised by unmechanical "quantum conditions," and the transitions between these states, the "quantum jumps," followed rules which have no analogy in mechanics. When this development culminated in the establishment of quantum mechanics there was an end to mechanical models and, by the way, also to the causal description of classical physics.

Thus, physical research has won a freedom necessary to handle the ever-increasing amount of observations and measurements. We try to find the mathematics appropriate to a domain of experience, then we investigate its structure and regard it as representing physical reality, whether it conforms to accustomed things or not. As examples I mention the curved space of the macroworld (cosmology) and the atoms, nuclei and elementary particles in the micro-world; they have little in common with our familiar surroundings.

Yet a further freedom had to be gained before physics could claim the right to call the structures images of the reality behind the phenomena.

E. Probability.

Philosophy has always, and still is, inclined to make final, categorical statements. Science was strongly influenced by this tendency. The early physicists, for example, considered the determinism of Newtonian mechanics a particular merit.

But already in the eighteenth century the concept of probability appears in physics. In attempts to establish a molecular theory of gases observable quantities, such as pressure, were conceived as averages of molecular collisions. In the nineteenth century the kinetic theory of gases was fully developed, followed by statistical mechanics applicable to all substances, gaseous, liquid and solid. The concept of probability was applied systematically and built into the system of physics.

This procedure was usually justified by the human inability to handle enormous numbers of particles with rigorous methods; but the elementary process, e.g., the collisions of two atoms, was assumed to obey the laws of classical, deterministic physics.†

After the discovery of quantum mechanics this assumption became obsolete. The elementary processes are not obeying deterministic, but statistical laws according to the statistical interpretation of quantum mechanics.

I am convinced that ideas such as absolute certainty, absolute precision, final truth, etc., are phantoms which should be excluded from science.

From the restricted knowledge of the present state of a system one can, with the help of a theory, deduce conjectures and expectations of a future situation, expressed in terms of probability. Each statement of probability is, from the standpoint of the theory used, either right or wrong.‡

This loosening of the rules of thinking seems to me the greatest blessing which modern science has given us. For the belief that there is only one truth and that oneself is in possession of it, seems to me the deepest root of all that is evil in the world.

6. Application to the Problem of the External World.

Before performing the last step in these considerations I wish to recall the point of departure, namely the shock experienced by every thoughtful person when comprehending that a single sense impression is not communicable, hence purely subjective. Anybody who has not had this experience will regard the whole dis-

† The deterministic interpretation of Newtonian mechanics is actually an unjustified idealisation, as Brillouin and I have independently shown. It is based on the idea of absolutely precise measurements, an assumption which has obviously no physical meaning. It is not difficult to write classical mechanics in a statistical form.

‡ Here I apply the logical rule of the "excluded third" (*tertium non datur*). The question has been investigated, particularly in connection with quantum theory, whether a "three-valued logic" can be established where between "right" and "wrong" there is a third possibility "indeterminate." But I cannot discuss this here.

cussion as sophistry. In a certain sense this is right. For naive realism is a natural attitude which corresponds to the biological situation of the human race, just as that of the animal world. A bee recognizes flowers by their colour or scent and needs no philosophy. As long as one restricts oneself to the things of everyday life the problem of objectivity is an artifact of philosophical brooding.

In science, however, it is different. Here one has often to do with phenomena beyond everyday experience. What you see through a high-power microscope, what you perceive with the help of a telescope, spectroscope or one of the various amplifying devices of electronics is incomprehensible without a theory; it must be interpreted. In the smallest domains as in the largest, in that of atoms as well as of stars, we encounter phenomena which do not resemble the accustomed aspect of our surroundings and which can be described only with the help of abstract concepts. Here one cannot elude the question whether there is an objective world, independent of the observer, behind the phenomena.

I do not believe that this question can be answered categorically by logical thinking. But it can be answered if we make use of the freedom to consider an extremely improbable statement as wrong.

The assumption that the coincidence of structures revealed by using different sense organs and communicable from one individual to another is accidental, is improbable to the highest degree.

This is the normal way of scientific reasoning and, apart from science, of all research. An archaeologist, for example, who discovers in two different countries remains of pottery of similar design will conclude that this cannot be accidental but indicates a common origin.

I am not afraid of identifying such well-defined structures with Kant's "thing in itself." The objections quoted before in the formulation of Bertrand Russell have no validity from our point of view. They consist in the following: the existence of the "thing in itself" is postulated because one needs an external cause to understand why different individuals experience "the same" phenomena; but the category of causality has a meaning only within the domain of phenomena. However, the concept of causality is a residue of former ways of thinking and is replaced today by the process of coordination as described before. This procedure leads to structures which are communicable, controllable, hence objective. It is justified to call these by the old term "thing in itself." They are pure form, void of all sensual qualities. That is all we can wish and expect.

The result is, of course, contradictory to the traditional conception of Kant's "thing in itself." Hegel, for instance, says in the *Encyclopedia of Philosophy,* § 44: "The thing in itself . . . means the object as far as everything referring to consciousness, feeling, emotion as well as all notions is abstracted. It is easy to see what is left—the perfect abstractum, the complete emptiness, just something from a 'world beyond' (*Jenseits*) . . . ."

If the objects of modern physics, in particular those of atomic physics, are identified with Kant's "thing in itself," one can agree with Hegel that they are a "perfect abstractum." But that they are perfectly empty, something from a world beyond, does not fit the facts. Remember what practical use can be made of them in the production of things like engines, airplanes, nuclear reactors, plastics, electronic computers and so on ad infinitum. It might happen that nuclear research will lead to our being transferred to the "world beyond." Yet Hegel did not mean this and could not foresee it.

7. RETURN TO IMAGES.

The systems of formulae in physics do not necessarily represent conceivable things, familiar through experience. Yet they are derived from experience through abstraction and continually checked by experiment. On the other hand, the instruments used by the physicists are made of materials known in ordinary life and can be described in everyday language. The results obtained with the help of these instruments, such as exposed photographic plates, tables of figures or curves, are also of this kind. The trace of droplets in a Wilson expansion chamber suggests a particle in flight; a periodical distribution of the blackening on a photographic plate suggests interferences of waves. One cannot give up such interpretations without paralyzing intuition, which is the source of research, and rendering communication between scientists more difficult.

Therefore, physicists are bound to describe the content of their abstract formulae as far as possible in terms of ordinary language with concepts based on intuition. The specific difficulties encountered here have been studied by the Copenhagen school under the leadership of Niels Bohr. He has shown that it is possible to describe atomic processes with the "classical" concepts, provided one desists from investigating *all* properties of a physical system simultaneously. Different, mutually exclusive but complementary experimental arrangements are needed. The experimentalist has the choice which of them to employ. Thus a subjective trend is re-introduced into physics and cannot be eliminated. Another loss of objectivity is due to the fact that the theory makes only probability predictions, which produce graded expectations. From our standpoint, where subjectivity is primary and the possibility of objective knowledge problematic, it is not surprising that the rigorous separation of subject and object is not possible if one tries to express the mathematical formalism with the help of images.

Bohr's principle of complementarity is another new method of thinking. Discovered in physics, it is applicable to many other fields. It is another loosening of traditional methods of thought which promises important results. But this leads beyond the framework of these considerations.

I wish to mention that the latest branch of physical research, the theory of elementary particles, seems to be still entirely in the abstract. Though it leads to definite observable predictions, the elementary processes themselves can hardly be grasped by intuition. The content of Heisenberg's world-formula seems to me at present an abstract "thing in itself" without an immediate correlation with sense impressions.

Here it may be remarked that a turning towards the abstract appears to be an obvious trend of our time. We observe it also in art, particularly in abstract painting and sculpture. But this parallelism is only seeming. For modern painters seem to me to avoid associations and intellectual interpretations, and concentrate on appealing to the optical sensation. The physicist, on the other hand, uses the perceptions of the senses as material to construct an intellectual world. The word "abstract" refers in the two cases to opposite intentions.

Yet we scientists should always remember that all experience is based on the senses. A theoretician who, immersed in his formulae, forgets the phenomena which he wants to explain is no real scientist, physicist or chemist, and if he is estranged by his books from the beauty and variety of nature I would call him a poor fool. At present we have a reasonable equilibrium between experiment and theory, between sensual and intellectual reality, and we ought to take care that it is preserved.

We also have to be careful that scientific thinking in abstract terms does not extend to other domains where it is not applicable. Human and ethical values cannot be based on scientific thinking. It is true that Kant attempted to build up an ethical system according to the model of categories, by introducing his "categorical imperative." But the validity of this command is not "decidable," in the sense of the word as defined by us. It need only be accepted and believed in. However attractive and satisfactory abstract thinking may be for the scientist, however valuable his results for the material aspect of our civilisation, it is most dangerous to apply these methods beyond the range of their validity, to religion, ethics, art, literature and all humanities.

Thus, my excursion into philosophy is intended to be not only an illustration of the foundation of science, but also an exhortation to restrict the scientific methods to that domain to which they reasonably belong.

INDEX

CATALOGUE OF DOVER BOOKS

BOOKS EXPLAINING SCIENCE AND MATHEMATICS

General

WHAT IS SCIENCE?, Norman Campbell. This excellent introduction explains scientific method, role of mathematics, types of scientific laws. Contents: 2 aspects of science, science & nature, laws of science, discovery of laws, explanation of laws, measurement & numerical laws, applications of science. 192pp. 5⅜ x 8. S43 Paperbound **$1.25**

THE COMMON SENSE OF THE EXACT SCIENCES, W. K. Clifford. Introduction by James Newman, edited by Karl Pearson. For 70 years this has been a guide to classical scientific and mathematical thought. Explains with unusual clarity basic concepts, such as extension of meaning of symbols, characteristics of surface boundaries, properties of plane figures, vectors, Cartesian method of determining position, etc. Long preface by Bertrand Russell. Bibliography of Clifford. Corrected, 130 diagrams redrawn. 249pp. 5⅜ x 8.
T61 Paperbound **$1.60**

SCIENCE THEORY AND MAN, Erwin Schrödinger. This is a complete and unabridged reissue of SCIENCE AND THE HUMAN TEMPERAMENT plus an additional essay: "What is an Elementary Particle?" Nobel laureate Schrödinger discusses such topics as nature of scientific method, the nature of science, chance and determinism, science and society, conceptual models for physical entities, elementary particles and wave mechanics. Presentation is popular and may be followed by most people with little or no scientific training. "Fine practical preparation for a time when laws of nature, human institutions . . . are undergoing a critical examination without parallel," Waldemar Kaempffert, N. Y. TIMES. 192pp. 5⅜ x 8.
T428 Paperbound **$1.35**

FADS AND FALLACIES IN THE NAME OF SCIENCE, Martin Gardner. Examines various cults, quack systems, frauds, delusions which at various times have masqueraded as science. Accounts of hollow-earth fanatics like Symmes; Velikovsky and wandering planets; Hoerbiger; Bellamy and the theory of multiple moons; Charles Fort; dowsing, pseudoscientific methods for finding water, ores, oil. Sections on naturopathy, iridiagnosis, zone therapy, food fads, etc. Analytical accounts of Wilhelm Reich and orgone sex energy; L. Ron Hubbard and Dianetics; A. Korzybski and General Semantics; many others. Brought up to date to include Bridey Murphy, others. Not just a collection of anecdotes, but a fair, reasoned appraisal of eccentric theory. Formerly titled IN THE NAME OF SCIENCE. Preface. Index. x + 384pp. 5⅜ x 8. T394 Paperbound **$1.50**

A DOVER SCIENCE SAMPLER, edited by George Barkin. 64-page book, sturdily bound, containing excerpts from over 20 Dover books, explaining science. Edwin Hubble, George Sarton, Ernst Mach, A. d'Abro, Galileo, Newton, others, discussing island universes, scientific truth, biological phenomena, stability in bridges, etc. Copies limited; no more than 1 to a customer,
FREE

POPULAR SCIENTIFIC LECTURES, Hermann von Helmholtz. Helmholtz was a superb expositor as well as a scientist of genius in many areas. The seven essays in this volume are models of clarity, and even today they rank among the best general descriptions of their subjects ever written. "The Physiological Causes of Harmony in Music" was the first significant physiological explanation of musical consonance and dissonance. Two essays, "On the Interaction of Natural Forces" and "On the Conservation of Force," were of great importance in the history of science, for they firmly established the principle of the conservation of energy. Other lectures include "On the Relation of Optics to Painting," "On Recent Progress in the Theory of Vision," "On Goethe's Scientific Researches," and "On the Origin and Significance of Geometrical Axioms." Selected and edited with an introduction by Professor Morris Kline. xii + 286pp. 5⅜ x 8½. T799 Paperbound **$1.45**

BOOKS EXPLAINING SCIENCE AND MATHEMATICS

Physics

CONCERNING THE NATURE OF THINGS, Sir William Bragg. Christmas lectures delivered at the Royal Society by Nobel laureate. Why a spinning ball travels in a curved track; how uranium is transmuted to lead, etc. Partial contents: atoms, gases, liquids, crystals, metals, etc. No scientific background needed; wonderful for intelligent child. 32pp. of photos, 57 figures. xii + 232pp. 5⅜ x 8. T31 Paperbound **$1.35**

THE RESTLESS UNIVERSE, Max Born. New enlarged version of this remarkably readable account by a Nobel laureate. Moving from sub-atomic particles to universe, the author explains in very simple terms the latest theories of wave mechanics. Partial contents: air and its relatives, electrons & ions, waves & particles, electronic structure of the atom, nuclear physics. Nearly 1000 illustrations, including 7 animated sequences. 325pp. 6 x 9.
T412 Paperbound **$2.00**

FROM EUCLID TO EDDINGTON: A STUDY OF THE CONCEPTIONS OF THE EXTERNAL WORLD, Sir Edmund Whittaker. A foremost British scientist traces the development of theories of natural philosophy from the western rediscovery of Euclid to Eddington, Einstein, Dirac, etc. The inadequacy of classical physics is contrasted with present day attempts to understand the physical world through relativity, non-Euclidean geometry, space curvature, wave mechanics, etc. 5 major divisions of examination: Space; Time and Movement; the Concepts of Classical Physics; the Concepts of Quantum Mechanics; the Eddington Universe. 212pp. 5⅜ x 8.
T491 Paperbound **$1.35**

PHYSICS, THE PIONEER SCIENCE, L. W. Taylor. First thorough text to place all important physical phenomena in cultural-historical framework; remains best work of its kind. Exposition of physical laws, theories developed chronologically, with great historical, illustrative experiments diagrammed, described, worked out mathematically. Excellent physics text for self-study as well as class work. Vol. 1: Heat, Sound: motion, acceleration, gravitation, conservation of energy, heat engines, rotation, heat, mechanical energy, etc. 211 illus. 407pp. 5⅜ x 8. Vol. 2: Light, Electricity: images, lenses, prisms, magnetism, Ohm's law, dynamos, telegraph, quantum theory, decline of mechanical view of nature, etc. Bibliography. 13 table appendix. Index. 551 illus. 2 color plates. 508pp. 5⅜ x 8.
Vol. 1 S565 Paperbound **$2.00**
Vol. 2 S566 Paperbound **$2.00**
The set **$4.00**

A SURVEY OF PHYSICAL THEORY, Max Planck. One of the greatest scientists of all time, creator of the quantum revolution in physics, writes in non-technical terms of his own discoveries and those of other outstanding creators of modern physics. Planck wrote this book when science had just crossed the threshold of the new physics, and he communicates the excitement felt then as he discusses electromagnetic theories, statistical methods, evolution of the concept of light, a step-by-step description of how he developed his own momentous theory, and many more of the basic ideas behind modern physics. Formerly "A Survey of Physics." Bibliography. Index. 128pp. 5⅜ x 8.
S650 Paperbound **$1.15**

THE ATOMIC NUCLEUS, M. Korsunsky. The only non-technical comprehensive account of the atomic nucleus in English. For college physics students, etc. Chapters cover: Radioactivity, the Nuclear Model of the Atom, the Mass of Atomic Nuclei, the Disintegration of Atomic Nuclei, the Discovery of the Positron, the Artificial Transformation of Atomic Nuclei, Artificial Radioactivity, Mesons, the Neutrino, the Structure of Atomic Nuclei and Forces Acting Between Nuclear Particles, Nuclear Fission, Chain Reaction, Peaceful Uses, Thermoculear Reactions. Slightly abridged edition. Translated by G. Yankovsky. 65 figures. Appendix includes 45 photographic illustrations. 413 pp. 5⅜ x 8.
S1052 Paperbound **$2.00**

PRINCIPLES OF MECHANICS SIMPLY EXPLAINED, Morton Mott-Smith. Excellent, highly readable introduction to the theories and discoveries of classical physics. Ideal for the layman who desires a foundation which will enable him to understand and appreciate contemporary developments in the physical sciences. Discusses: Density, The Law of Gravitation, Mass and Weight, Action and Reaction, Kinetic and Potential Energy, The Law of Inertia, Effects of Acceleration, The Independence of Motions, Galileo and the New Science of Dynamics, Newton and the New Cosmos, The Conservation of Momentum, and other topics. Revised edition of "This Mechanical World." Illustrated by E. Kosa, Jr. Bibliography and Chronology. Index. xiv + 171pp. 5⅜ x 8½.
T1067 Paperbound **$1.00**

THE CONCEPT OF ENERGY SIMPLY EXPLAINED, Morton Mott-Smith. Elementary, non-technical exposition which traces the story of man's conquest of energy, with particular emphasis on the developments during the nineteenth century and the first three decades of our own century. Discusses man's earlier efforts to harness energy, more recent experiments and discoveries relating to the steam engine, the engine indicator, the motive power of heat, the principle of excluded perpetual motion, the bases of the conservation of energy, the concept of entropy, the internal combustion engine, mechanical refrigeration, and many other related topics. Also much biographical material. Index. Bibliography. 33 illustrations. ix + 215pp. 5⅜ x 8½.
T1071 Paperbound **$1.25**

HEAT AND ITS WORKINGS, Morton Mott-Smith. One of the best elementary introductions to the theory and attributes of heat, covering such matters as the laws governing the effect of heat on solids, liquids and gases, the methods by which heat is measured, the conversion of a substance from one form to another through heating and cooling, evaporation, the effects of pressure on boiling and freezing points, and the three ways in which heat is transmitted (conduction, convection, radiation). Also brief notes on major experiments and discoveries. Concise, but complete, it presents all the essential facts about the subject in readable style. Will give the layman and beginning student a first-rate background in this major topic in physics. Index. Bibliography. 50 illustrations. x + 165pp. 5⅜ x 8½. T978 Paperbound **$1.00**

THE STORY OF ATOMIC THEORY AND ATOMIC ENERGY, J. G. Feinberg. Wider range of facts on physical theory, cultural implications, than any other similar source. Completely non-technical. Begins with first atomic theory, 600 B.C., goes through A-bomb, developments to 1959. Avogadro, Rutherford, Bohr, Einstein, radioactive decay, binding energy, radiation danger, future benefits of nuclear power, dozens of other topics, told in lively, related, informal manner. Particular stress on European atomic research. "Deserves special mention . . . authoritative," Saturday Review. Formerly "The Atom Story." New chapter to 1959. Index. 34 illustrations. 251pp. 5⅜ x 8.
T625 Paperbound **$1.45**

THE STRANGE STORY OF THE QUANTUM, AN ACCOUNT FOR THE GENERAL READER OF THE GROWTH OF IDEAS UNDERLYING OUR PRESENT ATOMIC KNOWLEDGE, B. Hoffmann. Presents lucidly and expertly, with barest amount of mathematics, the problems and theories which led to modern quantum physics. Dr. Hoffmann begins with the closing years of the 19th century, when certain trifling discrepancies were noticed, and with illuminating analogies and examples takes you through the brilliant concepts of Planck, Einstein, Pauli, de Broglie, Bohr, Schroedinger, Heisenberg, Dirac, Sommerfeld, Feynman, etc. This edition includes a new, long postscript carrying the story through 1958. "Of the books attempting an account of the history and contents of our modern atomic physics which have come to my attention, this is the best," H. Margenau, Yale University, in "American Journal of Physics." 32 tables and line illustrations. Index. 275pp. 5⅜ x 8. T518 Paperbound **$1.50**

THE EVOLUTION OF SCIENTIFIC THOUGHT FROM NEWTON TO EINSTEIN, A. d'Abro. Einstein's special and general theories of relativity, with their historical implications, are analyzed in non-technical terms. Excellent accounts of the contributions of Newton, Riemann, Weyl, Planck, Eddington, Maxwell, Lorentz and others are treated in terms of space and time, equations of electromagnetics, finiteness of the universe, methodology of science. 21 diagrams. 482pp. 5⅜ x 8. T2 Paperound **$2.00**

THE RISE OF THE NEW PHYSICS, A. d'Abro. A half-million word exposition, formerly titled THE DECLINE OF MECHANISM, for readers not versed in higher mathematics. The only thorough explanation, in everyday language, of the central core of modern mathematical physical theory, treating both classical and modern theoretical physics, and presenting in terms almost anyone can understand the equivalent of 5 years of study of mathematical physics. Scientifically impeccable coverage of mathematical-physical thought from the Newtonian system up through the electronic theories of Dirac and Heisenberg and Fermi's statistics. Combines both history and exposition; provides a broad yet unified and detailed view, with constant comparison of classical and modern views on phenomena and theories. "A must for anyone doing serious study in the physical sciences," JOURNAL OF THE FRANKLIN INSTITUTE. "Extraordinary faculty . . . to explain ideas and theories of theoretical physics in the language of daily life," ISIS. First part of set covers philosophy of science, drawing upon the practice of Newton, Maxwell, Poincaré, Einstein, others, discussing modes of thought, experiment, interpretations of causality, etc. In the second part, 100 pages explain grammar and vocabulary of mathematics, with discussions of functions, groups, series, Fourier series, etc. The remainder is devoted to concrete, detailed coverage of both classical and quantum physics, explaining such topics as analytic mechanics, Hamilton's principle, wave theory of light, electromagnetic waves, groups of transformations, thermodynamics, phase rule, Brownian movement, kinetics, special relativity, Planck's original quantum theory, Bohr's atom, Zeeman effect, Broglie's wave mechanics, Heisenberg's uncertainty, Eigen-values, matrices, scores of other important topics. Discoveries and theories are covered for such men as Alembert, Born, Cantor, Debye, Euler, Foucault, Galois, Gauss, Hadamard, Kelvin, Kepler, Laplace, Maxwell, Pauli, Rayleigh, Volterra, Weyl, Young, more than 180 others. Indexed. 97 illustrations. ix + 982pp. 5⅜ x 8. T3 Volume 1, Paperbound **$2.00**
T4 Volume 2, Paperbound **$2.00**

SPINNING TOPS AND GYROSCOPIC MOTION, John Perry. Well-known classic of science still unsurpassed for lucid, accurate, delightful exposition. How quasi-rigidity is induced in flexible and fluid bodies by rapid motions; why gyrostat falls, top rises; nature and effect on climatic conditions of earth's precessional movement; effect of internal fluidity on rotating bodies, etc. Appendixes describe practical uses to which gyroscopes have been put in ships, compasses, monorail transportation. 62 figures. 128pp. 5⅜ x 8. T416 Paperbound **$1.00**

THE UNIVERSE OF LIGHT, Sir William Bragg. No scientific training needed to read Nobel Prize winner's expansion of his Royal Institute Christmas Lectures. Insight into nature of light, methods and philosophy of science. Explains lenses, reflection, color, resonance, polarization, x-rays, the spectrum, Newton's work with prisms, Huygens' with polarization, Crookes' with cathode ray, etc. Leads into clear statement of 2 major historical theories of light, corpuscle and wave. Dozens of experiments you can do. 199 illus., including 2 full-page color plates. 293pp. 5⅜ x 8. S538 Paperbound **$1.85**

THE STORY OF X-RAYS FROM RÖNTGEN TO ISOTOPES, A. R. Bleich. Non-technical history of x-rays, their scientific explanation, their applications in medicine, industry, research, and art, and their effect on the individual and his descendants. Includes amusing early reactions to Röntgen's discovery, cancer therapy, detections of art and stamp forgeries, potential risks to patient and operator, etc. Illustrations show x-rays of flower structure, the gall bladder, gears with hidden defects, etc. Original Dover publication. Glossary. Bibliography. Index. 55 photos and figures. xiv + 186pp. 5⅜ x 8. T662 Paperbound **$1.35**

ELECTRONS, ATOMS, METALS AND ALLOYS, Wm. Hume-Rothery. An introductory-level explanation of the application of the electronic theory to the structure and properties of metals and alloys, taking into account the new theoretical work done by mathematical physicists. Material presented in dialogue-form between an "Old Metallurgist" and a "Young Scientist." Their discussion falls into 4 main parts: the nature of an atom, the nature of a metal, the nature of an alloy, and the structure of the nucleus. They cover such topics as the hydrogen atom, electron waves, wave mechanics, Brillouin zones, co-valent bonds, radioactivity and natural disintegration, fundamental particles, structure and fission of the nucleus,etc. Revised, enlarged edition. 177 illustrations. Subject and name indexes. 407pp. 5⅜ x 8½. S1046 Paperbound **$2.25**

OUT OF THE SKY, H. H. Nininger. A non-technical but comprehensive introduction to "meteoritics", the young science concerned with all aspects of the arrival of matter from outer space. Written by one of the world's experts on meteorites, this work shows how, despite difficulties of observation and sparseness of data, a considerable body of knowledge has arisen. It defines meteors and meteorites; studies fireball clusters and processions, meteorite composition, size, distribution, showers, explosions, origins, craters, and much more. A true connecting link between astronomy and geology. More than 175 photos, 22 other illustrations. References. Bibliography of author's publications on meteorites. Index. viii + 336pp. 5⅜ x 8. T519 Paperbound **$1.85**

SATELLITES AND SCIENTIFIC RESEARCH, D. King-Hele. Non-technical account of the manmade satellites and the discoveries they have yielded up to the autumn of 1961. Brings together information hitherto published only in hard-to-get scientific journals. Includes the life history of a typical satellite, methods of tracking, new information on the shape of the earth, zones of radiation, etc. Over 60 diagrams and 6 photographs. Mathematical appendix. Bibliography of over 100 items. Index. xii + 180pp. 5⅜ x 8½. T703 Paperbound **$2.00**

BOOKS EXPLAINING SCIENCE AND MATHEMATICS

Mathematics

CHANCE, LUCK AND STATISTICS: THE SCIENCE OF CHANCE, Horace C. Levinson. Theory of probability and science of statistics in simple, non-technical language. Part I deals with theory of probability, covering odd superstitions in regard to "luck," the meaning of betting odds, the law of mathematical expectation, gambling, and applications in poker, roulette, lotteries, dice, bridge, and other games of chance. Part II discusses the misuse of statistics, the concept of statistical probabilities, normal and skew frequency distributions, and statistics applied to various fields—birth rates, stock speculation, insurance rates, advertising, etc. "Presented in an easy humorous style which I consider the best kind of expository writing," Prof. A. C. Cohen, Industry Quality Control. Enlarged revised edition. Formerly titled "The Science of Chance." Preface and two new appendices by the author. Index. xiv + 365pp. 5⅜ x 8. T1007 Paperbound **$1.85**

PROBABILITIES AND LIFE, Emile Borel. Translated by M. Baudin. Non-technical, highly readable introduction to the results of probability as applied to everyday situations. Partial contents: Fallacies About Probabilities Concerning Life After Death; Negligible Probabilities and the Probabilities of Everyday Life; Events of Small Probability; Application of Probabilities to Certain Problems of Heredity; Probabilities of Deaths, Diseases, and Accidents; On Poisson's Formula. Index. 3 Appendices of statistical studies and tables. vi + 87pp. 5⅜ x 8½. T121 Paperbound **$1.00**

GREAT IDEAS OF MODERN MATHEMATICS: THEIR NATURE AND USE, Jagjit Singh. Reader with only high school math will understand main mathematical ideas of modern physics, astronomy, genetics, psychology, evolution, etc., better than many who use them as tools, but comprehend little of their basic structure. Author uses his wide knowledge of non-mathematical fields in brilliant exposition of differential equations, matrices, group theory, logic, statistics, problems of mathematical foundations, imaginary numbers, vectors, etc. Original publication. 2 appendices. 2 indexes. 65 illustr. 322pp. 5⅜ x 8. S587 Paperbound **$1.75**

MATHEMATICS IN ACTION, O. G. Sutton. Everyone with a command of high school algebra will find this book one of the finest possible introductions to the application of mathematics to physical theory. Ballistics, numerical analysis, waves and wavelike phenomena, Fourier series, group concepts, fluid flow and aerodynamics, statistical measures, and meteorology are discussed with unusual clarity. Some calculus and differential equations theory is developed by the author for the reader's help in the more difficult sections. 88 figures. Index. viii + 236pp. 5⅜ x 8. T440 Clothbound **$3.50**

THE FOURTH DIMENSION SIMPLY EXPLAINED, edited by H. P. Manning. 22 essays, originally Scientific American contest entries, that use a minimum of mathematics to explain aspects of 4-dimensional geometry: analogues to 3-dimensional space, 4-dimensional absurdities and curiosities (such as removing the contents of an egg without puncturing its shell), possible measurements and forms, etc. Introduction by the editor. Only book of its sort on a truly elementary level, excellent introduction to advanced works. 82 figures. 251pp. 5⅜ x 8. T711 Paperbound **$1.35**

MATHEMATICS—INTERMEDIATE TO ADVANCED

General

INTRODUCTION TO APPLIED MATHEMATICS, Francis D. Murnaghan. A practical and thoroughly sound introduction to a number of advanced branches of higher mathematics. Among the selected topics covered in detail are: vector and matrix analysis, partial and differential equations, integral equations, calculus of variations, Laplace transform theory, the vector triple product, linear vector functions, quadratic and bilinear forms, Fourier series, spherical harmonics, Bessel functions, the Heaviside expansion formula, and many others. Extremely useful book for graduate students in physics, engineering, chemistry, and mathematics. Index. 111 study exercises with answers. 41 illustrations. ix + 389pp. 5⅜ x 8½.
S1042 Paperbound **$2.00**

OPERATIONAL METHODS IN APPLIED MATHEMATICS, H. S. Carslaw and J. C. Jaeger. Explanation of the application of the Laplace Transformation to differential equations, a simple and effective substitute for more difficult and obscure operational methods. Of great practical value to engineers and to all workers in applied mathematics. Chapters on: Ordinary Linear Differential Equations with Constant Coefficients;; Electric Circuit Theory; Dynamical Applications; The Inversion Theorem for the Laplace Transformation; Conduction of Heat; Vibrations of Continuous Mechanical Systems; Hydrodynamics; Impulsive Functions; Chains of Differential Equations; and other related matters. 3 appendices. 153 problems, many with answers. 22 figures. xvi + 359pp. 5⅜ x 8½. S1011 Paperbound **$2.25**

APPLIED MATHEMATICS FOR RADIO AND COMMUNICATIONS ENGINEERS, C. E. Smith. No extraneous material here!—only the theories, equations, and operations essential and immediately useful for radio work. Can be used as refresher, as handbook of applications and tables, or as full home-study course. Ranges from simplest arithmetic through calculus, series, and wave forms, hyperbolic trigonometry, simultaneous equations in mesh circuits, etc. Supplies applications right along with each math topic discussed. 22 useful tables of functions, formulas, logs, etc. Index. 166 exercises, 140 examples, all with answers. 95 diagrams. Bibliography. x + 336pp. 5⅜ x 8. S141 Paperbound **$1.75**

Algebra, group theory, determinants, sets, matrix theory

ALGEBRAS AND THEIR ARITHMETICS, L. E. Dickson. Provides the foundation and background necessary to any advanced undergraduate or graduate student studying abstract algebra. Begins with elementary introduction to linear transformations, matrices, field of complex numbers; proceeds to order, basal units, modulus, quaternions, etc.; develops calculus of linears sets, describes various examples of algebras including invariant, difference, nilpotent, semi-simple. "Makes the reader marvel at his genius for clear and profound analysis," Amer. Mathematical Monthly. Index. xii + 241pp. 5⅜ x 8. S616 Paperbound **$1.50**

THE THEORY OF EQUATIONS WITH AN INTRODUCTION TO THE THEORY OF BINARY ALGEBRAIC FORMS, W. S. Burnside and A. W. Panton. Extremely thorough and concrete discussion of the theory of equations, with extensive detailed treatment of many topics curtailed in later texts. Covers theory of algebraic equations, properties of polynomials, symmetric functions, derived functions, Horner's process, complex numbers and the complex variable, determinants and methods of elimination, invariant theory (nearly 100 pages), transformations, introduction to Galois theory, Abelian equations, and much more. Invaluable supplementary work for modern students and teachers. 759 examples and exercises. Index in each volume. Two volume set. Total of xxiv + 604pp. 5⅜ x 8. S714 Vol I Paperbound **$1.85**
S715 Vol II Paperbound **$1.85**
The set **$3.70**

COMPUTATIONAL METHODS OF LINEAR ALGEBRA, V. N. Faddeeva, translated by **C. D. Benster.** First English translation of a unique and valuable work, the only work in English presenting a systematic exposition of the most important methods of linear algebra—classical and contemporary. Shows in detail how to derive numerical solutions of problems in mathematical physics which are frequently connected with those of linear algebra. Theory as well as individual practice. Part I surveys the mathematical background that is indispensable to what follows. Parts II and III, the conclusion, set forth the most important methods of solution, for both exact and iterative groups. One of the most outstanding and valuable features of this work is the 23 tables, double and triple checked for accuracy. These tables will not be found elsewhere. Author's preface. Translator's note. New bibliography and index. x + 252pp. 5⅜ x 8. S424 Paperbound **$1.95**

ALGEBRAIC EQUATIONS, E. Dehn. Careful and complete presentation of Galois' theory of algebraic equations; theories of Lagrange and Galois developed in logical rather than historical form, with a more thorough exposition than in most modern books. Many concrete applications and fully-worked-out examples. Discusses basic theory (very clear exposition of the symmetric group); isomorphic, transitive, and Abelian groups; applications of Lagrange's and Galois' theories; and much more. Newly revised by the author. Index. List of Theorems. xi + 208pp. 5⅜ x 8. S697 Paperbound **$1.45**

Differential equations, ordinary and partial; integral equations

INTRODUCTION TO THE DIFFERENTIAL EQUATIONS OF PHYSICS, L. Hopf. Especially valuable to the engineer with no math beyond elementary calculus. Emphasizing intuitive rather than formal aspects of concepts, the author covers an extensive territory. Partial contents: Law of causality, energy theorem, damped oscillations, coupling by friction, cylindrical and spherical coordinates, heat source, etc. Index. 48 figures. 160pp. 5⅜ x 8.
S120 Paperbound **$1.25**

INTRODUCTION TO THE THEORY OF LINEAR DIFFERENTIAL EQUATIONS, E. G. Poole. Authoritative discussions of important topics, with methods of solution more detailed than usual, for students with background of elementary course in differential equations. Studies existence theorems, linearly independent solutions; equations with constant coefficients; with uniform analytic coefficients; regular singularities; the hypergeometric equation; conformal representation; etc. Exercises. Index. 210pp. 5⅜ x 8. S629 Paperbound **$1.65**

DIFFERENTIAL EQUATIONS FOR ENGINEERS, P. Franklin. Outgrowth of a course given 10 years at M. I. T. Makes most useful branch of pure math accessible for practical work. Theoretical basis of D.E.'s; solution of ordinary D.E.'s and partial derivatives arising from heat flow, steady-state temperature of a plate, wave equations; analytic functions; convergence of Fourier Series. 400 problems on electricity, vibratory systems, other topics. Formerly "Differential Equations for Electrical Engineers." Index 41 illus. 307pp. 5⅜ x 8.
S601 Paperbound **$1.65**

DIFFERENTIAL EQUATIONS, F. R. Moulton. A detailed, rigorous exposition of all the non-elementary processes of solving ordinary differential equations. Several chapters devoted to the treatment of practical problems, especially those of a physical nature, which are far more advanced than problems usually given as illustrations. Includes analytic differential equations; variations of a parameter; integrals of differential equations; analytic implicit functions; problems of elliptic motion; sine-amplitude functions; deviation of formal bodies; Cauchy-Lipschitz process; linear differential equations with periodic coefficients; differential equations in infinitely many variations; much more. Historical notes. 10 figures. 222 problems. Index. xv + 395pp. 5⅜ x 8. S451 Paperbound **$2.00**

DIFFERENTIAL AND INTEGRAL EQUATIONS OF MECHANICS AND PHYSICS (DIE DIFFERENTIAL- UND INTEGRALGLEICHUNGEN DER MECHANIK UND PHYSIK), edited by P. Frank and R. von Mises. Most comprehensive and authoritative work on the mathematics of mathematical physics available today in the United States: the standard, definitive reference for teachers, physicists, engineers, and mathematicians—now published (in the original German) at a relatively inexpensive price for the first time! Every chapter in this 2,000-page set is by an expert in his field: Carathéodory, Courant, Frank, Mises, and a dozen others. Vol I, on mathematics, gives concise but complete coverages of advanced calculus, differential equations, integral equations, and potential, and partial differential equations. Index. xxiii + 916pp. Vol. II (physics): classical mechanics, optics, continuous mechanics, heat conduction and diffusion, the stationary and quasi-stationary electromagnetic field, electromagnetic oscillations, and wave mechanics. Index. xxiv + 1106pp. Two volume set. Each volume available separately. 5⅝ x 8⅜.
S787 Vol I Clothbound **$7.50**
S788 Vol II Clothbound **$7.50**
The set **$15.00**

LECTURES ON CAUCHY'S PROBLEM, J. Hadamard. Based on lectures given at Columbia, Rome, this discusses work of Riemann, Kirchhoff, Volterra, and the author's own research on the hyperbolic case in linear partial differential equations. It extends spherical and cylindrical waves to apply to all (normal) hyperbolic equations. Partial contents: Cauchy's problem, fundamental formula, equations with odd number, with even number of independent variables; method of descent. 32 figures. Index. iii + 316pp. 5⅜ x 8. S105 Paperbound **$1.75**

THEORY OF DIFFERENTIAL EQUATIONS, A. R. Forsyth. Out of print for over a decade, the complete 6 volumes (now bound as 3) of this monumental work represent the most comprehensive treatment of differential equations ever written. Historical presentation includes in 2500 pages every substantial development. Vol. 1, 2: EXACT EQUATIONS, PFAFF'S PROBLEM; ORDINARY EQUATIONS, NOT LINEAR: methods of Grassmann, Clebsch, Lie, Darboux; Cauchy's theorem; branch points; etc. Vol. 3, 4: ORDINARY EQUATIONS, NOT LINEAR; ORDINARY LINEAR EQUATIONS: Zeta Fuchsian functions, general theorems on algebraic integrals, Brun's theorem, equations with uniform periodic coffiecients, etc. Vol. 4, 5: PARTIAL DIFFERENTIAL EQUATIONS: 2 existence-theorems, equations of theoretical dynamics, Laplace transformations, general transformation of equations of the 2nd order, much more. Indexes. Total of 2766pp. 5⅜ x 8. S576-7-8 Clothbound: the set **$15.00**

PARTIAL DIFFERENTIAL EQUATIONS OF MATHEMATICAL PHYSICS, A. G. Webster. A keystone work in the library of every mature physicist, engineer, researcher. Valuable sections on elasticity, compression theory, potential theory, theory of sound, heat conduction, wave propagation, vibration theory. Contents include: deduction of differential equations, vibrations, normal functions, Fourier's series, Cauchy's method, boundary problems, method of Riemann-Volterra. Spherical, cylindrical, ellipsoidal harmonics, applications, etc. 97 figures. vii + 440pp. 5⅜ x 8. S263 Paperbound **$2.00**

ELEMENTARY CONCEPTS OF TOPOLOGY, P. Alexandroff. First English translation of the famous brief introduction to topology for the beginner or for the mathematician not undertaking extensive study. This unusually useful intuitive approach deals primarily with the concepts of complex, cycle, and homology, and is wholly consistent with current investigations. Ranges from basic concepts of set-theoretic topology to the concept of Betti groups. "Glowing example of harmony between intuition and thought," David Hilbert. Translated by A. E. Farley. Introduction by D. Hilbert. Index. 25 figures. 73pp. 5⅜ x 8. S747 Paperbound **$1.00**

Number theory

INTRODUCTION TO THE THEORY OF NUMBERS, L. E. Dickson. Thorough, comprehensive approach with adequate coverage of classical literature, an introductory volume beginners can follow. Chapters on divisibility, congruences, quadratic residues & reciprocity, Diophantine equations, etc. Full treatment of binary quadratic forms without usual restriction to integral coefficients. Covers infinitude of primes, least residues, Fermat's theorem, Euler's phi function, Legendre's symbol, Gauss's lemma, automorphs, reduced forms, recent theorems of Thue & Siegel, many more. Much material not readily available elsewhere. 239 problems. Index. I figure. viii + 183pp. 5⅜ x 8. S342 Paperbound **$1.65**

ELEMENTS OF NUMBER THEORY, I. M. Vinogradov. Detailed 1st course for persons without advanced mathematics; 95% of this book can be understood by readers who have gone no farther than high school algebra. Partial contents: divisibility theory, important number theoretical functions, congruences, primitive roots and indices, etc. Solutions to both problems and exercises. Tables of primes, indices, etc. Covers almost every essential formula in elementary number theory! Translated from Russian. 233 problems, 104 exercises. viii + 227pp. 5⅜ x 8. S259 Paperbound **$1.60**

THEORY OF NUMBERS and DIOPHANTINE ANALYSIS, R. D. Carmichael. These two complete works in one volume form one of the most lucid introductions to number theory, requiring only a firm foundation in high school mathematics. "Theory of Numbers," partial contents: Eratosthenes' sieve, Euclid's fundamental theorem, G.C.F. and L.C.M. of two or more integers, linear congruences, etc "Diophantine Analysis": rational triangles, Pythagorean triangles, equations of third, fourth, higher degrees, method of functional equations, much more. "Theory of Numbers": 76 problems. Index. 94pp. "Diophantine Analysis": 222 problems. Index. 118pp. 5⅜ x 8. S529 Paperbound **$1.35**

Numerical analysis, tables

MATHEMATICAL TABLES AND FORMULAS, Compiled by Robert D. Carmichael and Edwin R. Smith. Valuable collection for students, etc. Contains all tables necessary in college algebra and trigonometry, such as five-place common logarithms, logarithmic sines and tangents of small angles, logarithmic trigonometric functions, natural trigonometric functions, four-place antilogarithms, tables for changing from sexagesimal to circular and from circular to sexagesimal measure of angles, etc. Also many tables and formulas not ordinarily accessible, including powers, roots, and reciprocals, exponential and hyperbolic functions, ten-place logarithms of prime numbers, and formulas and theorems from analytical and elementary geometry and from calculus. Explanatory introduction. viii + 269pp. 5⅜ x 8½. S111 Paperbound **$1.00**

MATHEMATICAL TABLES, H. B. Dwight. Unique for its coverage in one volume of almost every function of importance in applied mathematics, engineering, and the physical sciences. Three extremely fine tables of the three trig functions and their inverse functions to thousandths of radians; natural and common logarithms; squares, cubes; hyperbolic functions and the inverse hyperbolic functions; $(a^2 + b^2)$ exp. ½a; complete elliptic integrals of the 1st and 2nd kind; sine and cosine integrals; exponential integrals Ei(x) and Ei(—x); binomial coefficients; factorials to 250; surface zonal harmonics and first derivatives; Bernoulli and Euler numbers and their logs to base of 10; Gamma function; normal probability integral; over 60 pages of Bessel functions; the Riemann Zeta function. Each table with formulae generally used, sources of more extensive tables, interpolation data, etc. Over half have columns of differences, to facilitate interpolation. Introduction. Index. viii + 231pp. 5⅜ x 8. S445 Paperbound **$1.75**

TABLES OF FUNCTIONS WITH FORMULAE AND CURVES, E. Jahnke & F. Emde. The world's most comprehensive 1-volume English-text collection of tables, formulae, curves of transcendent functions. 4th corrected edition, new 76-page section giving tables, formulae for elementary functions—not in other English editions. Partial contents: sine, cosine, logarithmic integral; factorial function; error integral; theta functions; elliptic integrals, functions; Legendre, Bessel, Riemann, Mathieu, hypergeometric functions, etc. Supplementary books. Bibliography. Indexed. "Out of the way functions for which we know no other source," SCIENTIFIC COMPUTING SERVICE, Ltd. 212 figures. 400pp. 5⅜ x 8. S133 Paperbound **$2.00**

CHEMISTRY AND PHYSICAL CHEMISTRY

ORGANIC CHEMISTRY, F. C. Whitmore. The entire subject of organic chemistry for the practicing chemist and the advanced student. Storehouse of facts, theories, processes found elsewhere only in specialized journals. Covers aliphatic compounds (500 pages on the properties and synthetic preparation of hydrocarbons, halides, proteins, ketones, etc.), alicyclic compounds, aromatic compounds, heterocyclic compounds, organophosphorus and organometallic compounds. Methods of synthetic preparation analyzed critically throughout. Includes much of biochemical interest. "The scope of this volume is astonishing," INDUSTRIAL AND ENGINEERING CHEMISTRY. 12,000-reference index. 2387-item bibliography. Total of x + 1005pp. 5⅜ x 8. Two volume set. S700 Vol I Paperbound **$2.00**
S701 Vol II Paperbound **$2.00**
The set **$4.00**

THE MODERN THEORY OF MOLECULAR STRUCTURE, Bernard Pullman. A reasonably popular account of recent developments in atomic and molecular theory. Contents: The Wave Function and Wave Equations (history and bases of present theories of molecular structure); The Electronic Structure of Atoms (Description and classification of atomic wave functions, etc.); Diatomic Molecules; Non-Conjugated Polyatomic Molecules; Conjugated Polyatomic Molecules; The Structure of Complexes. Minimum of mathematical background needed. New translation by David Antin of "La Structure Moleculaire." Index. Bibliography. vii + 87pp. 5⅜ x 8½. S987 Paperbound **$1.00**

CATALYSIS AND CATALYSTS, Marcel Prettre, Director, Research Institute on Catalysis. This brief book, translated into English for the first time, is the finest summary of the principal modern concepts, methods, and results of catalysis. Ideal introduction for beginning chemistry and physics students. Chapters: Basic Definitions of Catalysis (true catalysis and generalization of the concept of catalysis); The Scientific Bases of Catalysis (Catalysis and chemical thermodynamics, catalysis and chemical kinetics); Homogeneous Catalysis (acid-base catalysis, etc.); Chain Reactions; Contact Masses; Heterogeneous Catalysis (Mechanisms of contact catalyses, etc.); and Industrial Applications (acids and fertilizers, petroleum and petroleum chemistry, rubber, plastics, synthetic resins, and fibers). Translated by David Antin. Index. vi + 88pp. 5⅜ x 8½. S998 Paperbound **$1.00**

POLAR MOLECULES, Pieter Debye. This work by Nobel laureate Debye offers a complete guide to fundamental electrostatic field relations, polarizability, molecular structure. Partial contents: electric intensity, displacement and force, polarization by orientation, molar polarization and molar refraction, halogen-hydrides, polar liquids, ionic saturation, dielectric constant, etc. Special chapter considers quantum theory. Indexed. 172pp. 5⅜ x 8.
S64 Paperbound **$1.50**

THE ELECTRONIC THEORY OF ACIDS AND BASES, W. F. Luder and Saverio Zuffanti. The first full systematic presentation of the electronic theory of acids and bases—treating the theory and its ramifications in an uncomplicated manner. Chapters: Historical Background; Atomic Orbitals and Valence; The Electronic Theory of Acids and Bases; Electrophilic and Electrodotic Reagents; Acidic and Basic Radicals; Neutralization; Titrations with Indicators; Displacement; Catalysis; Acid Catalysis; Base Catalysis; Alkoxides and Catalysts; Conclusion. Required reading for all chemists. Second revised (1961) eidtion, with additional examples and references. 3 figures. 9 tables. Index. Bibliography xii + 165pp. 5⅜ x 8.
S201 Paperbound **$1.50**

KINETIC THEORY OF LIQUIDS, J. Frenkel. Regarding the kinetic theory of liquids as a generalization and extension of the theory of solid bodies, this volume covers all types of arrangements of solids, thermal displacements of atoms, interstitial atoms and ions, orientational and rotational motion of molecules, and transition between states of matter. Mathematical theory is developed close to the physical subject matter. 216 bibliographical footnotes. 55 figures. xi + 485pp. 5⅜ x 8. S95 Paperbound **$2.55**

THE PRINCIPLES OF ELECTROCHEMISTRY, D. A. MacInnes. Basic equations for almost every subfield of electrochemistry from first principles, referring at all times to the soundest and most recent theories and results; unusually useful as text or as reference. Covers coulometers and Faraday's Law, electrolytic conductance, the Debye-Hueckel method for the theoretical calculation of activity coefficients, concentration cells, standard electrode potentials, thermodynamic ionization constants, pH, potentiometric titrations, irreversible phenomena, Planck's equation, and much more. "Excellent treatise," AMERICAN CHEMICAL SOCIETY JOURNAL. "Highly recommended," CHEMICAL AND METALLURGICAL ENGINEERING. 2 Indices. Appendix. 585-item bibliography. 137 figures. 94 tables. ii + 478pp. 5⅝ x 8⅜.
S52 Paperbound **$2.45**

THE PHASE RULE AND ITS APPLICATION, Alexander Findlay. Covering chemical phenomena of 1, 2, 3, 4, and multiple component systems, this "standard work on the subject" (NATURE, London), has been completely revised and brought up to date by A. N. Campbell and N. O. Smith. Brand new material has been added on such matters as binary, tertiary liquid equilibria, solid solutions in ternary systems, quinary systems of salts and water. Completely revised to triangular coordinates in ternary systems, clarified graphic representation, solid models, etc. 9th revised edition. Author, subject indexes. 236 figures. 505 footnotes, mostly bibliographic. xii + 494pp. 5⅜ x 8. S91 Paperbound **$2.45**

PHYSICS

General physics

FOUNDATIONS OF PHYSICS, R. B. Lindsay & H. Margenau. Excellent bridge between semi-popular works & technical treatises. A discussion of methods of physical description, construction of theory; valuable for physicist with elementary calculus who is interested in ideas that give meaning to data, tools of modern physics. Contents include symbolism, mathematical equations; space & time foundations of mechanics; probability; physics & continua; electron theory; special & general relativity; quantum mechanics; causality. "Thorough and yet not overdetailed. Unreservedly recommended," NATURE (London). Unabridged, corrected edition. List of recommended readings. 35 illustrations. xi + 537pp. 5⅜ x 8.
S377 Paperbound **$2.75**

FUNDAMENTAL FORMULAS OF PHYSICS, ed. by D. H. Menzel. Highly useful, fully inexpensive reference and study text, ranging from simple to highly sophisticated operations. Mathematics integrated into text—each chapter stands as short textbook of field represented. Vol. 1: Statistics, Physical Constants, Special Theory of Relativity, Hydrodynamics, Aerodynamics, Boundary Value Problems in Math. Physics; Viscosity, Electromagnetic Theory, etc. Vol. 2: Sound, Acoustics, Geometrical Optics, Electron Optics, High-Energy Phenomena, Magnetism, Biophysics, much more. Index. Total of 800pp. 5⅜ x 8. Vol. 1 S595 Paperbound **$2.00**
Vol. 2 S596 Paperbound **$2.00**

MATHEMATICAL PHYSICS, D. H. Menzel. Thorough one-volume treatment of the mathematical techniques vital for classic mechanics, electromagnetic theory, quantum theory, and relativity. Written by the Harvard Professor of Astrophysics for junior, senior, and graduate courses, it gives clear explanations of all those aspects of function theory, vectors, matrices, dyadics, tensors, partial differential equations, etc., necessary for the understanding of the various physical theories. Electron theory, relativity, and other topics seldom presented appear here in considerable detail. Scores of definitions, conversion factors, dimensional constants, etc. "More detailed than normal for an advanced text . . . excellent set of sections on Dyadics, Matrices, and Tensors," JOURNAL OF THE FRANKLIN INSTITUTE. Index. 193 problems, with answers. x + 412pp. 5⅜ x 8. S56 Paperbound **$2.00**

THE SCIENTIFIC PAPERS OF J. WILLARD GIBBS. All the published papers of America's outstanding theoretical scientist (except for "Statistical Mechanics" and "Vector Analysis"). Vol I (thermodynamics) contains one of the most brilliant of all 19th-century scientific papers—the 300-page "On the Equilibrium of Heterogeneous Substances," which founded the science of physical chemistry, and clearly stated a number of highly important natural laws for the first time; 8 other papers complete the first volume. Vol II includes 2 papers on dynamics, 8 on vector analysis and multiple algebra, 5 on the electromagnetic theory of light, and 6 miscellaneous papers. Biographical sketch by H. A. Bumstead. Total of xxxvi + 718pp. 5⅝ x 8⅜.
S721 Vol I Paperbound **$2.00**
S722 Vol II Paperbound **$2.00**
The set **$4.00**

BASIC THEORIES OF PHYSICS, Peter Gabriel Bergmann. Two-volume set which presents a critical examination of important topics in the major subdivisions of classical and modern physics. The first volume is concerned with classical mechanics and electrodynamics: mechanics of mass points, analytical mechanics, matter in bulk, electrostatics and magnetostatics, electromagnetic interaction, the field waves, special relativity, and waves. The second volume (Heat and Quanta) contains discussions of the kinetic hypothesis, physics and statistics, stationary ensembles, laws of thermodynamics, early quantum theories, atomic spectra, probability waves, quantization in wave mechanics, approximation methods, and abstract quantum theory. A valuable supplement to any thorough course or text.
Heat and Quanta: Index. 8 figures. x + 300pp. 5⅜ x 8½. S968 Paperbound **$1.75**
Mechanics and Electrodynamics: Index. 14 figures. vii + 280pp. 5⅜ x 8½.
S969 Paperbound **$1.75**

THEORETICAL PHYSICS, A. S. Kompaneyets. One of the very few thorough studies of the subject in this price range. Provides advanced students with a comprehensive theoretical background. Especially strong on recent experimentation and developments in quantum theory. Contents: Mechanics (Generalized Coordinates, Lagrange's Equation, Collision of Particles, etc.), Electrodynamics (Vector Analysis, Maxwell's equations, Transmission of Signals, Theory of Relativity, etc.), Quantum Mechanics (the Inadequacy of Classical Mechanics, the Wave Equation, Motion in a Central Field, Quantum Theory of Radiation, Quantum Theories of Dispersion and Scattering, etc.), and Statistical Physics (Equilibrium Distribution of Molecules in an Ideal Gas, Boltzmann statistics, Bose and Fermi Distribution, Thermodynamic Quantities, etc.). Revised to 1961. Translated by George Yankovsky, authorized by Kompaneyets. 137 exercises. 56 figures. 529pp. 5⅜ x 8½. S972 Paperbound **$2.50**

ANALYTICAL AND CANONICAL FORMALISM IN PHYSICS, André Mercier. A survey, in one volume, of the variational principles (the key principles—in mathematical form—from which the basic laws of any one branch of physics can be derived) of the several branches of physical theory, together with an examination of the relationships among them. Contents: the Lagrangian Formalism, Lagrangian Densities, Canonical Formalism, Canonical Form of Electrodynamics, Hamiltonian Densities, Transformations, and Canonical Form with Vanishing Jacobian Determinant. Numerous examples and exercises. For advanced students, teachers, etc. 6 figures. Index. viii + 222pp. 5⅜ x 8½. S1077 Paperbound **$1.75**

MATHEMATICAL PUZZLES AND RECREATIONS

AMUSEMENTS IN MATHEMATICS, Henry Ernest Dudeney. The foremost British originator of mathematical puzzles is always intriguing, witty, and paradoxical in this classic, one of the largest collections of mathematical amusements. More than 430 puzzles, problems, and paradoxes. Mazes and games, problems on number manipulation, unicursal and other route problems, puzzles on measuring, weighing, packing, age, kinship, chessboards, joining, crossing river, plane figure dissection, and many others. Solutions. More than 450 illustrations. vii + 258pp. 5⅜ x 8. T473 Paperbound **$1.25**

SYMBOLIC LOGIC and THE GAME OF LOGIC, Lewis Carroll. "Symbolic Logic" is not concerned with modern symbolic logic, but is instead a collection of over 380 problems posed with charm and imagination, using the syllogism, and a fascinating diagrammatic method of drawing conclusions. In "The Game of Logic," Carroll's whimsical imagination devises a logical game played with 2 diagrams and counters (included) to manipulate hundreds of tricky syllogisms. The final section, "Hit or Miss" is a lagniappe of 101 additional puzzles in the delightful Carroll manner. Until this reprint edition, both of these books were rarities costing up to $15 each. Symbolic Logic: Index, xxxi + 199pp. The Game of Logic: 96pp. Two vols. bound as one. 5⅜ x 8. T492 Paperbound **$1.50**

MAZES AND LABYRINTHS: A BOOK OF PUZZLES, W. Shepherd. Mazes, formerly associated with mystery and ritual, are still among the most intriguing of intellectual puzzles. This is a novel and different collection of 50 amusements that embody the principle of the maze: mazes in the classical tradition; 3-dimensional, ribbon, and Möbius-strip mazes; hidden messages; spatial arrangements; etc.—almost all built on amusing story situations. 84 illustrations. Essay on maze psychology. Solutions. xv + 122pp. 5⅜ x 8. T731 Paperbound **$1.00**

MATHEMATICAL RECREATIONS, M. Kraitchik. Some 250 puzzles, problems, demonstrations of recreational mathematics for beginners & advanced mathematicians. Unusual historical problems from Greek, Medieval, Arabic, Hindu sources: modern problems based on "mathematics without numbers," geometry, topology, arithmetic, etc. Pastimes derived from figurative numbers, Mersenne numbers, Fermat numbers; fairy chess, latruncles, reversi, many topics. Full solutions. Excellent for insights into special fields of math. 181 illustrations. 330pp. 5⅜ x 8. T163 Paperbound **$1.75**

MATHEMATICAL PUZZLES OF SAM LOYD, Vol. I, selected and edited by M. Gardner. Puzzles by the greatest puzzle creator and innovator. Selected from his famous "Cyclopedia of Puzzles," they retain the unique style and historical flavor of the originals. There are posers based on arithmetic, algebra, probability, game theory, route tracing, topology, counter, sliding block, operations research, geometrical dissection. Includes his famous "14-15" puzzle which was a national craze, and his "Horse of a Different Color" which sold millions of copies. 117 of his most ingenious puzzles in all, 120 line drawings and diagrams. Solutions. Selected references. xx + 167pp. 5⅜ x 8. T498 Paperbound **$1.00**

MY BEST PUZZLES IN MATHEMATICS, Hubert Phillips ("Caliban"). Caliban is generally considered the best of the modern problemists. Here are 100 of his best and wittiest puzzles, selected by the author himself from such publications as the London Daily Telegraph, and each puzzle is guaranteed to put even the sharpest puzzle detective through his paces. Perfect for the development of clear thinking and a logical mind. Complete solutions are provided for every puzzle. x + 107pp. 5⅜ x 8½. T91 Paperbound **$1.00**

MY BEST PUZZLES IN LOGIC AND REASONING, H. Phillips ("Caliban"). 100 choice, hitherto unavailable puzzles by England's best-known problemist. No special knowledge needed to solve these logical or inferential problems, just an unclouded mind, nerves of steel, and fast reflexes. Data presented are both necessary and just sufficient to allow one unambiguous answer. More than 30 different types of puzzles, all ingenious and varied, many one of a kind, that will challenge the expert, please the beginner. Original publication. 100 puzzles, full solutions. x + 107pp. 5⅜ x 8½. T119 Paperbound **$1.00**

MATHEMATICAL PUZZLES FOR BEGINNERS AND ENTHUSIASTS, G. Mott-Smith. 188 mathematical puzzles to test mental agility. Inference, interpretation, algebra, dissection of plane figures, geometry, properties of numbers, decimation, permutations, probability, all enter these delightful problems. Puzzles like the Odic Force, How to Draw an Ellipse, Spider's Cousin, more than 180 others. Detailed solutions. Appendix with square roots, triangular numbers, primes, etc. 135 illustrations. 2nd revised edition. 248pp. 5⅜ x 8. T198 Paperbound **$1.00**

MATHEMATICS, MAGIC AND MYSTERY, Martin Gardner. Card tricks, feats of mental mathematics, stage mind-reading, other "magic" explained as applications of probability, sets, theory of numbers, topology, various branches of mathematics. Creative examination of laws and their applications with scores of new tricks and insights. 115 sections discuss tricks wtih cards, dice, coins; geometrical vanishing tricks, dozens of others. No sleight of hand needed; mathematics guarantees success. 115 illustrations. xii + 174pp. 5⅜ x 8. T335 Paperbound **$1.00**

RECREATIONS IN THE THEORY OF NUMBERS: THE QUEEN OF MATHEMATICS ENTERTAINS, Albert H. Beiler. The theory of numbers is often referred to as the "Queen of Mathematics." In this book Mr. Beiler has compiled the first English volume to deal exclusively with the recreational aspects of number theory, an inherently recreational branch of mathematics. The author's clear style makes for enjoyable reading as he deals with such topics as: perfect numbers, amicable numbers, Fermat's theorem, Wilson's theorem, interesting properties of digits, methods of factoring, primitive roots, Euler's function, polygonal and figurate numbers, Mersenne numbers, congruence, repeating decimals, etc. Countless puzzle problems, with full answers and explanations. For mathematicians and mathematically-inclined laymen, etc. New publication. 28 figures. 9 illustrations. 103 tables. Bibliography at chapter ends. vi + 247pp. 5⅜ x 8½. T1096 Paperbound **$1.85**

PAPER FOLDING FOR BEGINNERS, W. D. Murray and F. J. Rigney. A delightful introduction to the varied and entertaining Japanese art of origami (paper folding), with a full crystal-clear text that anticipates every difficulty; over 275 clearly labeled diagrams of all important stages in creation. You get results at each stage, since complex figures are logically developed from simpler ones. 43 different pieces are explained: place mats, drinking cups, bonbon boxes, sailboats, frogs, roosters, etc. 6 photographic plates. 279 diagrams. 95pp. 5⅝ x 8⅜. T713 Paperbound **$1.00**

1800 RIDDLES, ENIGMAS AND CONUNDRUMS, Darwin A. Hindman. Entertaining collection ranging from hilarious gags to outrageous puns to sheer nonsense—a welcome respite from sophisticated humor. Children, toastmasters, and practically anyone with a funny bone will find these zany riddles tickling and eminently repeatable. Sample: "Why does Santa Claus always go down the chimney?" "Because it soots him." Some old, some new—covering a wide variety of subjects. New publication. iii + 154pp. 5⅜ x 8½. T1059 Paperbound **$1.00**

EASY-TO-DO ENTERTAINMENTS AND DIVERSIONS WITH CARDS, STRING, COINS, PAPER AND MATCHES, R. M. Abraham. Over 300 entertaining games, tricks, puzzles, and pastimes for children and adults. Invaluable to anyone in charge of groups of youngsters, for party givers, etc. Contains sections on card tricks and games, making things by paperfolding—toys, decorations, and the like; tricks with coins, matches, and pieces of string; descriptions of games; toys that can be made from common household objects; mathematical recreations; word games; and 50 miscellaneous entertainments. Formerly "Winter Nights Entertainments." Introduction by Lord Baden Powell. 329 illustrations. v + 186pp. 5⅜ x 8. T921 Paperbound **$1.00**

DIVERSIONS AND PASTIMES WITH CARDS, STRING, PAPER AND MATCHES, R. M. Abraham. Another collection of amusements and diversion for game and puzzle fans of all ages. Many new paperfolding ideas and tricks, an extensive section on amusements with knots and splices, two chapters of easy and not-so-easy problems, coin and match tricks, and lots of other parlor pastimes from the agile mind of the late British problemist and gamester. Corrected and revised version. Illustrations. 160pp. 5⅜ x 8½. T1127 Paperbound **$1.00**

STRING FIGURES AND HOW TO MAKE THEM: A STUDY OF CAT'S-CRADLE IN MANY LANDS, Caroline Furness Jayne. In a simple and easy-to-follow manner, this book describes how to make 107 different string figures. Not only is looping and crossing string between the fingers a common youthful diversion, but it is an ancient form of amusement practiced in all parts of the globe, especially popular among primitive tribes. These games are fun for all ages and offer an excellent means for developing manual dexterity and coordination. Much insight also for the anthropological observer on games and diversions in many different cultures. Index. Bibliography. Introduction by A. C. Haddon, Cambridge University. 17 full-page plates. 950 illustrations. xxiii + 407pp. 5⅜ x 8½. T152 Paperbound **$2.00**

CRYPTANALYSIS, Helen F. Gaines. (Formerly ELEMENTARY CRYPTANALYSIS.) A standard elementary and intermediate text for serious students. It does not confine itself to old material, but contains much that is not generally known, except to experts. Concealment, Transposition, Substitution ciphers; Vigenere, Kasiski, Playfair, multafid, dozens of other techniques. Appendix with sequence charts, letter frequencies in English, 5 other languages, English word frequencies. Bibliography. 167 codes. New to this edition: solution to codes. vi + 230pp. 5⅜ x 8. T97 Paperbound **$1.95**

MAGIC SQUARES AND CUBES, W. S. Andrews. Only book-length treatment in English, a thorough non-technical description and analysis. Here are nasik, overlapping, pandiagonal, serrated squares; magic circles, cubes, spheres, rhombuses. Try your hand at 4-dimensional magical figures! Much unusual folklore and tradition included. High school algebra is sufficient. 754 diagrams and illustrations. viii + 419pp. 5⅜ x 8. T658 Paperbound **$1.85**

CALIBAN'S PROBLEM BOOK: MATHEMATICAL, INFERENTIAL, AND CRYPTOGRAPHIC PUZZLES, H. Phillips ("Caliban"), S. T. Shovelton, G. S. Marshall. 105 ingenious problems by the greatest living creator of puzzles based on logic and inference. Rigorous, modern, piquant, and reflecting their author's unusual personality, these intermediate and advanced puzzles all involve the ability to reason clearly through complex situations; some call for mathematical knowledge, ranging from algebra to number theory. Solutions. xi + 180pp. 5⅜ x 8. T736 Paperbound **$1.25**

FICTION

THE LAND THAT TIME FORGOT and THE MOON MAID, Edgar Rice Burroughs. In the opinion of many, Burroughs' best work. The first concerns a strange island where evolution is individual rather than phylogenetic. Speechless anthropoids develop into intelligent human beings within a single generation. The second projects the reader far into the future and describes the first voyage to the Moon (in the year 2025), the conquest of the Earth by the Moon, and years of violence and adventure as the enslaved Earthmen try to regain possession of their planet. "An imaginative tour de force that keeps the reader keyed up and expectant," NEW YORK TIMES. Complete, unabridged text of the original two novels (three parts in each). 5 illustrations by J. Allen St. John. vi + 552pp. 5⅜ x 8½.
T1020 Clothbound **$3.75**
T358 Paperbound **$2.00**

AT THE EARTH'S CORE, PELLUCIDAR, TANAR OF PELLUCIDAR: THREE SCIENCE FICTION NOVELS BY EDGAR RICE BURROUGHS. Complete, unabridged texts of the first three Pellucidar novels. Tales of derring-do by the famous master of science fiction. The locale for these three related stories is the inner surface of the hollow Earth where we discover the world of Pellucidar, complete with all types of bizarre, menacing creatures, strange peoples, and alluring maidens—guaranteed to delight all Burroughs fans and a wide circle of advenutre lovers. Illustrated by J. Allen St. John and P. F. Berdanier. vi + 433pp. 5⅜ x 8½.
T1051 Paperbound **$2.00**

THE PIRATES OF VENUS and LOST ON VENUS: TWO VENUS NOVELS BY EDGAR RICE BURROUGHS. Two related novels, complete and unabridged. Exciting adventure on the planet Venus with Earthman Carson Napier broken-field running through one dangerous episode after another. All lovers of swashbuckling science fiction will enjoy these two stories set in a world of fascinating societies, fierce beasts, 5000-ft. trees, lush vegetation, and wide seas. Illustrations by Fortunino Matania. Total of vi + 340pp. 5⅜ x 8½. T1053 Paperbound **$1.75**

A PRINCESS OF MARS and A FIGHTING MAN OF MARS: TWO MARTIAN NOVELS BY EDGAR RICE BURROUGHS. "Princess of Mars" is the very first of the great Martian novels written by Burroughs, and it is probably the best of them all; it set the pattern for all of his later fantasy novels and contains a thrilling cast of strange peoples and creatures and the formula of Olympian heroism amidst ever-fluctuating fortunes which Burroughs carries off so successfully. "Fighting Man" returns to the same scenes and cities—many years later. A mad scientist, a degenerate dictator, and an indomitable defender of the right clash—with the fate of the Red Planet at stake! Complete, unabridged reprinting of original editions. Illustrations by F. E. Schoonover and Hugh Hutton. v + 356pp. 5⅜ x 8½.
T1140 Paperbound **$1.75**

THREE MARTIAN NOVELS, Edgar Rice Burroughs. Contains: Thuvia, Maid of Mars; The Chessmen of Mars; and The Master Mind of Mars. High adventure set in an imaginative and intricate conception of the Red Planet. Mars is peopled with an intelligent, heroic human race which lives in densely populated cities and with fierce barbarians who inhabit dead sea bottoms. Other exciting creatures abound amidst an inventive framework of Martian history and geography. Complete unabridged reprintings of the first edition. 16 illustrations by J. Allen St. John. vi + 499pp. 5⅜ x 8½. T39 Paperbound **$1.85**

THREE PROPHETIC NOVELS BY H. G. WELLS, edited by E. F. Bleiler. Complete texts of "When the Sleeper Wakes" (1st book printing in 50 years), "A Story of the Days to Come," "The Time Machine" (1st complete printing in book form). Exciting adventures in the future are as enjoyable today as 50 years ago when first printed. Predict TV, movies, intercontinental airplanes, prefabricated houses, air-conditioned cities, etc. First important author to foresee problems of mind control, technological dictatorships. "Absolute best of imaginative fiction," N. Y. Times. Introduction. 335pp. 5⅜ x 8. T605 Paperbound **$1.50**

28 SCIENCE FICTION STORIES OF H. G. WELLS. Two full unabridged novels, MEN LIKE GODS and STAR BEGOTTEN, plus 26 short stories by the master science-fiction writer of all time. Stories of space, time, invention, exploration, future adventure—an indispensable part of the library of everyone interested in science and adventure. PARTIAL CONTENTS: Men Like Gods, The Country of the Blind, In the Abyss, The Crystal Egg, The Man Who Could Work Miracles, A Story of the Days to Come, The Valley of Spiders, and 21 more! 928pp. 5⅜ x 8.
T265 Clothbound **$4.50**

THE WAR IN THE AIR, IN THE DAYS OF THE COMET, THE FOOD OF THE GODS: THREE SCIENCE FICTION NOVELS BY H. G. WELLS. Three exciting Wells offerings bearing on vital social and philosophical issues of his and our own day. Here are tales of air power, strategic bombing, East vs. West, the potential miracles of science, the potential disasters from outer space, the relationship between scientific advancement and moral progress, etc. First reprinting of "War in the Air" in almost 50 years. An excellent sampling of Wells at his storytelling best. Complete, unabridged reprintings. 16 illustrations. 645pp. 5⅜ x 8½.
T1135 Paperbound **$2.00**

SEVEN SCIENCE FICTION NOVELS, H. G. Wells. Full unabridged texts of 7 science-fiction novels of the master. Ranging from biology, physics, chemistry, astronomy to sociology and other studies, Mr. Wells extrapolates whole worlds of strange and intriguing character. "One will have to go far to match this for entertainment, excitement, and sheer pleasure . . . ," NEW YORK TIMES. Contents: The Time Machine, The Island of Dr. Moreau, First Men in the Moon, The Invisible Man, The War of the Worlds, The Food of the Gods, In the Days of the Comet. 1015pp. 5⅜ x 8. T264 Clothbound **$4.50**

BEST GHOST STORIES OF J. S. LE FANU, Selected and introduced by E. F. Bleiler. LeFanu is deemed the greatest name in Victorian supernatural fiction. Here are 16 of his best horror stories, including 2 nouvelles: "Carmilla," a classic vampire tale couched in a perverse eroticism, and "The Haunted Baronet." Also: "Sir Toby's Will," "Green Tea," "Schalken the Painter," "Ultor de Lacy," "The Familiar," etc. The first American publication of about half of this material: a long-overdue opportunity to get a choice sampling of LeFanu's work. New selection (1964). 8 illustrations. 5⅜ x 8⅜. T415 Paperbound **$1.85**

THE WONDERFUL WIZARD OF OZ, L. F. Baum. Only edition in print with all the original W. W. Denslow illustrations in full color—as much a part of "The Wizard" as Tenniel's drawings are for "Alice in Wonderland." "The Wizard" is still America's best-loved fairy tale, in which, as the author expresses it, "The wonderment and joy are retained and the heartaches and nightmares left out." Now today's young readers can enjoy every word and wonderful picture of the original book. New introduction by Martin Gardner. A Baum bibliography. 23 full-page color plates. viii + 268pp. 5⅜ x 8. T691 Paperbound **$1.45**

GHOST AND HORROR STORIES OF AMBROSE BIERCE, Selected and introduced by E. F. Bleiler. 24 morbid, eerie tales—the cream of Bierce's fiction output. Contains such memorable pieces as "The Moonlit Road," "The Damned Thing," "An Inhabitant of Carcosa," "The Eyes of the Panther," "The Famous Gilson Bequest," "The Middle Toe of the Right Foot," and other chilling stories, plus the essay, "Visions of the Night" in which Bierce gives us a kind of rationale for his aesthetic of horror. New collection (1964). xxii + 199pp. 5⅜ x 8⅜. T767 Paperbound **$1.00**

HUMOR

MR. DOOLEY ON IVRYTHING AND IVRYBODY, Finley Peter Dunne. Since the time of his appearance in 1893, "Mr. Dooley," the fictitious Chicago bartender, has been recognized as America's most humorous social and political commentator. Collected in this volume are 102 of the best Dooley pieces—all written around the turn of the century, the height of his popularity. Mr. Dooley's Irish brogue is employed wittily and penetratingly on subjects which are just as fresh and relevant today as they were then: corruption and hypocrisy of politicans, war preparations and chauvinism, automation, Latin American affairs, superbombs, etc. Other articles range from Rudyard Kipling to football. Selected with an introduction by Robert Hutchinson. xii + 244pp. 5⅜ x 8½. T626 Paperbound **$1.00**

RUTHLESS RHYMES FOR HEARTLESS HOMES and MORE RUTHLESS RHYMES FOR HEARTLESS HOMES, Harry Graham ("Col. D. Streamer"). A collection of Little Willy and 48 other poetic "disasters." Graham's funniest and most disrespectful verse, accompanied by original illustrations. Nonsensical, wry humor which employs stern parents, careless nurses, uninhibited children, practical jokers, single-minded golfers, Scottish lairds, etc. in the leading roles. A precursor of the "sick joke" school of today. This volume contains, bound together for the first time, two of the most perennially popular books of humor in England and America. Index. vi + 69pp. 5⅜ x 8. T930 Paperbound **75¢**

A WHIMSEY ANTHOLOGY, Collected by Carolyn Wells. 250 of the most amusing rhymes ever written. Acrostics, anagrams, palindromes, alphabetical jingles, tongue twisters, echo verses, alliterative verses, riddles, mnemonic rhymes, interior rhymes, over 40 limericks, etc. by Lewis Carroll, Edward Lear, Joseph Addison, W. S. Gilbert, Christina Rossetti, Chas. Lamb, James Boswell, Hood, Dickens, Swinburne, Leigh Hunt, Harry Graham, Poe, Eugene Field, and many others. xiv + 221pp. 5⅜ x 8½. T195 Paperbound **$1.25**

MY PIOUS FRIENDS AND DRUNKEN COMPANIONS and MORE PIOUS FRIENDS AND DRUNKEN COMPANIONS, Songs and ballads of Conviviality Collected by Frank Shay. Magnificently illuminated by John Held, Jr. 132 ballads, blues, vaudeville numbers, drinking songs, cowboy songs, sea chanties, comedy songs, etc. of the Naughty Nineties and early 20th century. Over a third are reprinted with music. Many perennial favorites such as: The Band Played On, Frankie and Johnnie, The Old Grey Mare, The Face on the Bar-room Floor, etc. Many others unlocatable elsewhere: The Dog-Catcher's Child, The Cannibal Maiden, Don't Go in the Lion's Cage Tonight, Mother, etc. Complete verses and introductions to songs. Unabridged republication of first editions, 2 Indexes (song titles and first lines and choruses). Introduction by Frank Shay. 2 volumes bounds as 1. Total of xvi + 235pp. 5⅜ x 8½. T946 Paperbound **$1.00**